Imperial-Mexicali Valleys:
Development and Environment of the
U.S.-Mexican Border Region

Imperial-Mexicali Valleys: Development and Environment of the U.S.-Mexican Border Region

Edited by

Kimberly Collins

Paul Ganster

Cheryl Mason

Eduardo Sánchez López

Margarito Quintero-Núñez

San Diego State University Press

Institute for Regional Studies of the Californias

2004

Research for this project and publication of this work were supported by a grant from the Southwest Consortium for Environmental Research and Policy (SCERP).

Contents

List of Maps / ix

Foreword: Two Valleys, Two Nations—One River, One Region, *by Denise Moreno Ducheny* / xi

Preface and Acknowledgements / xiii

PART ONE **Introduction / 1**

CHAPTER 1. The Imperial Valley and Mexicali: An Introduction to the Region and Its People, *by Kimberly Collins* 3

PART TWO **History and Government / 15**

CHAPTER 2. Before the Waters…The Desert: An Early History of the Imperial Valley, *by Carlos R. Herrera* 17

CHAPTER 3. Development of the Structure of Agriculture in the Mexicali Valley in the Early Twentieth Century, *by Oscar Sánchez Ramírez* 33

CHAPTER 4. Capitalist Development and Population Growth in the County of Imperial, California, and Mexicali, Baja California, *by Norma Fimbres Durazo*..
43

CHAPTER 5. Tribal Adaptation: The Quechan of Imperial County, *by Jay von Werlhof* 55

CHAPTER 6. Governance in Imperial County, California, and Mexicali, Baja California, *by Glen Sparrow* 65

CHAPTER 7. Municipal Governance and Management in Mexicali, Baja California, *by José María Ramos García and Vicente Sánchez Munguía*..........79

PART THREE **Economy and Agriculture / 97**

CHAPTER 8. Explaining Low Income and High Unemployment in
Imperial County, *by James Gerber* 99

CHAPTER 9. Economic Overview: Employment Patterns in the
Municipality of Mexicali, *by Sergio Noriega-Verdugo* 113

CHAPTER 10. The Economy of Yuma County, Arizona, and San Luis Río
Colorado, Sonora, *by Gerald L. Schmaedick and Vanessa Owen* 133

CHAPTER 11. Imperial County Employment Profile, *by Cheryl Mason* 155

CHAPTER 12. Economic Bases for Cross-Border Planning at the
Imperial-Mexicali Border, *by Araceli Almaraz Alvarado* 171

CHAPTER 13. Employee Turnover in Mexicali, *by Mindy S. West* 199

CHAPTER 14. Industrial Growth, Urban Expansion, and Industrial
Facilities in Mexicali, Baja California, *by Arturo Ranfla González
and César Peña Salmón* 209

CHAPTER 15. Agriculture in the Imperial Valley, *by Refugio A. González* 229

CHAPTER 16. Agricultural Policy in Mexicali and San Luis Río Colorado,
by Eduardo Sánchez López 237

CHAPTER 17. Imperial County Livestock Industry, 1910 to the Present,
by Juan N. Guerrero and Alecsandro Rufino dos Santos 253

PART FOUR **Environmental Concerns and Natural Resources / 261**

CHAPTER 18. Air Quality Evaluation in the Mexicali and Imperial
Valleys as an Element for an Outreach Program, *by Margarito
Quintero-Núñez and Alan Sweedler* 263

CHAPTER 19. Energy Profile of the Baja California-California Border
Region with Emphasis on the Mexicali-Imperial Valley, *by Margarito
Quintero-Núñez and Alan Sweedler* 281

CHAPTER 20. Energy Savings Plans and Domestic Consumers: An Analysis,
by Silvia Ahumada Valdez and Ramona Fuentes Valdez 297

CHAPTER 21. Environmental Management of Hazardous Waste along the
Imperial-Mexicali Valley Border, *by M. Socorro Romero,
Fabio de la Cruz, Roger Vintze, and Magdalena Carrasco* 307

CHAPTER 22. Handling of Waste Tires at the Border, *by Elizabeth
Ramírez Barreto and Sara Ojeda Benítez* 319

CHAPTER 23. The Colorado River Delta: An Important Ecosystem for
the Mexicali-Imperial Valley Region, *by José L. Fermán Almada,
David W. Fischer, and Alejandro García Gastelum* 335

PART FIVE **Social Trends and Culture / 349**

CHAPTER 24. Education in the Imperial and Mexicali Valleys,
by Olga Amaral 351

CHAPTER 25. Housing Trends in the Imperial Valley, *by G. Jean Laurin*..............379

CHAPTER 26. Housing in Mexicali: An Intraurban Geographic Analysis,
by Guillermo B. Álvarez de la Torre and Martha Cristina Dorantes G. 389

CHAPTER 27. Nongovernmental Organizations in the Mexicali and
Imperial Valleys: An Approach to Their Characteristics and
Interactions, *by José A. Moreno Mena and Guadalupe Alonso* 399

CHAPTER 28. The Place and Places of Culture in the Imperial
Valley-Mexicali Region, *by Sheila Dollente and Eduardo Kintero*..................415

CHAPTER 29. Transborder Public Art: Murals and Graffiti in the Imperial-
Mexicali Valley, *by Marcia Isabel Campillo López*..427

Index / 447

List of Maps

Population of Imperial County 7

Population of Mexicali 8

Imperial County Households 9

Mexicali Households 10

Imperial County Transportation 11

Mexicali Transportation 12

Native American Tribes' Lands 55

Location of Industrial Spaces, Mexicali, 1998 217

Historic Growth of the City of Mexicali, 1900–1990 219

The Mexicali Valley 238

Geographical Boundaries of the Rural Development Support Centers 241

Irrigation Modules of Colorado River Irrigation Districts 242

Location of the Air Quality Monitoring Stations in Mexicali 269

Location of the Air Quality Monitoring Net in Imperial Valley 271

Western Section of the Electric Power System 284

Geographic Location of the Mexicali and Imperial Valleys 298

The Colorado River Delta Zone 336

Upper Gulf of California and Colorado River Delta Biosphere Reserve
Nuclear Zone and Buffer Zone 344

Proportion of Rental Housing in Mexicali 394

Mexicali's Historic Urban Growth, 1920–1980 395

Housing Quality in Mexicali, 1993 396

Foreword

Two Valleys, Two Nations—
One River, One Region

Denise Moreno Ducheny*

The series of essays that follows provides an overview of a unique region of the North American continent. It is a region that appears unusually unsuited for human habitation, yet has been inhabited for many hundreds of years.

Native peoples of this region adapted their lives to the desert environment, cultivating crops along the edge of the Colorado River, fishing in Lake Cahuilla (which in ancient times filled the basin presently occupied by the body of water known as the Salton Sea), and finding nourishment in desert plants. Later, immigrants from Switzerland, India, China, and all parts of the growing United States and Mexico came to call this region home. They have turned it into one of the most productive agricultural regions in the world.

When Don Juan Bautista de Anza first encountered the Colorado Desert in 1774—as he sought a route from Sonora, Mexico, to the California coast—his expedition found the area unforgivingly harsh and desolate. He did not know where to look for watering holes, although he was fortunate to encounter the region during the winter months when the climate was most tolerable.

Few Spaniards lived in the region during the colonial period and many Mexicans chose not to settle in the area after Mexico won its independence from Spain in 1821. In 1848, following the U.S.-Mexican war, a political line was drawn that crossed the desert.

The region remained empty until the early twentieth century when U.S. businessmen and engineers designed ways to harness the life-giving waters of the Colorado River and channel them for use in agriculture. Their first attempt was foiled by the

*Moreno Ducheny was Presidential Fellow at San Diego State University, former member of the California State Assembly, and is now California State Senator, District 40.

strength of the river itself that broke through the makeshift canals and dams in 1905, flooding into the dry bed of the former Lake Cahuilla, creating the body of water we now know as the Salton Sea. But they did not give up and, today, approximately one million acres of land are cultivated in the Imperial and Mexicali valleys.

Currently, Mexicali, a city of nearly one million people, serves as the center of this primarily agricultural region. The peoples of two nations live side by side, bound together by their mutual dependence on the last portion of the Colorado River as it flows finally into the Sea of Cortez.

The 2000 Census found over 142,000 people living in Imperial County—nearly double the number found there in 1970. Over the same period, Mexicali also nearly doubled to approximately 800,000 inhabitants, as it has increasingly become a manufacturing center with the arrival of *maquiladora* industries.

The two valleys share an ecosystem that includes the Colorado River Delta and an internationally recognized biosphere reserve in the Upper Gulf of California. They share air and water quality issues that must be resolved despite differences in political structures and economic bases. They share a workforce, with many residents living on one side of the international political boundary and working on the other. They share a need for greater educational services for growing populations and the changing economies.

The challenge of creating and maintaining a sustainable economy in the area and improving the quality of life for all residents is one that will be best accomplished by joint and cooperative efforts of the two valleys. This requires considerable understanding by each culture of the other, of each nation's unique governmental structures, and of the socioeconomic needs of each society.

As a member of the California State Legislature during the 1990s representing portions of the border region, I frequently found myself exchanging basic information with Mexican colleagues regarding our government structures. To propose solutions to mutual problems, for instance, we needed to know what level of government (state, local, or federal) had jurisdiction over a given issue. At the border, it is often all three. We needed to take the time to become personally acquainted so that we would have the ability to comfortably call on each other as issues of mutual concern arose. We cannot afford to meet only in times of crisis and not spend the time to have meetings that lead to forward-looking planning efforts. Each needs to be aware of the other society's needs and aspirations in order to seek workable solutions to joint problems.

In the essays that follow, you will learn of the history, the environment, the culture, the economy, the social structures, and the governance structures of these two valleys and, hopefully, will come to appreciate this very unique and special corner of the North American continent. I, along with the editors and authors, also hope these studies will assist decision makers throughout the region by providing the background information they need to approach problem solving on a regional basis in order to create a sustainable economy and ecology in the desert region they share.

Preface and Acknowledgements

The Imperial and Mexicali valleys constitute a binational region in the U.S.-Mexican border that is recognized first and foremost for its extreme climate. Its economy has traditionally been based on intensive irrigated agriculture, but manufacturing, cross-border trade, and a government sector are growing in importance. Water and agricultural issues remain an important part of the identity of the region, even though they are declining in relative economic importance. Many local residents are therefore struggling to maintain a traditional rural way of life that is quickly changing. Internal and external pressures that are altering the region include influences from the global economy; movement from the traditional agricultural workforce toward employment by multinational corporations (maquiladoras); population growth in Southern California and Baja California coastal areas that is accompanied by increased demands for water and energy; and suburban sprawl from residential housing and retail growth within the region.

Many of the changes from a rural to an urban economy have already occurred in Mexicali, but the Imperial Valley is currently in the midst of this change. As these transformations become a reality, a general understanding of the region's past and present is key to working toward the future. In addition to economic and employment concerns, there are many environmental challenges that need to be addressed. Thus, one purpose of this book is to provide insight on this binational region in order to assist scholars, students, community members, and decision makers with their respective tasks of guiding the region into the future. It is hoped that informing all stakeholders will contribute to improving the quality of life for all residents within the community.

This work is a compilation of essays authored by experts and scholars on the region. It combines the views of policymakers, historians, public administrators, archeologists, economists, sociologists, physicists, environmental engineers, biologists, and practitioners. Since development encompasses many different issues, the editors have gathered essays from a range of disciplines. The many perspectives and scholarly traditions of this combined work are designed to produce a more complete, holistic view of the binational region.

The text begins with a foreword by State Senator Denise Moreno Ducheny, a legislator who not only understands the border region, but also truly enjoys it and its people. She has worked to provide policy answers to many of the problems challenging the region.

The first section is an introductory overview by Kimberly Collins of San Diego State University's California Center for Border and Regional Economic Studies. She presents a summary of the demographics, geography, and general characteristics of the region, which will be especially helpful to those who are unfamiliar with the Imperial-Mexicali valleys.

The second section includes essays on the region's history and governance. Carlos R. Herrera reviews the history of the desert region from indigenous times through settlement by Europeans and North Americans who effected the first transfer of water from the Colorado River to the desert for farming activities. Oscar Sánchez Ramírez continues this discussion with an analysis of the agricultural development in the Mexicali Valley, which is linked to the overall historical development of the region. A large part of the history of Mexicali is tied to the migrants who came to the region to farm, to find employment and other opportunities, to establish homes for their families, or to merely pause to rest before reaching their final destination. Norma Fimbres Durazo reviews the migration to the border region as a part of its historical development. Jay von Werlhof describes in his essay the impact of this development on the local Native American people and their resilience that enabled them to survive not only a harsh climate, but also aggressive Spanish, Mexican, and Anglo cultures. Finally, touching upon policy and governance today, Glen Sparrow, as well as José María Ramos García and Vicente Sánchez Munguía, write about local governance and public administration in Imperial County and Mexicali.

The next section includes essays on the economy and agriculture in the region. Jim Gerber begins with an analysis of the low income and high unemployment that has plagued Imperial County for many years. Sergio Noriega-Verdugo provides an overview of the economy of Mexicali while Gerald L. Schmaedick and Vanessa Owen analyze the Yuma, Arizona-San Luis Río Colorado, Sonora regional economy. Cheryl Mason provides a review of employment in Imperial County. For Mexicali, Araceli Almaraz Alvarado and Mindy S. West explore the dynamics of employment in this municipality. Development and land use planning in Mexicali and the move from agriculture to industry are outlined by Arturo Ranfla González and César Peña Salmón. This leads the reader to the final three essays in this section. Refugio A. González writes about agriculture in the Imperial Valley; Eduardo Sánchez López looks at agricultural policy in Mexicali and San Luis Río Colorado; and Juan N. Guerrero and Alecsandro Rufino dos Santos provide a review of the livestock industry in the Imperial Valley from 1910 to the present.

Since a main goal of this work is to link economy and development with the environment and natural resources of the region, the fourth section explores several important environmental concerns. A review of the energy sector and air quality in the Imperial and Mexicali valleys is provided by Margarito Quintero-Núñez and Alan Sweedler. The next essay analyzes the energy savings plans for domestic consumers in the Imperial and Mexicali valleys. This essay by Silvia Ahumada Valdez and Ramona Fuentes Valdez, stresses the critical importance of energy efficiencies in a region where temperatures reach 120 degrees Fahrenheit in the summer months. Another critical environmental issue in this binational region is the management of hazardous waste, a subject discussed by M. Socorro Romero, Fabio de la Cruz, Roger Vintze, and Magdalena Carrasco. Elizabeth Ramírez Barreto and Sara Ojeda Benítez discuss a problem of solid waste: the handling of waste tires. The final essay in this section, by José L. Fermán Almada, David W. Fischer, and Alejandro García Gastelum, addresses the Colorado River Delta ecosystem, a critical component of the Colorado River and Upper Gulf of California systems.

The final section of this monograph explores social trends and culture in the region. An important part of any society is its educational system, which is discussed by Olga Amaral who provides a comparative view of the Mexicali and Imperial Valley regions. The availability and quality of housing indicates the quality of life for the community's residents and two essays examine housing issues and development. The first, by G. Jean Laurin, describes housing trends in Imperial Valley. The second essay, by Guillermo B. Alvarez de la Torre and Martha Cristina Dorantes G., provides a geographical perspective of housing development in the city of Mexicali. Another important component in gauging quality of life and participation of community members in society is seen through the analysis of nongovernmental organizations. The essay by José A. Moreno Mena and Guadalupe Alonso describes the characteristics and interactions between nongovernmental organizations in both valleys. The last two essays depict culture and public art in the Imperial and Mexicali valleys. Sheila Dollente and Eduardo Kintero describe the physical facilities that support cultural events and the differences that exist between Mexico and the United States in their administration and funding of the arts. Marcia Isabel Campillo López analyzes the depiction of cross-border life in public art, as seen in the murals and graffiti that are found throughout the region.

One purpose of this book is to provide baseline information to assist regional stakeholders in understanding the complexities of environment and development in this binational region. Another purpose is to bring together material on key Mexicali-Imperial Valley regional subjects into one convenient volume. Most existing printed materials for the region deal with only Mexicali or only with the Imperial Valley. Studies most often end at the international boundary, with authors ignoring the other side. And, most printed sources are not available in both languages of the region. One purpose of the editors of this book is to provide readers with basic materials that will aid in understanding the entire region in a more integrated fashion. To this end, a Spanish-language version of these essays will be published by the press of the Autonomous University of Baja California.

This book is the result of a complex process involving many individuals in California, Baja California, and Arizona. Kimberly Collins and her staff of CCBRES took charge of organizational requirements for the project, issuing the call for contributors, coordinating working meetings, and managing the editorial process. The staff of the Institute for Regional Studies of the Californias coordinated the peer review process for the individual articles, copyediting, production of graphics, and final typesetting. The binational editorial team for this book—Kimberly Collins, Paul Ganster, Cheryl Mason, Eduardo Sánchez López, and Margarito Quintero-Núñez—all assisted with recruitment of authors and critical review of essay drafts.

Special thanks are due to IRSC's Bertha Hernández who supervised copyediting, translations, and final production of the work. IRSC and CCBRES staff Angélica Villegas, Alison McNee, Richard Harmon, Roberto González, and Marisa Oliff all assisted with aspects of the project. Harry Johnson created most of the maps that appear in the volume.

This book grew out of a project supported by the Southwest Center for Environmental Research and Policy (SCERP), a university-based consortium of five U.S. and five Mexican institutions. SCERP recognizes that an important part of environmental quality is understanding the human systems that affect the natural systems of the border region. SCERP firmly believes that knowledge of historical, social, economic, and other components of human societies will empower regional stakeholders to begin to make the decisions that will lead to sustainable development.

The Editors

PART ONE

Introduction

1

The Imperial Valley and Mexicali:
An Introduction to the Region and Its People

Kimberly Collins*

Regional Overview

The Imperial Valley-Mexicali region is located on the U.S.-Mexican border, where the States of California and Baja California meet. The region is bounded on the north by Riverside County, California, on the east by the Colorado River, on the west by San Diego County and the municipalities of Tecate and Ensenada, and on the south by the Gulf of California and Ensenada. The region covers approximately 26,432 square kilometers (10,205 square miles), of which 11,096 km² (4,284 mi²) are in Imperial County, and 15,336 km² (5,921 mi²) are in the Municipality of Mexicali (U.S. Census Bureau 2000a; INEGI 2002).

Because much of the region is located below sea level and mountains to the west prevent Pacific moisture from entering the area, average annual rainfall is approximately 70 millimeters (2.8 inches) (INEGI 1996: 7). Despite this, the region is among the most productive agricultural areas in both the United States and Mexico. Agriculture, which initiated the region's development at the end of the nineteenth and early part of the twentieth century, became possible due to the diversion of Colorado River water through an extensive network of canals. Approximately 396,803 hectares (980,518 acres) are used for agriculture in the region, with roughly 60 percent of the cultivated land located in the Imperial Valley (Imperial County Agricultural Commissioner's Office 2001: 8; INEGI 1996: 91). Mean monthly temperatures range from approximately 13°C (55°F) to 35°C (95°F), creating a year-round growing season (INEGI 1996: 6).

*Collins is Director of the California Center for Border and Regional Economic Studies at the Imperial Valley Campus of San Diego State University. Juan Lagunas, Computer Engineer, and Richard Harmon, Roberto González, and Marissa Oliff, former Project Coordinators for the Center, contributed to this article.

Population

Population trends in the Imperial Valley-Mexicali region have been marked by rapid growth, especially since World War II, when an increased need for labor in the United States resulted in a dramatic increase of immigration of people from throughout Mexico and Latin America (Alegría Olazábal 1992). Immigration has continued to the region, particularly to Mexicali. There, the growth of the *maquiladora* (in-bond manufacturing) industry, that accelerated in the 1980s, required large amounts of labor. Other factors attracting migrants to the Mexicali region include employment—legal or undocumented—across the border in the Imperial Valley or elsewhere in California.

Imperial County was twice the size of Mexicali in 1930, with a population of 60,903 compared to Mexicali's 29,985. By 1950, Mexicali had grown to a population of 124,362, nearly twice the size of Imperial County (62,975 persons). The rapid growth experienced in Mexicali since the mid-1900s reflects the influx of persons from elsewhere in Mexico to work in the agricultural and, since the mid-1960s, the growing *maquiladora* industries. Both Mexicali and Imperial County are projected to grow significantly over the next few decades. From its 2000 population of 142,361, Imperial County is expected to grow to mushroom to more than 500,000 in 2040. Similarly, Mexicali's population is projected to increase from 764,602 in 2000 to

Figure 1. Historical and Projected Population Trends in Imperial County and Mexicali, 1930–2040

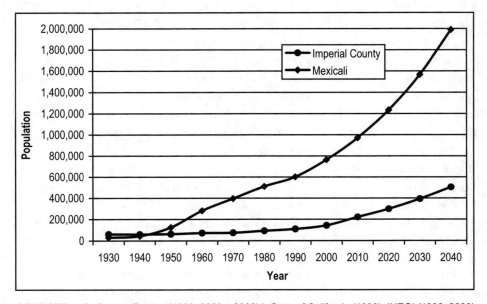

SOURCES: U.S. Census Bureau (1990, 2000a, 2000b); State of California (1998); INEGI (1996, 2000).

almost two million in 2040 (U.S. Census Bureau 1990, 2000a, 2000b; State of California 1998; INEGI 1996, 2000). Figure 1 provides the historical and projected population in Imperial County and Mexicali for the years from 1930 through 2040.

Figures 2 and 3 compare the distribution of the population in Imperial County and California and the population in Mexicali and Baja California by age group. As shown in the figures, Imperial County has a younger population than California; 41.5 percent of Imperial County residents are in the age categories between zero and 24 while only 37.1 percent of Californians are in these categories. Mexicali has an older

Figure 2. Population in Imperial County and California
by Age Group, 2000

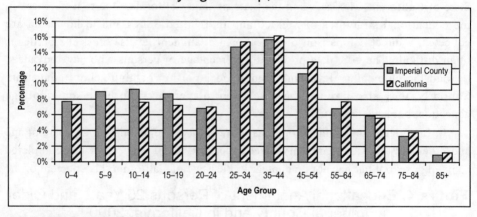

SOURCE: U.S. Census Bureau (2000).

Figure 3. Population in Mexicali and Baja California
by Age Group, 2000

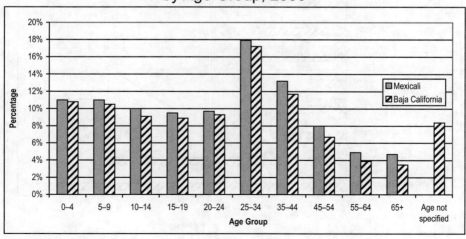

SOURCE: INEGI (2000).

population than Baja California; 48.7 percent of Mexicali residents are in the age categories between 25 and 65 and older while 43 percent of the State of Baja California residents are in these categories (U.S. Census Bureau 2000a; INEGI 2000). When the county and municipality are compared to each other, Imperial County shows an older population than Mexicali; 58.6 percent of Imperial County residents are in the age categories between 25–85 while only 48.7 percent of Mexicali residents are in the age categories of 25 and older.

Education

Figures 4, 5, and 6 show educational attainment of residents of Imperial County, the State of California, Mexicali, and the State of Baja California. Due to differences in the educational structures of Mexico and the United States and in how data are collected, a direct comparison of educational attainment levels across the border is often difficult. The U.S. data provide the percentage of persons who have advanced beyond the elementary level and completed a portion of high school education. Similarly, they also provide the percentage of persons who have some college education, but have not obtained a degree.

In Imperial County, almost one quarter (23.8% of the population 25 years of age and older only has an elementary-level education, and 17.1 percent has completed some high school but has not graduated. In the State of California, 11.5 percent of the

Figure 4. Educational Attainment of Persons 25 Years and Older in Imperial County and in California, 2000

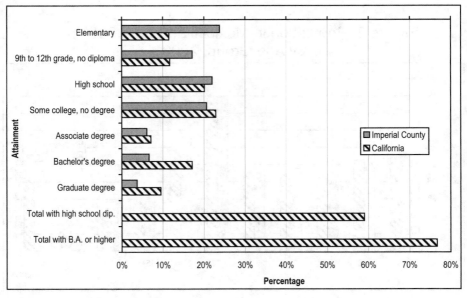

SOURCE: U.S. Census Bureau (2000).

Figure 5. Educational Attainment of Persons 15 Years and Older in Mexicali, 2000

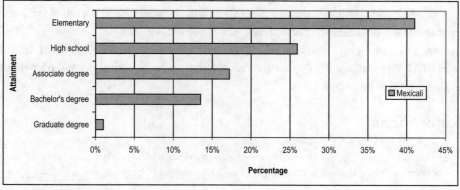

SOURCE: INEGI (2000).

Figure 6. Educational Attainment of Persons 15 Years and Older in Baja California,[1] 2000

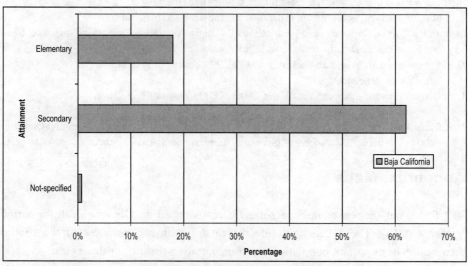

[1]Baja California does not specify higher education obtained by its residents.

SOURCE: INEGI (2000).

population has an elementary school education and another 11.7 percent has completed some high school but has not graduated. Roughly 77 percent of Californians possess a high school diploma and 26.6 percent have a bachelor's degree or higher. In Imperial County, 59 percent has a high school diploma and 10.3 percent has a bachelor's degree or higher.

In Mexicali, 41.0 percent of the population 15 years of age and older has a primary level education, 25.9 percent has a secondary level education, and 31.7 percent has some postsecondary education. In the entire State of Baja California, a total of 17.9 percent of the population has elementary level education and 62 percent has a secondary level education.

References

Alegría Olazábal, Tito. 1992. *Desarrollo urbano en la frontera México-Estados Unidos: Una interpretación y algunos resultados*. México, D.F.: Consejo Nacional para la Cultura y las Artes.

Imperial County Agricultural Commissioner's Office. 2001. *Imperial County Agricultural Crop & Livestock Report 2000*. El Centro: Imperial County Central Duplicating Office.

Instituto Nacional de Estadística, Geografía e Informática (INEGI). 1996. *Mexicali, Estado de Baja California: Cuaderno Estadístico Municipal, Edición 1996*. México D.F.: Instituto Nacional de Estadística, Geografía e Informática.

Instituto Nacional de Estadística, Geografía e Informática (INEGI). 2000. XII Censo General de Población y Vivienda 2000. http://www.inegi.gob.mx/difusion/espanol/poblacion/definitivos/ bc/tabulados/indice.html.

Instituto Nacional de Estadística, Geografía e Informática (INEGI). 2002. Acerca de México. http://www.inegi.gob/difusión/español/acercamexico/facermex.html.

State of California, Department of Finance. 1998. County Population Projections with Age, Sex and Race/Ethnic Detail. http://www.dof.ca.gov.

U.S. Census Bureau, American Factfinder. 1990. 1990 Census of Population. http://factfinder.census.gov.

U.S. Census Bureau, American Factfinder. 2000a. 2000 Census of Population. http://factfinder.census.gov.

U.S. Census Bureau, Population Division. 2000b. Population of Counties by Decennial Census: 1900 to 1990. http://www.census.gov/population/cencounts/ca190090.txt.

Appendix: Maps

The following section contains a series of maps based on Geographic Information Systems (GIS). These maps provide the reader with a clear view of the spatial distribution of important population and transportation features of the region.

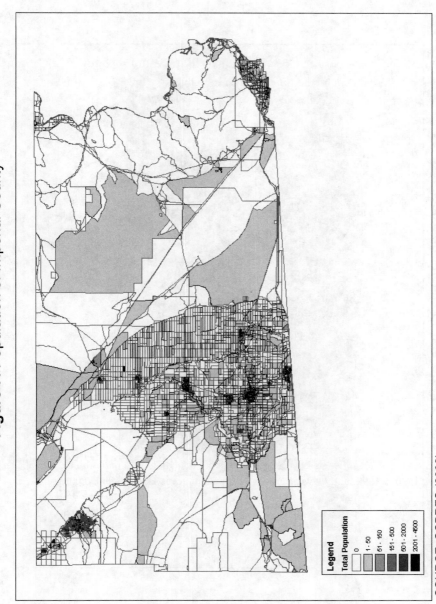

Figure 7. Population of Imperial County

Legend
Total Population
0
1 - 50
51 - 150
151 - 500
501 - 2000
2001 - 4500

SOURCE: CCBRES (2002).

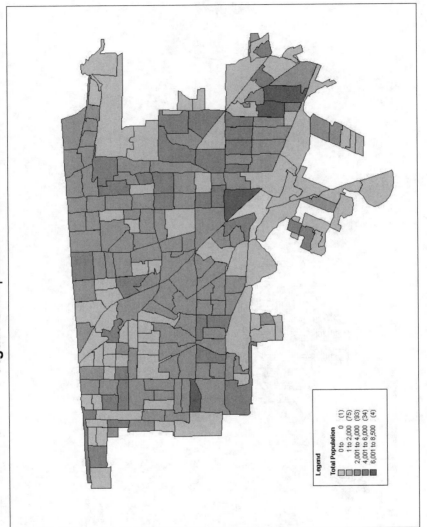

Figure 8. Population of Mexicali

Legend

Total Population
- 0 to 0 (1)
- 1 to 2,000 (75)
- 2,001 to 4,000 (93)
- 4,001 to 6,000 (34)
- 6,001 to 8,500 (4)

SOURCES: UABC (2002); CCBRES (2002).

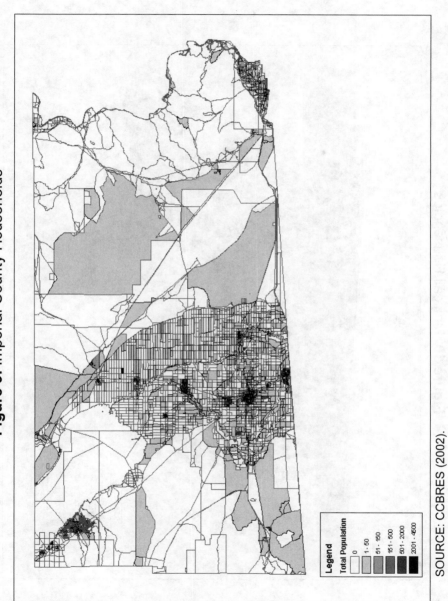

Figure 9. Imperial County Households

Legend

Total Population

0
1 - 50
51 - 150
151 - 500
501 - 2000
2001 - 4500

SOURCE: CCBRES (2002).

Figure 10. Mexicali Households

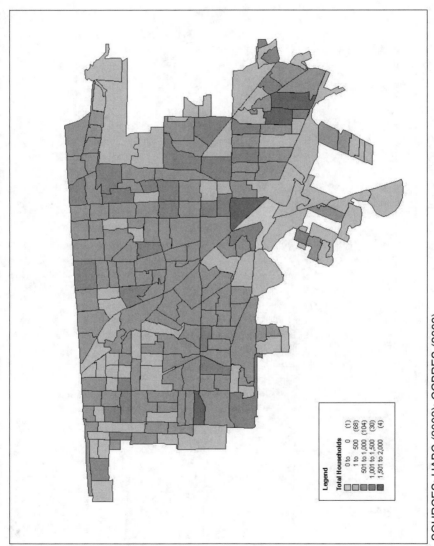

SOURCES: UABC (2002); CCBRES (2002).

Figure 11. Imperial County Transportation

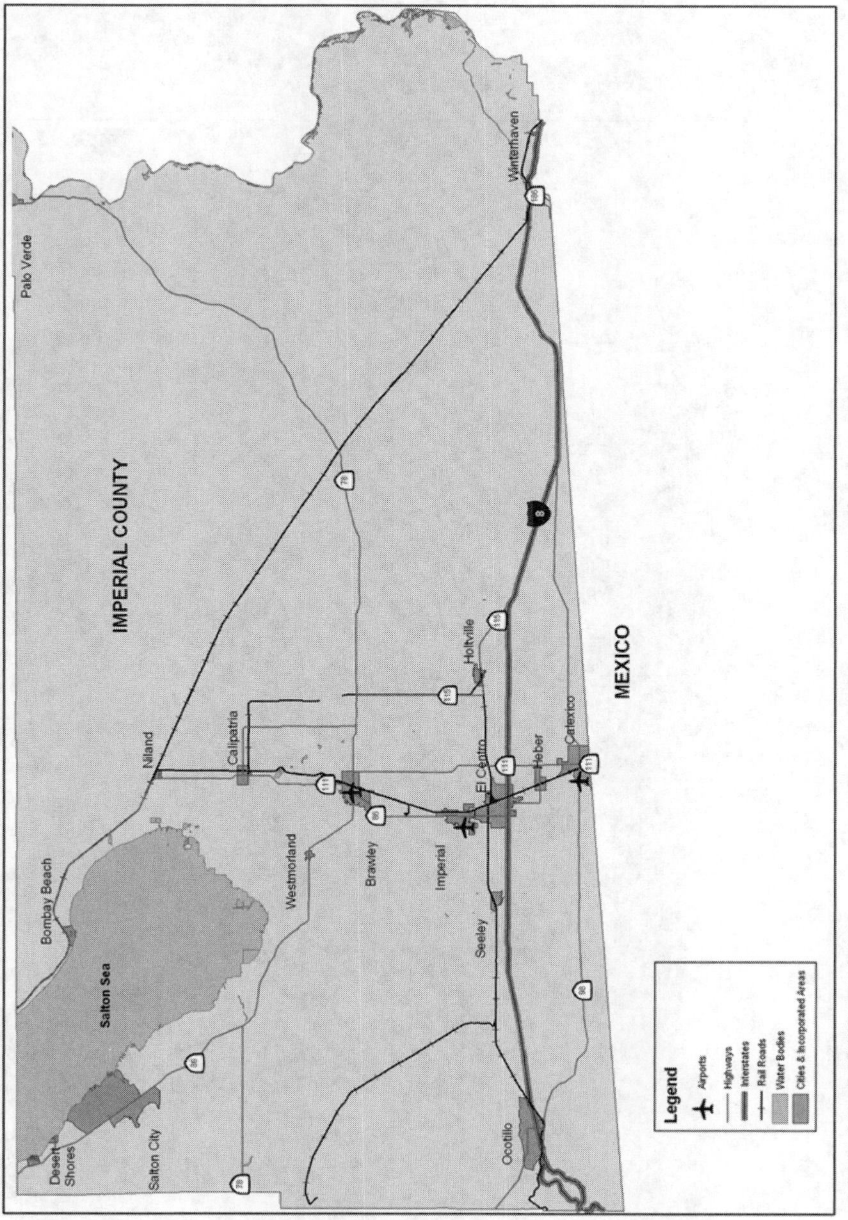

SOURCE: CCBRES (2002).

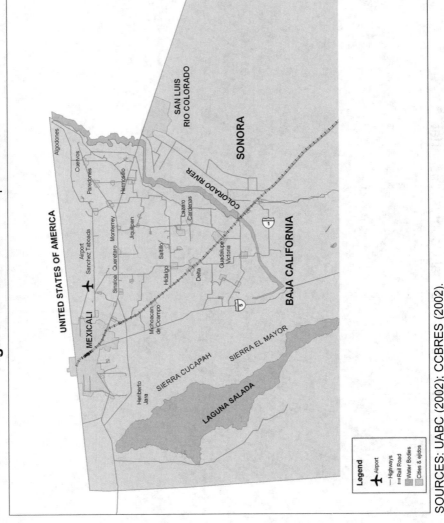

Figure 12. Mexicali Transportation

SOURCES: UABC (2002); CCBRES (2002).

PART TWO

History and Government

2

Before the Waters ... The Desert: An Early History of the Imperial Valley

Carlos R. Herrera*

Abstract

This essay explores the history of the Imperial-Mexicali Valley before the advent of planes, trains, and automobiles; agribusiness; and the cooling presence of Colorado River water in the All-American Canal and its numerous arteries. Specifically, the study looks at the most significant attempts made by Europeans and Americans to traverse the valley's sun-baked surface in the eighteenth and nineteenth centuries. Of particular interest are the questions of why these people came to the desert and why most refused to stay, preferring instead to cross the valley as quickly as possible to reach points along the Pacific coast. For some, it is called the Colorado Desert. Others refer to it as the Imperial-Mexicali Desert, the Yuha, or the Northern Sonoran. For the thousands of people who inhabit the Imperial-Mexicali Valley, the desert is simply home.

Introduction

Until George Chaffey diverted water from the Colorado River to the Imperial-Mexicali Valley late in the 1800s, all wayfarers of European ancestry who ventured into this unforgiving landscape regarded it as the last obstacle en route to the Pacific coast. Spanish, Mexican, and North American travelers who dared to chance this relentless environment understood the hardships and privations that awaited them on the open trail. The arid climate and sparse resources of the Colorado Desert did not

*Herrera is Professor of History at San Diego State University-Imperial Valley Campus.

compare favorably to the more moderate conditions of northern California. On this frontier, temperatures soared in the summer and dropped precipitously in the winter.[1] Game and water were scarce and pasturage for livestock was almost nonexistent. Still, in their desire to reach San Diego and Los Angeles, these would-be Californios proved willing to endure the harsher elements that abounded in the Colorado Desert. Few, however, desired to make this desolate valley their home; they regarded it a place to be crossed, not lived in.[2]

First Inhabitants of the Colorado Desert

The Europeans and Americans who ventured into the Colorado Desert encountered indigenous peoples who made this arid frontier their home. The earliest physical record of human presence in the Imperial-Mexicali Valley dates back some twenty thousand years. At this time, the Colorado Desert was, in fact, a lake. Fed by the primitive Colorado River, as well as water from giant ice caps that covered much of the earth's surface that began to melt sometime around 8000 B.C., Lake Cahuilla offered humans a hospitable climate and plenty of resources. Archeological evidence suggests that the earliest inhabitants of the Imperial-Mexicali Valley, the ancestors of today's Kumeyaay Indians, hunted big game and gathered the natural foods Mother Earth provided in and around the lake.[3]

Lake Cahuilla began to dry up sometime around 7500 B.C., causing dramatic alterations to the environment of the lush and prehistoric Imperial-Mexicali Valley. The transformation of the region into a true desert forced the people of the lake to adapt and change as well. The early Kumeyaay probably sought shelter in caves of surrounding mountain ranges to escape the increasing heat during the summer months. When forced to live in the open desert—normally from fall to spring—they constructed temporary pole and brush huts. From these makeshift homes, the people scoured sloughs for what food they could find from a dwindling resource supply, mostly seeds from mesquite pods. When necessary, the Kumeyaay ate rodents, lizards, snakes, and insects. They hunted small game such as rabbit and fish, but rarely did they bring down mountain deer and sheep.

Around 1000 B.C., the desert dwellers came into contact with the Quechan Indians of the lower Colorado River valley, at present-day Yuma. From the Quechan, the Kumeyaay borrowed ideas that helped them better adapt to severe desert conditions, including the use of sunken hut floors and pottery for improved preservation and storage of food. The most significant lesson, however, came in the form of agriculture. By A.D. 600, the desert Kumeyaay supplemented their food supply by growing maize and beans. The arid desert, though, did not lend itself well to large-scale cultivation, so agriculture was practiced on a limited basis; it never replaced hunting and gathering as the primary means of procuring sustenance (Luomala 1978: 594, 600–601). When the harvest was abundant, the people traded garden vegetables and fruits with their upland cousins and Colorado River neighbors. In so doing, they became cultural brokers between the Pacific coast Kumeyaay and subsistence agriculturists such as the Quechan, Pima, Hopi, and the ancient Anasazi and their descendants, the Pueblo of New Mexico.[4] Through this expansive economic network, the Indians of today's U.S. Southwest shared more than material goods; they also disseminated valuable knowledge of the Europeans, who began to appear in the region in the 1500s. Of these foreign interlopers, it was the Spaniards that the Kumeyaay first met on the sands of the Colorado Desert.

Spanish Explorers and the Colorado Desert

As an imperial-minded world power of the sixteenth century, Spain was destined to lay claim to the Imperial-Mexicali Valley. The Iberians began to build their North American empire when Hernán Cortés conquered the Mexica (Aztec) capital City of Tenochtitlán in 1521.[5] The *conquistadores* (conquerors) believed this large, and rich urban center might be one of the fabled cities of Antilia, where gold abounded beyond anyone's dreams.[6] For Spain's Catholic Monarchs, Fernando and Isabela, Tenochtitlán and its inhabitants represented much more than trophies of war; they believed the city housed thousands of souls that must be brought into the Christian fold. Waving the dual banners of empire and church, the Spaniards thus embarked upon a North American agenda of imperial and spiritual expansion that ultimately brought them to the Colorado Desert.

Spain's push into New Spain's northernmost regions began in 1535. That year, four members of a failed exploratory expedition to Florida—who had survived among the indigenous peoples of the far northern frontier since 1528—were reunited with their fellow countrymen in the region of present-day Culiacán, Mexico. The most outspoken castaway, Álvar Núñez Cabeza de Vaca, shared tales of the peoples he encountered throughout his odyssey, but never claimed to have seen any cities that compared to old Tenochtitlán.[7] Undaunted by the uncertainty of immediate riches, the Spaniards set out to explore and conquer the lands Cabeza de Vaca had so recently left behind. In 1538, the Franciscan friar, Fray Marcos de Niza, and one of Cabeza de Vaca's companions, the Moorish slave Estevanico, reconnoitered the Arizona-New Mexico frontier. There, the friar glanced at Zuni Pueblo from a distance; he then returned to Mexico City and proclaimed the Indian settlement was grander than the capital of New Spain. In 1540, the Spanish monarchy ordered Francisco Vázquez de Coronado to lead an exploratory expedition of hundreds to the now legendary Zuni. To Coronado's dismay, the pueblo proved nothing more than a small settlement of adobe structures with no gold and few Indians. Disillusioned, the *conquistador* cursed Niza's name through clenched teeth and returned to Mexico City in 1542.[8]

Although Coronado did not find treasures in New Spain's northern frontier, he did acquire much information regarding the land and peoples of the region. From

Zuni, the Spaniards explored north to the Grand Canyon, east to New Mexico and the Great Plains, and in September 1540, Coronado ordered Melchor Díaz to lead a company of troops west to the Colorado River. Here, Díaz hoped to meet a naval party that sailed into the river by way of the Sea of Cortez under the command of Hernando de Alarcón bearing supplies for Coronado's expeditionary forces. Díaz reached Yuma late in the month, but failed to find the supply vessels. Instead, he located a note carved on a tree by Alarcón that indicated the latter's presence in the region. Alarcón is credited as the first European to see the Imperial-Mexicali Valley, but it was Díaz who first represented Spain in the Colorado Desert. From Yuma, the Spaniard traveled to the region of the present-day Salton Sea (Polich 1992: 2–3).

After Díaz's visit in 1540, Spain ignored the Imperial-Mexicali Valley for almost 230 years. In the seventeenth and eighteenth centuries, Jesuit and Franciscan friars made sporadic journeys to the Colorado River valley, aiming to plant the seed of Christianity among the local Indian populace and thus fulfill a royal mandate that the region be transformed into a missionary frontier.[9] Few friars dared to venture into the uninviting Colorado Desert. Nonetheless, one devout Franciscan of abundant energy and ambition, Fray Francisco Garcés, appeared eager to bring God to the indigenous peoples of the Imperial-Mexicali Valley:

> Father Garcés is so well fitted to get along with the Indians and to go among them that he appears to be but an Indian himself. Like the Indians he is phlegmatic in everything. He sits with them in the circle, or at night around the fire, with his legs crossed, and there he will sit musing two or three hours or more, oblivious to everything else, talking with them with much serenity and deliberation. (Bolton 1930: 121)

Since his appointment to Sonora in 1768, the strong-willed Garcés made several trips to Yuma and, in 1771, he explored the Imperial-Mexicali Valley as far as present-day Calexico (Polich 1992: 5). Unimpressed by the barren Colorado Desert, Garcés encouraged his superiors to expand the mission program among the Hopi Indians of northeastern Arizona and northwestern New Mexico.[10] In so doing, Garcés believed Spain could create a Christian corridor between New Mexico, Sonora, and the newly founded colony of Alta California.[11] King Carlos III agreed that ties among these northern colonies would help consolidate the imperial frontier. Toward this end, he ordered the friar to accompany an exploratory force charged with locating a land route from Sonora to Alta California. Garcés' participation in this expedition of 1774 brought him together with one of New Spain's most respected frontiersman, Captain Juan Bautista de Anza. Don Juan had made a name for himself as a successful military officer in his native Sonora. He knew the people of the north, both Indian and European. More than anything else, however, Anza's knowledge of the land made him the perfect candidate to conduct Spain's first exploratory expedition across the Imperial-Mexicali Valley.[12]

Spain considered Alta California a religious and imperial frontier that must be preserved at all costs. By populating the colony with Spanish-American immigrants, the monarchy hoped to defend it against foreigners bent on wresting from Spain territory on the continent. Carlos III had good reason to fear encroachment on his North American domains. Acting under orders of Queen Elizabeth, British privateers, such as Sir Francis Drake, had raided Spanish vessels along the Pacific Ocean as early as the 1570s. In 1587, the pirate Thomas Cavendish plundered a Spanish galleon en route to Mexico from the Philippines (Weber 1992: 40–42, 82–84). France too represented a formidable foe. In the late 1600s, it made inroads into the Texas territory, but failed to retain a permanent stronghold in the region and was eventually evicted in the 1760s as a result of war (Chipman 1992: 70–85). Spain's most pressing interloper in Alta California came to the colony by way of Alaska and Canada. Since the 1740s, Russian fur trappers had extended their activities south along the Pacific coast from these remote regions. By the 1770s, Spain understood clearly that Empress Catherine II intended to establish a permanent Russian presence in Alta California (Jones 1984: 1–11).

The Russian challenge could not go unanswered. Thus, Spain initiated a mission and presidio-building program in Alta California designed to reinforce the colony with Spanish-American settlers and indigenous converts. Carlos III turned to able frontiersmen such as Anza to cut land routes through the uninviting terrain of the Colorado Desert in order to keep supplies flowing to these settlers (Rolle 1978: 54–100). In this regard, Anza did not disappoint his king:

On 8 January 1774, Captain Anza and a small contingent of troops, scouts, friars, and servants set out from Tubac presidio. Don Juan pressed one individual, Sebastián Tarabal, a Cochimí Indian from the mission of San Gabriel in Alta California, into service. Sebastián played a significant role in the expedition, for he had recently traveled to Sonora from San Gabriel along the very route Anza ultimately followed to reach the Pacific coast. The journey to Alta California proved rough. Just east of the Colorado River at Yuma, the Spaniards struggled to find their way across a formidable stretch of sand dunes where not even a blade of grass could survive. Beyond this great barrier and the broad river lay the sun-baked deserts of the present Imperial Valley. Here, within site *El Monte Centinela* (Mount Signal), Tarabal directed the company in a more north-western direction and led the party through another stretch of desert that now bears Don Juan's name (Anza-Borrego). Next, the Spaniards from Tubac worked their way over the San Jacinto Mountains and into the Los Angeles basin. Finally, Anza and company found their way to San Gabriel and ultimately to Monterrey. (Herrera 2000: 51)

Anza's 1774 odyssey through the dreaded Colorado Desert proved invaluable for Spain; he demonstrated that a land route between Sonora and Alta California did exist. More importantly, Don Juan's efforts convinced King Carlos III to call for a colonizing expedition that would traverse the Imperial-Mexicali Valley and expand his imperial frontier to San Francisco Bay.[13]

Spanish Colonists Cross the Imperial-Mexicali Valley

They had come to the Colorado Desert to serve their celestial God and earthly king. But as the 240 Spaniards gathered on the banks of the Colorado River in December 1775 and gazed upon a desert that stretched west from Yuma Indian villages, they must have wondered why God and emperor led them to this vast and arid landscape. Not even the presence of their famed leader, Don Juan Bautista de Anza, could settle the strained nerves and thoughts of these Spanish-Americans as they pondered the desert crossing they were about to make. Anza had traversed this desolate panorama in 1774 and knew all too well the hardships his people would face in the coming days. Before them lay some ninety miles of parched earth that offered almost no water and little pasturage for the nearly one thousand beasts of burden that accompanied the colonists. Although they would escape the extreme heat of summer, the travelers could not avoid exposure to a desert winter that, in the evenings, could chill even the hardiest to the bone. Most had left families and friends behind in Sonora and Sinaloa, hoping to build new homes among the indigenous peoples of Alta California. The quest for a better life, however, seemed a distant and illusive dream while the Colorado Desert beckoned the Spanish pilgrims into its barren grasp. Still, as they took their first steps into the scorched wilderness west of Yuma, the Spaniards found solace in the thought that this wasteland represented nothing more than a thirsty barrier, a sandy highway that stood between them and their promised land.

Fray Pedro Font, the Franciscan who served as diarist and head priest for the colonizing expedition of 1775, compared the odyssey he and his compatriots embarked upon to the biblical exodus of Jews from ancient Egypt (Bolton 1966: 20). Although the Spaniards did not cross a Red Sea, they had struggled across the Colorado River. And while they would never gaze upon the desolate Egyptian landscape, the arid Colorado Desert now stood before them. Without a doubt, Anza's land-bound argonauts were a faithful bunch. Still, they embraced memories of the kind reception they had received from the Quechan back in November. At Yuma, the Indians shared their harvest of fruits and vegetables with the Spaniards. Their leader, Don Salvador Palma, had called them his *queyé* (friends). And on the very day they were about to depart from the cottonwood and mesquite laden banks of the Colorado River, the chief came out to bid his Spanish guests farewell. On that crisp December morning, Palma took care to present an elegant and proud visage. He donned a European styled suit gifted to him by Anza, which consisted of an embroidered jacket with a stylish yellow front, a cape of blue cloth decorated with gold braid, and a black velvet cap adorned with imitation jewels (Bolton 1966: 80).

The Spaniards entered the Colorado Desert on December 6, 1775, bearing a large painting of the Virgin Mary at the head of their caravan. Early in the afternoon, they reached the sand dunes west of Yuma, from which they gazed upon the Sierra Madre (Chocolate Mountains) in the horizon. Two days later, Anza divided the colonists into three groups and ordered them to traverse the Imperial-Mexicali Valley at one-day intervals. In so doing, Don Juan hoped to prevent a large convoy from depleting what little water the desert wells provided. Before leaving Yuma, Anza also ordered the Spaniards to collect as much maize and grass as they could carry so that their horses and livestock might have something to eat while on the trail (Bolton 1966: 124).

On December 9 and 10, the Spaniards trudged across territory encompassing today's City of Mexicali and crossed the future U.S.-Mexican border somewhere west of Calexico. Anza's lead party reached Santa Rosa de las Raxas (Yuha) the following day. There, the Spaniards dug six wells that produced a decent supply of water for the thirsty travelers and their beasts. A mere seven miles to the south, the Cerro del Imposible (Mount Signal) cast a shadow on the desert floor that served as an omen of ill tidings to come. On December 12, Anza and company rode into the environs of Plaster City, at Coyote Wash, where they were greeted by a cold wind that bit into the flesh of the weary Spaniards. The following day, the group made camp at San Sebastián (Harpers Well), where they encountered a band of hungry and emaciated Indians. On the fourteenth, storm clouds that had been gathering for two days finally burst open and dropped a blanket of snow on the colonists. As the white flakes fell, the second group of colonists arrived at camp, suffering from exposure to the desert cold. The final group of colonists arrived at San Sebastián on the seventeenth. That day, the Spaniards rejoiced at having survived the desert crossing and in the evening they celebrated with song and *fandango* (Bolton 1966: 124–38). In the coming days, Anza led his party across the Santa Rosa Mountains to San Gabriel Mission at Los Angeles. Finally, in March 1776, the now seasoned travelers stood on a patch of land just south of the future location of the Golden Gate Bridge. They made camp, lit fires, rejoiced that their long odyssey had ended, and formally founded the present-day settlement of San Francisco in the name of their God and king (Bolton 1966: 122–38). Back in the Imperial-Mexicali Valley, the sand had already consumed the flesh and hides of livestock lost by the Spaniards during their trek through the Colorado Desert. All that remained on the desert floor were the sun-bleached bones of these animals, emblems of a deteriorating empire gasping for life on the North American frontier.

The Californios and the Colorado Desert

The empire that Anza helped expand into the Imperial-Mexicali Valley did not last. In 1781, Indians attacked Spanish colonists living at two missions constructed near Yuma the previous year. The Quechan had allowed Spain to establish La Purísima

Concepción and San Pedro y San Pablo de Bicuñer on the western bank of the Colorado River so long as the foreigners increased trade with the locals. The Spaniards, however, failed to manifest a strong economic presence in the Colorado River valley. Instead, they became dependent on Quechan lands and goods. Tired of the growing demands for their resources, the Indians turned on the people Salvador Palma once considered his friends. By June 20, 1781, some one hundred Europeans at Yuma lay dead or were reported missing. In the aftermath of the bloody massacre, Spain chose to abandon the Colorado River valley and the desert trail Anza had forged through the Colorado Desert. In so doing, the crown forced those travelers seeking passage to Alta California to sail first to Baja California and finish their journey via overland peninsular routes.[14]

Following the Yuma massacre, California's European population did not try to use or settle the Imperial-Mexicali Valley until the 1820s. In 1821, the Colorado Desert, along with the rest of Mexico, gained its independence from Spain. But while the Californios lost the imperial vestiges that once bound them to the mother country, they clung dearly to the pastoral society they had created. Life was pleasant for the Mexican farmers and ranchers of California, where "orchards yielded abundantly and their gardens were full of vegetables ... beef and mutton were to be had for the killing, and wild game was very abundant" (Weber 1992: 342). The Californios wished to preserve this world of abundance and proved willing to defend it against undesirables. In 1831, they removed Lieutenant Colonel Manuel Victoria from office, a tyrannical governor who tried to rule the state with an iron fist and thus deny the people their right to a representative government, as mandated by the Mexican Constitution of 1824 (Rolle 1978: 137–41). More than their Mexico City-appointed governors, however, the Californios recognized that the increasing presence of North Americans in California represented a great threat to the rule they enjoyed over their homeland. In an effort to defend the extreme southern portion of the state against these adventurers, fortune seekers, and land grabbers, the Californios entered the Colorado Desert and erected a fort near present-day El Centro.

California's push to create a military presence in the Imperial-Mexicali Valley occurred during the short-lived reign of Emperor Agustín de Iturbide (1822–1823). Upon assuming office, Iturbide expressed concern regarding the possibility of U.S. encroachment into Mexico's far northern frontier. In 1822, the emperor ordered Anza's Colorado Desert trail reopened so as to reinforce defensive ties between Sonora and Alta California. Toward this end, Father Felix Caballero, from Baja California's Mission Santa Catarina, traversed the Imperial-Mexicali Valley and reached Yuma accompanied by two Indian guides in the spring of 1823. Caballero left the Colorado River valley believing that the Indians welcomed renewed ties with Mexico. The priest returned to Yuma with a small escort from Tucson in July 1823 and asked the locals to help his men construct rafts to cross the river. The Quechan obliged and even led the Mexicans into the raging Colorado. At mid-crossing, however, the Indians turned on their guests and tried to drown them, hoping to steal their horses. Caballero and company barely escaped and found their way back to Mission Santa Catarina, but not before the Quechan had stripped them of their supplies and pride (Chamberlin 1981: 9).

Two years after the Caballero incident at Yuma, Sonora's Governor José Figueroa invited the Quechan, Upper Pima, and Cocomaricopa chiefs to a peace conference at his capital of Arizpe. The indigenous leaders rejected the offer, prompting Figueroa to lead a force of 400 troops to the Colorado River valley; the Indians, he argued, must accept peace, even if by force of arms. The Mexicans reached Yuma on November 16, 1825, where the local chief, Cargo Muchachos, made them feel welcomed and thus avoided a violent confrontation (Chamberlin 1981: 10). Figueroa left Yuma soon after his meeting with Cargo Muchachos, content that peace had been restored, but fearing it would not last. The governor concluded that a military buildup in the Colorado Desert was required to protect citizens traveling on the old Anza trail. Mexican officials thus ordered the construction of a presidio near present-day Banning. The job of designing the fort-like structure went to Lieutenant Romualdo Pacheco, an engineer in the Mexican army assigned to San Diego.

In December 1825, Pacheco and newly appointed California Governor José María Echeandía led an inspection tour from San Diego to Yuma. The group entered the Colorado Desert via the Carrizo Wash north of Ocotillo. East of this corridor, they came upon a temporary lake on the New River that had been formed by diverted Colorado River floodwater. Having named the lake "Laguna Chapala," Echeandía agreed with Pacheco that a fort at this site, rather than at Banning, would better suit the defensive needs of travelers on the Anza trail. Pacheco and a small detachment of troops remained in the Imperial-Mexicali Valley to begin work on the presidio. Ironically, the lieutenant hired desert Kumeyaay to help construct the military outpost designed to protect Mexicans against these very Indians. Pacheco's crew completed the fort in January 1826 and the lieutenant returned to San Diego. In April, news reached Echeandía that a band of Kumeyaay Indians had attacked Fort Chapala. He ordered Pacheco and a detachment of 25 troops to the Colorado Desert, where they faced off against the desert dwellers. After several indecisive skirmishes, six Mexican soldiers and 28 Kumeyaay lay dead on the hot desert sand. Pacheco decided to abandon Fort Chapala, but not before he cut off the ears of his slain enemies and had them shipped to San Diego for public display (Farris 1977: 3–9). By evacuating his men from the Imperial-Mexicali Valley, the lieutenant surrendered the Colorado Desert to the Indians. For the next 20 years, the Kumeyaay enjoyed an unchallenged reign over this barren landscape. But then, in the 1840s, another breed of foreigners began to appear on the sands of the Imperial-Mexicali Valley. Armed with the ideal of manifest destiny, among other weapons of empire, the new interlopers believed it was God's will for them to conquer the entirety of North America's western frontier.

North Americans and the Colorado Desert

North Americans first appeared in Alta California as early as the 1790s. In 1848, the United States acquired the region through a war imposed on Mexico.[15] That same year, James Marshall discovered gold at John Sutter's mill near Sacramento and thus initiated a rush of humans seeking their fortunes in the soil of the Far West. Those gold diggers that chose to stay in California preferred the rich lands and moderate climates that abounded in the Pacific and northern regions of the state; none harbored the desire to settle the Colorado Desert. This latter frontier, after all, offered few resources and arable land. Like the Spaniards before them, North Americans regarded the Imperial-Mexicali Valley as a sandy highway that stood between them and the golden sunsets of the Pacific coast.

During the U.S.-Mexican War, General Stephen Watts Kearny used Colorado Desert trails to transport his Army of the West to California. Kearny and 100 dragoons wisely crossed the Imperial-Mexicali Valley in the cooler months of 1846, but almost lost the Pacific coast campaign when they faced off against Californio forces at San Pasqual in December. Following in the General's footsteps, a second U.S. military force of 500 Mormon volunteers reached the Colorado River valley in January 1847. From Yuma, this battalion embarked upon a Colorado Desert crossing that tested their physical and spiritual endurance.

Brigham Young's "Saints" had answered a military circular issued by General Kearny, which called for the creation of five infantry companies that would participate in the conquest of California.[16] The Mormons began their odyssey at Council Bluffs, Iowa, on July 16, 1846. They gathered at Fort Leavenworth, Kansas, where they received the accoutrements of war and ultimately reached Yuma on January 8, 1847. From the moment they entered the waters of the Colorado on the tenth, the Mormon Battalion, which also included several women, suffered at the hands of Mother Nature. Two pack mules drowned during the river crossing and the soldiers resorted to using their wagons as rafts. Having survived the untamed Colorado, the Mormons gathered what mesquite beans they could find to feed their starving beasts and headed off in the direction of the dreaded desert that lay before them. Like the Spaniards, the battalion did not stray far from the few wells that marked the trail across the Imperial-Mexicali Valley. Most of these watering holes lay on the Mexican side of the present U.S.-Mexican border, but had run dry by the time the thirsty Mormons needed them most. What little water the battalion found proved of the poorest quality. Nevertheless, the Mormons drank greedily when they came upon the life-giving liquid and allowed their livestock, the corpses of which soon began to litter the trail, to suffer the consequences of travel on the arid desert.

The Mormon Battalion reached the environs of Mexicali on Friday, January 15, 1847. From there, they crossed the present international boundary some five miles west of Calexico and ended the march near Plaster City. By then, the wayfarers found themselves at the doorsteps of death and struggled on in small groups. Many had already surrendered their lives to the unforgiving desert. Those that survived gathered around campfires and consumed a cow they had slaughtered to ward off starvation. The following morning, January 16, before the sun had begun its daily ascent over the eastern horizon, the Mormons set off in the direction of Carrizo Creek. There, they found plenty of water and pasturage and, so, were saved. Of the 500 individuals and 25 wagons that entered the Colorado Desert at Yuma, 364 in five carts reached their final destination of San Diego on January 29, 1847. Those Mormons that lived to tell the tale of their ordeal in the Imperial-Mexicali Valley continued to serve in the U.S. military in San Diego, San Luis Rey, and Los Angeles. On July 16, 1847, the Battalion was discharged and most of the Mormons found their way to Salt Lake City, where they were reunited with their spiritual brethren (Farris 1972: 1–20).

The Mormon Battalion's crossing of the Imperial-Mexicali Valley stands as a testament of the courage and perseverance needed to live in and traverse the Colorado Desert before the twentieth century. The privations the Mormons endured, however, did not keep other North Americans from venturing into the sandy frontier east of Yuma. By far, the greatest number of U.S. citizens to use the Colorado Desert as a highway to the Pacific coast did so impelled by the Gold Rush fever, which struck the Atlantic seaboard late in 1848. It is estimated that some 81,000 individuals from the United States and Mexico found their way to California in 1849 alone. The majority of these fortune seekers made the trek west on overland trails and about 10,500 arrived by way of Yuma and the Imperial-Mexicali Valley (Holliday 1995: 9).

At Yuma, the forty-niners met some 3,000 Quechan living in five major villages. Here, enterprising Americans, such as Dr. Able B. Lincoln from New York, set up Colorado River ferries that crossed compatriots into the Imperial-Mexicali Valley and set them on track toward the golden nuggets. Although Lincoln made efforts to deal respectfully with the Quechan, other more unscrupulous North Americans did not. One group from Tennessee, that was led by John Glanton, forced the doctor at gunpoint to take the ruffians on as partners. It did not take long for relations between North Americans and native Indians to deteriorate into violence. On April 23, 1850, the Quechan conducted a surprise attack on the Glanton gang and killed all but three of the Americans, including Dr. Lincoln. The Indians, it seems, grew tired of the wholesale disregard for life Glanton's men displayed at Yuma and the murder of indigenous people. The survivors escaped to San Diego and relayed news of the incident to local officials, who then sent a military force to Yuma to establish order and protect U.S. citizens flocking to California. The United States escalated its military presence in the Colorado River valley by establishing Fort Yuma on December 1, 1850 (Tabor 1968: 1–2). Like the Spaniards before them, the North Americans thus recognized the importance of the Imperial-Mexicali Valley and were ready to defend the old Anza trail at considerable cost.

Not all those North Americans who entered the Colorado Desert in 1849 did so as fortune hunters. That year, Lieutenant Amiel W. Whipple led a group of topographical engineers across the Imperial-Mexicali Valley that surveyed the desert and mapped the boundary between the United States and Mexico. Like their predecessors, these Americans experienced the full force of natural elements for which the desert was known. Impressed by the barren vastness of the region, Whipple described the Imperial-Mexicali Valley as "a dreary, desolate plain before us, far as the eye can reach" (Whipple 1849: 8). Lieutenant R.S. Williamson shared Whipple's sentimental depiction of the region. In the 1850s, Williamson led a survey group to the desert to ascertain the best possible route on which to build a railroad. He concluded that the horizontal nature of the Imperial-Mexicali Valley afforded an excellent landscape for such a project. Still, Williamson expressed concern regarding the lack of water needed to propel the steam-powered giants across the sandy highway.[17] Water or not, the Americans did bring the railroad to the Colorado Desert, and with it some semblance of the Industrial Age. Eventually, paved roads and highways joined the iron locomotives in replacing the very paths humans used to cross the Imperial-Mexicali Valley. This done, the ruts cut into the sun-baked earth by Spanish, Mexican, and U.S. wagons began to disappear from the face of the Colorado Desert.

Conclusion

At the dawn of the twenty-first century, travelers crossing the southwesternmost region of the United States continue to use the Imperial-Mexicali Valley as a highway. Like their preindustrial predecessors, today's wayfarers gaze upon the expansive Colorado Desert with awe and apprehension, and treat it with respect. In this regard, modern-day desert voyagers are not much different than the Spaniards, Mexicans, and North Americans who came before them. Although they press through the Imperial-Mexicali Valley in air-conditioned automobiles and on high-speed highways, they nevertheless pray their vehicles will not break down in the heat of summer or during a winter storm.

Present-day pilgrims who come to the Colorado Desert do so for reasons similar to those that brought the Spaniards, Mexicans, and North Americans. Like Spanish missionaries, evangelists from the different churches of the world spread their spiritual beliefs throughout the Imperial-Mexicali Valley. And although the United States is not a true empire, Border Patrol agents do scout the Colorado Desert daily to keep foreign interlopers at bay, much the same way Spain did in the eighteenth century. In addition, the U.S. Military does operate a Naval Air Facility near the City of El Centro, reminding one of the fort-like structure Lieutenant Romualdo Pacheco designed and had constructed there in the 1820s. Even the undesired aliens that supposedly threaten U.S. frontiers have a historical counterpart who came to the Colorado Desert. They come to the Imperial-Mexicali Valley and beyond for the same reason those forty-niners used the desert as a highway: to get to the gold nuggets of Alta California. Unfortunately, each year more and more fortune hunters do not find the riches they seek; rather, they perish in the barren desert like the Mormons who died trying to reach their promised land in 1847 and whose bones are still buried somewhere in the arid sand. Finally, much like the desert Kumeyaay, the people who call the Colorado Desert their home understand that before the coming of planes, trains, and automobiles, before the waters of the Colorado River transformed the Imperial-Mexicali Valley into an agricultural oasis, this very special place was, in fact, a desert.

Endnotes

1. North American surveyors who visited the Imperial-Mexicali Valley in the late 1800s, seeking a route for a railroad that would run from the Mississippi River Valley to San Diego and Los Angeles, first used the term "Colorado Desert." The place name identifies the territory that stretches from the present-day City of Yuma, Arizona, to the foot of the mountains west of San Diego, California, and from the shores of the Salton Sea to the Colorado River Delta in Mexico. The Imperial-Mexicali Valley lies within the boundaries of the Colorado Desert. Still, the indigenous peoples of this desert and the Spaniards, who first traversed it in the late 1700s, did not use these place names. For the sake of consistency, however, the designations "Colorado Desert" and "Imperial-Mexicali Valley" will be used throughout this essay. For a history of the origins of the term "Colorado Desert," see James 1906: xxii.

2. The Imperial-Mexicali Valley was formed by silt carried by the Colorado River to the lower Colorado River Delta and adjacent areas. See Polich 1992: 1.

3. The name of the indigenous group that inhabited the Imperial Valley prior to the coming of Europeans is debated. Traditional scholars referred to these people as the "Digueño," emphasizing their historical relations to the Indians who inhabited the San Diego region and its environs. William S. Simmons uses the name "Cahuilla," thus tying the desert dwellers to the ancient lake that formed the prehistoric Imperial-Mexicali Valley. Katherine Luomala prefers the term "Tipai," an indigenous word that roughly translates into "the people." For the sake of consistency, the more common appellation of "Kumeyaay" (also Kamia) will be used in this essay. See Simmons 1998: 53–54; Luomala 1978: 593.

4. Simmons places the Desert Kumeyaay at the "periphery of the greater Southwest culture area" because they shared cultural habits, such as subsistence agriculture and pottery making, with the Yuma, Pima, Hopi, and Pueblos (1998: 52–56).

5. The story of Cortés' conquest of the Aztec empire has been covered in numerous sources. One of the most modern and detailed accounts of this epic story is found in Thomas 1993.

6. Many Spaniards of the sixteenth century believed that the Americas might be the location of the fabled cities of Antilia, seven large urban centers founded by seven Portuguese bishops who had sailed across the Atlantic to escape the Moorish invasions of Iberia in the eighth century. Grounded in popular romance and historical novels of the day, the myth of Antilia stated that the bishops had constructed these cities primarily of gold and on an island far to the west of Iberia. By the late 1500s, the collective name of these Christian settlements evolved to "Cities of Cíbola," making reference to the belief that these urban centers were located far to the north of Tenochtitlán, specifically among the Zuni pueblos of Arizona and New Mexico. For the Seven Cities of Antilia and Cíbola, see Weber 1992: 24, 42; Nowell 1954: 47–50, 68–71.

7. Álvar Núñez Cabeza de Vaca and his fellow explorers set sail from Cuba in 1528 under the leadership of Pánfilo de Narváez. Having reached the northwestern shores of Florida, Narváez made the critical mistake of ordering a massive land party to traverse the peninsula from its gulf side to the Atlantic Ocean. There, the explorers would rendezvous with their ships and return to Cuba. The naval escort, however, was lost at sea during a storm and never made it to the Atlantic Ocean. Marooned, the Spaniards constructed rafts and drifted west on the Gulf of Mexico. Many of the castaways died of starvation or exposure to the elements. Those that lived washed ashore the beaches of Texas, near Galveston, where they lived among the Indians. Of the several hundred individuals who started the trip in 1528, only four survived to tell about it: three Spaniards, including Cabeza de Vaca, and Estevanico, a Moorish slave. For the Cabeza de Vaca story, see Pupo-Walker 1993.

8. The exploratory expedition headed by Francisco Vázquez de Coronado in 1540 set the pattern of Spanish-Indian relations in today's U.S. Southwest region. Upon reaching Zuni, Coronado and company engaged the local populace in battle, demanding provisions and lodging, and possibly interrupting an important Pueblo religious festival. This pattern of relations was repeated when Coronado reached other Pueblo settlements in the heart of New Mexico, along the Rio Grande. For the Coronado expedition to the Arizona-New Mexico frontier, see Bolton 1949; Flint and Cushing Flint 1997.

9. It was the Jesuit missionary, Eusebio Kino, who suggested and proved that Baja California is a peninsula, not an island. Kino did so in the 1690s when he visited the head of the Sea of Cortez and witnessed for himself the land mass that connects Baja California to Sonora. Kino first developed interest in his theory of the peninsula when Quechan Indians at Yuma told him they acquired blue abalone shells through overland trade with Pacific coast Indians. For a history of the Jesuits in New Spain's northwestern frontier, see Bolton 1984; Crosby 1994; Radding 1997.

10. As part of Spain's first colonizing expedition in Northern New Spain, the Franciscans established their mission field in the colony of New Mexico in the 1590s. There, they assumed considerable power until the Bourbon monarchy set out to subordinate them to the absolute power of the state in the 1780s.

11. Spain first explored Alta California in the 1500s, hoping to expand its empire but also to locate a water route that allowed Spanish ships to sail quickly from the Atlantic to the Pacific Ocean. For Spain's first efforts in Alta California, see Engstrand 1998: 78–110.

12. Juan Bautista de Anza was born in 1736 at the presidio town of Fronteras, Sonora, Mexico. As a child and young man, Juan received an education that prepared him to assume his place among the local frontier Spanish-American elites. Like his father, Juan the Elder, and maternal grandfather, Don Antonio Bezerra Nieto, Anza lived a life of service to his king. He entered the military as a teenage cadet in his native Sonora and earned promotions to the rank of captain. In 1774, he led an exploratory expedition of Spanish troops and Indian allies from Sonora, across the Colorado Desert, and ultimately to Alta California, where he founded the present-day City of San Francisco. From this 1774 journey, Anza acquired the knowledge he needed to lead a colonizing party to this Pacific coast settlement in 1775. In 1778, the king of Spain, Carlos III, granted Anza the governorship of New Mexico as a reward for his successful California expeditions. Don Juan held this post for 10 years. During his tenure, he defeated in battle the notorious Comanche chief, Cuerno Verde. In so doing, Anza also achieved what no other governor before could manage in the beleaguered colony, peace with the Comanche nation and various Apache tribes, all of which had threatened to destroy Spain's hold on New Spain's far northern frontier. Anza died in 1788 at the villa of Arizpe, Sonora. There, his wife, Ana

María Pérez Serrano, buried the celebrated creole in a side chapel of Nuestra Señora de la Asunción cathedral. For a biography of Anza, see Herrera 2000.

13. Fray Pedro Font, the chief Franciscan friar who served as missionary, surveyor, and diarist of the party, aptly described the colonizing expedition Anza led from Sonora to Alta California between 1775 and 1776. See Bolton 1966.

14. The Spaniards' inability to establish a strong presence at Yuma stemmed from a need to redirect the monetary and military resources needed for the economic plan to the colony of Sonora, where an Indian uprising threatened to destroy Spain's hold on the region. For the Yuma Massacre, see Santiago 1998.

15. Through the Treaty of Guadalupe Hidalgo that ended the U.S.-Mexican War of 1846–1848, the United States acquired slightly more than 50 percent of all the land that made up the country of Mexico. The ceded territory included the present-day states of California, Arizona, New Mexico, southern Colorado, and parts of Utah and Nevada.

16. Mormon participation in the U.S.-Mexican War coincided with Brigham Young's desire to transplant his Church of Jesus Christ of Latter-day Saints to the West. Young had contacted President James K. Polk early in 1846, seeking government funds for the migration. Polk recognized the potential for using the Mormons as a battalion in General Kearny's Army of the West. He communicated to Young that any male Mormon willing to help the United States conquer California would receive pay and provisions for military service and be allowed to settle in the West once the war ended.

17. Williamson's survey of the Colorado Desert is included in a collection of reports compiled by the U.S. War Department in 1856. See U.S. War Department 1856.

References

Bolton, Herbert E. 1930. *Anza's California Expeditions*. 5 vols. Berkeley: University of California Press.
Bolton, Herbert E. 1931. *Outpost of Empire: The Story of the Founding of San Francisco*. New York: Alfred A. Knopf.
Bolton, Herbert E. 1936. *Rim of Christendom, a Biography of Eusebio Francisco Kino, Pacific Coast Pioneer*. New York: Macmillan.
Bolton, Herbert E. 1949. *Coronado on the Turquoise Trail: Knight of Pueblos and Plains*. Albuquerque: University of New Mexico Press.
Bolton, Herbert E. 1966. *Anza's California Expeditions, Volume 4: Font's Complete Diary of the Second Anza Expedition*. New York: Russell and Russell.
Chamberlin, Eugene K. 1981. "Fort Romualdo Pacheco, 1825." Paper presented at the dedication of California Registered Historical Landmark number 944, 2–4 October, Fort Romualdo Pacheco, Imperial County, California.
Chipman, Donald E. 1992. *Spanish Texas, 1519–1821*. Austin: University of Texas Press.
Crosby, Harry W. 1994. *Antigua California: Mission and Colony on the Peninsular Frontier, 1697–1768*. Albuquerque: University of New Mexico Press.
Enstrand, Iris W. 1998. "Seekers of the 'Northern Mystery': European Explorations of California and the Pacific." Pp. 78–110 in *Contested Eden: California before the Gold Rush*, Ramón A. Gutiérrez and Richard J. Orsi, eds. Berkeley: University of California Press.
Farris, William M. 1972. *Historic 1847 Crossing of Imperial County, California, and Baja California, Mexico, by the Mormon Battalion*. El Centro: The Mormon Battalion Inc.

Farris, William M. 1977. *Laguna Chapala: The Mexican Fort.* Miscellaneous publication No. 6. El Centro: Imperial Valley College Museum Society and Imperial Valley College Museum.

Flint, Richard, and Shirley Cushing Flint. 1997. *The Coronado Expedition to Tierra Nueva: The 1540–1542 Route across the Southwest.* Niwot: University Press of Colorado.

Gutiérrez, Ramón A., and Richard J. Orsi, eds. 1998. *Contested Eden: California before the Gold Rush.* Berkeley: University of California Press.

Herrera, Carlos R. 2000. "The King's Governor: Juan Bautista de Anza and Bourbon New Mexico in the Era of Imperial Reform, 1778–1788." Ph.D. diss., History Department, University of New Mexico, Albuquerque, New Mexico.

Holliday, J.J. 1995. *Gold Rush Desert Trails to San Diego and Los Angeles in 1849: Brand Book Number Nine, The San Diego Corral of the Westerners.* San Diego: San Diego Corral of the Westerners.

James, George Wharton. 1906. *The Wonders of the Colorado Desert*, Vol. 1. Boston: Little, Brown and Company.

Jones, Robert E. 1984. *Provincial Development in Russia: Catherine II and Jakob Sievers.* New Brunswick: Rutgers University Press.

Luomala, Katherine. 1978. "Tipai–Ipai." Pp. 593–609 in *Handbook of North American Indians, Volume 8: California*, Robert F. Heizer, ed. Washington: Smithsonian Institute.

Lynch, John. 1989. *Bourbon Spain, 1700–1808.* Oxford: Basil Blackwell Ltd.

Nowell, Charles E. 1954. *The Great Discoveries and the First Colonial Empires.* Ithaca: Cornell University Press.

Polich, John. 1992. "Approaches to the Imperial-Mexicali Valley." Calexico. Unpublished.

Pupo-Walker, Enrique, ed. 1993. *Castaways: The Narrative of Alvar Núñez Cabeza de Vaca.* Berkeley: University of California Press.

Radding, Cynthia. 1997. *Wandering Peoples: Colonialism, Ethnic Spaces, and Ecological Frontiers in Northwestern Mexico, 1700–1850.* Durham: Duke University Press.

Rolle, Andrew F. 1978. *California: A History.* Arlington Heights: AHM Publishing Corporation.

Santiago, Mark. 1998. *Massacre at the Yuma Crossing: Spanish Relations with the Quechans, 1779–1782.* Tucson: University of Arizona Press.

Simmons, William S. 1998. "Indian Peoples in California." Pp. 48–77 in *Contested Eden: California before the Gold Rush*, Ramón A. Gutiérrez and Richard J. Orsi, eds. Berkeley: University of California Press.

Tabor, C.C. 1968. *The Ives Expedition of 1858.* El Centro: Imperial Irrigation District.

Thomas, Hugh. 1993. *Conquest: Montezuma, Cortés, and the Fall of Old Mexico.* New York: Simon and Schuster.

U.S. War Department. 1856. "Reports of Exploration and Surveys, to Ascertain the Most Practical and Economical Route for a Railroad from the Mississippi River to the Pacific Ocean." Washington, D.C.: A.D.P. Nicholson, Printer.

Weber, David J. 1992. *The Spanish Frontier in North America.* New Haven: Yale University Press.

Whipple, Amiel W. 1849. "Extract from a Journal of an Expedition from San Diego, California, to the Río Colorado, from September 11 to December 11, 1849, by A.W. Whipple, Lieutenant, United States Topographical Engineers." Included in a report by the Secretary of War, C.M. Conrad, to the U.S. Senate (1 February 1851).

3

Development of the Structure of Agriculture in the Mexicali Valley in the Early Twentieth Century

Oscar Sánchez Ramírez*

Abstract

This essay describes the most important steps that determined the path to socioeconomic development in the Mexicali Valley. It then describes the subsequent redevelopment of the valley, which allowed it to become one of the most productive regions of Mexico.

In the early twentieth century, the Colorado River Land Company purchased land from various owners in the Mexicali Valley, acquiring a majority of the property in this region. This concentration of land began an era of agricultural development. The Colorado River's natural flow led to several incidences that led to the construction of structures to protect the new agricultural activities and settlements of the Imperial-Mexicali valleys.

The valley's new agricultural economy drew an influx of Mexican migrants from all over Mexico, as well as a considerable number of Chinese migrants. The movement of Mexican workers demanding land to cultivate brought about the colonization and distribution of lands owned by the Colorado River Land Company until the company eventually disappeared from the Baja California landscape.

The repartition of Colorado River water between the United States and Mexico, after many years of diplomatic negotiations, was finalized by a water treaty that was signed by both countries in 1944. The solution of this problem demonstrated goodwill between Mexico and the United States and showed their ability to solve problems together.

*Sánchez Ramírez is the Historic Archive Coordinator for the Municipality of Mexicali.

Introduction

This essay describes the agricultural development of the Mexicali Valley, including San Luis Río Colorado, from the early twentieth century until the end of its redevelopment in 1976. Primary importance is given to the evolution of land tenure and the solution of international problems regarding the use and quality of the Colorado River water.

In order to develop the Imperial Valley, the California Land Development Company deemed it necessary to upgrade the Alamo Arroyo, formed by great floods of the Colorado River, that ran from Algodones, Mexico, to the Salton Sea in California. It formed a new partner company under Mexican law called the Irrigation and Land Society of Baja California (Sociedad de Riego y Terrenos de la Baja California, S.A.). It was commonly known as "the Mexican Company" in the United States and "la Compañía del Agua" (the Water Company) in Mexico. This was done to gain ownership of the Mexican land necessary for the construction of the Alamo Canal. The company reached a concession agreement with the Mexican government in 1904 allowing for water to be transported through Mexico from the Colorado River. It allowed for 50 percent of the 9,888 cubic feet (280 cubic meters) of water per second that would be transported by the canal to be allotted to Mexico to irrigate lands in the Mexicali Valley. It can be said that this contract, and this clause in particular, gave birth to the Mexicali Valley as an agricultural area. Prior to this, the land was there, but the water needed to develop it was not.

In the winter of 1905, the California Land Development Company opened the canal directly to the river. Due to problems with the headgate of the principal canal that was located on the U.S. side, an unexpected and uncontrolled flow burst into the canal, partially flooding the Mexicali and Imperial valleys and taking with it half of the new settlement of Mexicali. Regardless of its efforts, the company could not control the water flow and had to reroute the Southern Pacific railway, first obtaining a loan for $200,000. Its efforts then turned toward closing the break and returning the river to its previous course. Because the railway was so gravely affected, the Southern Pacific Railroad company built new routes so that trains could later bring thousands of tons of rock and gravel to the area to finally successfully block the inlet in February 1907. The cost of this operation was so high that it ultimately brought financial ruin to the company.

Once the river again began to flow toward the sea, a protective levee about 12.5 miles (20 kilometers) long—known as the California Development Levee—was constructed from the inlet to the south to prevent future floods that could affect the Imperial Valley. Another levee was constructed from Cerro Prieto toward the northeast, reaching the Cudahy check dam of the Alamo Canal. With these measures, normal agriculture was restored in the Imperial Valley and planting resumed in the Mexicali Valley.

The Colorado River Land Company

Upon the arrival of irrigation water to the Imperial Valley in June 1901, a group of investors from Los Angeles, California, became interested in acquiring the lands of the Mexicali Valley. These lands were owned largely by Don Guillermo Andrade. To this end, they established a Mexican company called the Colorado River Land Company, S.A., in Mexico City on November 18, 1902. The new company then acquired 285,208 hectares both directly and indirectly from Andrade, making its hold on the Mexican Colorado River Delta nearly complete.

The company leased the land to U.S. and Chinese companies, charging nothing for the first year and gradually increasing prices in subsequent years. The objective of this practice was to compensate the renters for the initial investment that they had to make to clear, level, and irrigate the lands. In this way, lands began to be used that could be irrigated by canal systems derived from the Alamo Canal located mainly in the western part of the valley. Areas of the Mexicali Valley that were most affected by summer floodings of the river and not protected by levees could not be planted until 1936 when the Hoover Dam was filled and the flow of the Colorado River was regulated.

Due to the economic depression of the early 1930s, Mexican return immigration from the United States grew and the Colorado Land Development Company began to lease land on an individual basis to these people. The renters, however, wanted to own the lands in the same way that the peasants did in the colonies formed by governors Esteban Cantú and Abelardo L. Rodríguez in the northeast area of the Mexicali Valley. Andrade had promised the Mexican government, from which he had acquired the land, that he would colonize it. The Secretariat of Agriculture and Development (Secretaría de Agricultura y Fomento) pressured the Colorado Land Development Company to sign an agreement for colonization on April 14, 1936. Based on this agreement, the colonization of the company's northwestern lands began between the City of Mexicali and Cerro Prieto. In reality, the company did not give up its land very quickly. Contracts granted buyers periods of 20 years to pay off the lands, while maintaining a clause reserving control of the land and preventing peasants from using the land as collateral for their loans, since the land was not yet theirs. The process was slow and not in accord with the spirit of the agreement with the Mexican government.

Floods and Protective Levees

Once the Cerro Prieto and California Development levees were constructed, a railway was extended to transport material to reinforce these structures, first from the Cucapá mountains and then from the Pilot Knob rock quarry. Extending the California

Development Levee, the Ockerson Levee was constructed toward the south, reaching beyond the town of San Luis Río Colorado. The river was thus confined between the levee and the sandy mesa. The new levee was funded by the U.S. government through the California Land Development Company, clearly indicating federal interest in protecting the Imperial Valley. Nonetheless, the heavy seasonal flows of 1909 broke the levee and water flowed through the Abejas Arroyo. The overflow reached the Volcano Lagoon before being stopped by the Cerro Prieto Levee and discharged into the Gulf of California via the Hardy River, flooding the southern part of the valley.

The construction of the Sáiz Levee began in 1910 from the Ockerson Levee, running southwest until it met the Cerro Prieto Levee at a place called Torchosa in 1922. With the construction of this structure, the northeastern Mexicali Valley, where some of the best lands are located, was protected from flooding and made available for farming. The river thus ceded space to humankind.

In 1916, the Cerro Prieto Canal was built to avoid crossing the main western canal over the dangerous New River Bridge/Canal, securing irrigation for the western part of the Imperial Valley. The Cerro Prieto Canal's inlet was located at Volcano Lagoon at the foothills of the Cerro Prieto volcano. This new route had the advantage of water coming from the lagoon, where its silt load was deposited, thereby lessening the need for the canal to be dredged. In addition, this canal also opened the land between the main canal and the Cerro Prieto volcano to cultivation.

In 1922, the Pescaderos Levee was built from the Ockerson Levee toward the southwest, taking advantage of the river's low water levels that winter by blocking the opening at Abejas and preventing the water from flowing toward Volcano Lagoon. As a result, the Cerro Prieto Canal remained without water supply. For this reason, the Solfatara Canal was built, connecting the Cerro Prieto and Alamo Canals at Cudahy. The river returned to its course, running to the sea as it had before, although summer floods still affected the southern part of the valley. To partially prevent this, General Abelardo Rodríguez's government and the Colorado River Land Company built the Rodríguez Levee. This levee went from the Delta railroad station on the Inter-California del Sur railway and headed approximately northeast until it joined with the Pescaderos Levee. A larger area for cultivation was saved from the river by this effort.

In 1928, a continuation of the Yuma Levee was constructed along the river's left side from east to west. It left a distance of 2,625 feet (800 meters) between it and the Pescaderos Levee so that the river could pass through to the south. From there toward the south, the levee of Bacanora 1 Canal nearly reached the Inter-California del Sur railroad. Almost thirty thousand hectares of land in the San Luis Valley were protected by this measure. The river continued to flood the southern part of the delta in the winter, but it did not flood beyond the zone defined by the protective levees. In 1936, the Hoover Dam began operating, bringing summer floods to a halt. Thenceforth, water releases were determined by the need for electricity generation, which resulted in increasing water flows in the winter due to greater demands for electricity.

Heavy precipitation in the upper Colorado Basin in 1940 produced enough added runoff that the river changed its course to the west, south of the railroad bridge, and flooded part of the Carranza colony. The local peasants were aided by the Pacific Soap Company (Compañía Jabonera del Pacífico), which built several levees to control the flood.

The enormous Glen Canyon Dam was completed in 1963, causing the Colorado River to practically disappear and serve primarily as an agricultural drain. Construction of the dam resulted in a number of large releases. However, the International Boundary and Water Commission (IBWC) (Comisión Internacional de Límites y Aguas–CILA) was then in operation to forewarn Mexican authorities. Also, protective levees were built on either side of the river from the international boundary to the sea as part of the Colorado River Flood Control Project. The area between the levees had a maximum capacity of 45,909 cubic feet (1,300 cubic meters) per second and damages from water releases were minimal. With these precautionary measures, the river has remained contained ever since.

Agrarian Reform

In the 1930s, along with the requests by colonists who wished to acquire land from the Colorado River Land Company, groups of people that wanted to establish *ejidos* (community-owned farms) were present in the Mexicali Valley. The requests had not been successful due to neglect on the part of local governors who were named by the federal government since Baja California still had not attained state status. The first step toward the breakup of the company's monopoly was taken in 1930 when a group of petitioners—headed by Doña Felipa Vázquez *viuda de* (widow of) Arellano—was arrested and sent to the Islas Marías prison along with several of Doña Felipa's minor children. They remained there until several months later when they were able to prove their innocence and were freed. Nonetheless, the requests continued and the number of groups increased until they decided on January 27, 1937, to invade the lands of the Colorado River Land Company. They were arrested, but freed almost immediately.

A delegation from this group went to Mexico City to present its case to the president of Mexico, Lázaro Cárdenas. President Cárdenas, who was aware of the situation, decided to resolve the problem in Baja California. He ordered the Chief of the Agrarian Department, Gabino Vázquez, to go to the territory and create a delegation of the Agrarian Department and the Mixed Agrarian Commission. He was also to expedite the processing of requests for land that had accumulated for so many years.

Governor Rafael Navarro Cortina was replaced by Colonel Rodolfo Sánchez Taboada, who facilitated the repartition of land. Vázquez tried to convert those colonies that were already established into *ejidos*, which sparked colonists to protest in the gardens of the government palace. The strike, referred to as the "Seated Strike" (Huelga de los Sentados), lasted for several weeks. The protesters were heard and the strike ended with favorable results.

By early 1938, a total of 44 *ejidos* had been created, encompassing approximately one hundred thousand hectares and satisfying the petitioners' claims. The Colorado River Land Company, which had been protected by the colonization contract, felt deceived. Since some of its directors had already died and the rest were quite old, the board began to entertain the idea of retiring the company from agricultural activity.

In an effort to assist the thousands of *ejidatarios* who had received land, the federal government established a branch of the National Bank of *Ejido* Credit (Banco Nacional de Crédito Ejidal) in Baja California. The bank furnished credit, machinery, farming equipment, animals, and (by means of a cooperative system) necessary food to the *ejidos*. The federal government also created the Colorado River Irrigation District to provide irrigation services and construct necessary canals to the new *ejidos*. However, at this time, water was still supplied by the Land and Water Company of Baja California.

Immigration to the Mexicali Valley

At the beginning of the twentieth century, the lower Colorado River valley was isolated from the rest of Mexico. Only the old overland route that Juan Bautista de Anza had forged in the eighteenth century—which crossed the river at Yuma—existed, along with some horse trails that crossed the mountains from Ensenada. Thus, the first immigrants arrived in the region from the port of Ensenada, as did some cowboys from the United States who crossed the international boundary.

When the Calexico-Yuma railroad was constructed, people began to arrive to the northern Mexican states from the United States. From 1914 to 1928, the Gulf of California Shipping Company (Compañía Naviera del Golfo de California) was functioning, operating two small ships that established communication among La Paz, Guaymas, Santa Rosalía, and Mexicali with a port located at the mouth of the Colorado River called La Bomba. Many of those who pioneered the Mexicali Valley came to the region via this route. Some arrived already under contract to help with the harvest of the cotton crop planted by the companies that leased land from the Colorado River Land Company.

Later, additional communication was established across the Altar Desert, using automobiles known as *diligencias* (diligences). They left the town of Santa Ana in Sonora, passing Caborca and Sonoita, crossing the river at San Luis, and finally reaching the Mexicali Valley.

For many years, it was thought that a railway that would unite Baja California with mainland Mexico would be too expensive. Thus, the first attempts to construct a railroad were to connect Mexicali with one of the ports along the Gulf of California, such as San Felipe, San Luis Gonzaga, La Bomba, or the imaginary Puerto Otis. For this reason, by 1936, the railroad to the mainland reached only a few kilometers beyond Riíto. However, President Cárdenas was more concerned with national integration than the economics of the railroad. As such, he ordered the construction of the Sonora-Baja California Railroad.

The railroad's construction began in 1937 and was completed on May 5, 1940, reaching Puerto Peñasco, Sonora. People traveled from Santa Ana to Puerto Peñasco and, from there, were transported by train to Mexicali. The construction of the route continued, but in 1941, the United States entered World War II and the supply of rails was suspended until the end of the war. In 1948, the Sonora-Baja California Railroad was inaugurated when it connected with the Southern Pacific Railroad at the Benjamín Hill station. The operation of this line united Baja California with the rest of Mexico. Immigration increased astonishingly and was made even easier when the paved highway from Santa Ana to Mexicali was completed in 1958, further uniting the territory with central Mexico.

End of the Colorado River Land Company

Once agrarian reform was satisfactorily completed in the Mexicali Valley with the establishment of ejidos, the Agrarian Department informed the Secretariat of Agriculture and Promotion on December 13, 1937, that the distribution of land would continue through the same colonization system as determined by the 1936 agreement. Based on this decision, the Baja California, Carranza, Nuevo León, and Coahuila colonies were developed, including a total of 20,593 hectares.

The directors of the Colorado River Land Company, however, did not show any interest in continuing the sale of land through 20-year contracts. The majority of original partners had already died and new partners wanted to recuperate money more quickly. Surprisingly, in 1945, the news spread that the Colorado River Land Company had been sold to U.S. business tycoon William O. Jenkins, who was residing in Mexico. He also had invested in Banco Mercantil (Mercantile Bank) and the Pacific Industrial Soap Company. However, Jenkins did not exercise power over these investments for long, for Nacional Financiera bought them on August 12, 1946. The name of the Colorado River Land Company was changed to the Mexican Company of Colorado River Lands (Compañía Mexicana de Terrenos del Río Colorado, S.A.) and was charged with furthering the sale of the lands, but only to Mexicans. Thus ended the hegemony that the Colorado River Land Company had enjoyed for 44 years in the Mexicali Valley.

The International Water Treaty between Mexico and the United States

When the Treaty of Guadalupe Hidalgo was signed between Mexico and the United States in 1848, the subject of international water use for irrigation purposes was not discussed. The only water-related provisions dealt with the free use of international rivers for navigation. It was not until 1906 that the first agreement was signed between the two nations to determine the quantity of water that would be guaranteed to Mexico for irrigation in the Juárez Valley.

There was no agreement regarding the distribution of Colorado River water within the United States either. To this end, a series of meetings culminated with the signing of an agreement in 1922 in Santa Fe, New Mexico, by the states of the Colorado River valley, excepting Arizona. In this agreement, a tentative distribution of waters was outlined in which the United States, out of courtesy, conceded water rights to Mexico. From this date forward, many discussions regarding the repartition of water between the two countries arose, including the possible construction of the Hoover Dam, the All-American Canal, and the legal conflict between California and Arizona concerning California's use of water allocated to Arizona. Not until all of these disputes were brought to a close did the problem of Mexico's water come to include representatives from Mexico.

According to the consensus formed by the states of the Colorado basin, Mexico had no rights to the water, except for the use that it had already made of it, if it had done so. Since the system produced return flows and some surpluses, it was thought that Mexico's share should be drawn from these sources. This offer was not accepted by Mexico, which demanded, at a minimum, sufficient quantities to irrigate the 350,000 hectares of the Mexicali Valley.

In the negotiations, the Rio Grande and the Tijuana River were also considered. In the case of the Rio Grande, the conditions contrasted those of the Colorado River. There, the apportioned waters largely originated in Mexico, and Texas farmers in the lower Rio Grande Valley depended on them. The Texas farmers feared that they would not be able to secure sufficient water for their use. As such, discussions began to balance concessions from both rivers and both countries. In the end, it was agreed that the United States would allocate 65.3 billion cubic feet (1.85 billion cubic meters) of water annually to Mexico. The treaty was signed on February 3, 1944, and was sent to be ratified by the senates of each country. Once ratified, the treaty entered into effect on November 8, 1945, and the new IBWC was charged with enforcing it. The new commission was made up of representatives from both countries. Since its establishment, the treaty has been adjusted by the IBWC on various occasions as deemed necessary through the signing of acts or minutes.

Salinity in the Mexicali Valley

In the fall of 1961, it was observed that newly sprouted alfalfa plants in the Mexicali Valley were dying as they were irrigated. It was soon discovered that the Colorado River water's salt content was higher than normal. The cause of such concentrated salinity levels was the operation of the new pumping station for the Wellton-Mohawk Drainage Project in Arizona. The Wellton-Mohawk region was a formerly successful agricultural area that suffered from the lack of an outlet for drainage due to its location in a deep basin. In hope of revitalizing the region for production, imported water was used for irrigation, causing the region's groundwater to decrease in quality and the water table to rise to the point of waterlogging the fields. As a solution, a 50-mile channel was constructed to export the drainage water to the Colorado River, causing serious repercussions for those downstream that were reflected in crop production in the Mexicali Valley (Hundley 1966).

Mexico brought the incident to the attention of the IBWC and demanded that water coming into the Mexicali Valley have a salt content similar to what it had received prior to the project's initiation. The U.S. government responded through the IBWC that according to the tenth clause of the 1944 treaty, Mexico should receive "return flows from any and all sources." Those opposed to the idea that Mexico should received better quality waters included constituents of the Colorado Basin who insisted that Mexico accept its allotted amount of drainage water with high salt content. The diplomatic process lasted for 12 years and the problem was resolved in the following stages.

First, the U.S. government built a lined canal in 1965 that brought the salty water to the Morelos Dam in Mexico, where some of the water could be mixed with less salty water and the remainder would be diverted to the Gulf of California via the river. This salty water was still considered part of Mexico's allotted quantity. Second, in 1972, the United States discharged salty water below the Morelos Dam and substituted for it fresh water above the dam. Third, in 1974 Minute 242 was signed by the IBWC, which specified that waters "delivered to Mexico upstream of Morelos Dam have an annual average salinity of no more than 115 ppm ± 30 ppm U.S. count (121 ppm ± 30 ppm Mexican count) over the annual average salinity of Colorado River waters which arrive at Imperial Dam" (IBWC 2002). The United States also constructed a concrete-lined canal to carry the salty waters to the Santa Clara Estuary, without including them as part of Mexico's allotment.

Rehabilitation of the Mexicali Valley

One result of the salinity problem was to highlight the poor agricultural conditions that prevented efficient production. The fields were not level, the canal network only functioned at 50 percent efficiency, and the drainage network was incomplete. For these reasons, credits were authorized by the World Bank and the Inter-American Development Bank. On June 29, 1970, the rehabilitation plan for Irrigation District 14, "Río Colorado, Baja California y Sonora," was executed and declared a public utility (SARH 1980).

In order to fulfill the plan, its users' consent was obtained to downsize the district, level the lands, construct new canals and line them with concrete, complete and integrate the drainage network, and relocate many of its users. All of these measures were completed in a period of about ten years and resulted in efficient irrigation for about 207,000 hectares in the Mexicali and San Luis Río Colorado valleys. This land remains adequately irrigated to this day.

References

Barrios Matrecitos, Valdemar. 1988. *Por las rutas del desierto*. Hermosillo: Gobierno del Estado de Sonora and Secretaría de Fomento Educativo y Cultura.

Blaisdell, Lowell L. 1962. *The Desert Revolution*. Madison: University of Wisconsin Press.

Herrera Carrillo, Pablo. 1958. *Colonización del Valle de Mexicali*. Mexicali: Universidad Autónoma de Baja California.

Hundley, Norris, Jr. 1966. *Dividing the Waters*. Berkeley and Los Angeles: University of California Press.

International Boundary and Water Commission (IBWC). 1944. *Tratado internacional de aguas entre México y los Estados Unidos*. Washington, D.C.: IBWC.

International Boundary and Water Commission (IBWC). 2002. "Minute No. 242" (cited 8 February). http://www.ibwc.state.gov/FORAFFAI/MINUTES/miniindex.htm.

Orive de Alba, Adolfo. 1945. "Informe técnico sobre el Tratado Internacional de Aguas." *Revista Irrigación en México* 3 (26).

Sánchez Ramírez, Oscar. 1990. *Crónica agrícola del Valle de Mexicali*. Mexicali: Universidad Autónoma de Baja California.

Secretaría de Agricultura y Recursos Hidráulicos (SARH). 1980. *Obras de rehabilitación del distrito de riego No. 14 Río Colorado, Baja California y Sonora*. México, D.F.: Dirección General de Irrigación y Control de Ríos.

4

Capitalist Development and Population Growth in the County of Imperial, California, and Mexicali, Baja California

Norma Fimbres Durazo*

Abstract

The U.S.-Mexican border was established in 1848 by the Treaty of Guadalupe Hidalgo. Its establishment resulted in the formation of cities on both sides of the border, some adjacent to the international boundary and others more distant from it. The development of these settlements is rooted in the movement of Mexican populations from the southern portion of the country to the border region in search of employment. At the same time, U.S. citizens and investors from the north moved south and west, resulting in the growth and development of the states in the southwestern United States.

As a result of the flow of capital into the region, the border became a magnet for both Mexican and U.S. workers. These migratory fluxes contributed to the formation, growth, and development of the region in the twentieth century. This can be considered a relatively solitary phenomenon, as very few borders in the world have established cities (Alegría Olazábal 1992: 15). One of these transborder regions that was formed in the early twentieth century is composed of Imperial County, California, and the Municipality of Mexicali, Baja California. Its formation, like that of all border regions, was derived from the creation of the modern nation-state, in which geographical divisions were instituted to exercise sovereignty and market controls. The nation-state is the

*Fimbres Durazo is Researcher at the Institute for Social Research at the Universidad Autónoma de Baja California, Mexicali campus.

product of industrial capitalism. As such, the purpose of the border (to permit or impede movement) has adapted to the requirements of each period of capitalism (Alegría Olazábal 1992: 15).

Within this border framework, one of the most significant social phenomena that has developed is the migration of people from other regions of Mexico to the Imperial-Mexicali region. Calexico, California, and Mexicali, Baja California, were established by these migratory currents in the early twentieth century. The two cities sit next to one another across the border and have transformed the region into a transborder space with the exchange of goods and capital and an international job market that remains viable even today.

Introduction

The permeability of borders has developed according to the needs of capitalism and can be divided into three periods. The first period began in the second half of the nineteenth century during the industrial development era when nation-states intervened and asserted greater control over their economies. This, thereby, created a need to develop an international labor supply. In this period, borders were rather permeable to the flow of goods, capital, and workers. In the second period, when nation-states had consolidated themselves and began to focus on inward development, borders lost this permeability due to economic factors, especially for goods and workers. In the mid-twentieth century, the third period emerged in which borders became more permeable, though selectively, in response to expanded economic activities. This brought about increased commercial and economic integration of nations. This integration is manifested in a new international division of labor led not by nation-states, but by transnational corporations, thereby decreasing states' potential to coordinate (Alegría Olazábal 1992: 18).

With regard to Imperial County and Mexicali, the permeability of their common border has been subject to the same fluctuations determined by the international economic arrangement that has prevailed throughout history, as previously described in the stages of capitalism. This arrangement has greatly affected labor, occupation levels, and the employment of Mexican labor due to the great difference in the capitalist development of the two countries. Thus, it is important to describe how Imperial County and the Municipality of Mexicali have emerged to highlight this region's relevance as a magnet for the Mexican migrant population.

The Region's Characteristics

Imperial County is located in the southwestern part of the State of California along part of the Colorado Desert. To the north it borders Riverside County, to the south it borders the Mexican State of Baja California, to the east the Chocolate Mountains, and to the west the Foothills Mountain Range. The central part of the Imperial Valley is part of the Colorado River Delta, considered to be one of the most arid regions in the United States, where "… the temperatures in the summer months are very high, reaching 120°F, while in the winter some days they drop to 0°F; the rest of the year the climate could be considered favorable, with scarce rains in the region" (Dowd 1956: 2). However, its geoclimatic characteristics did not hinder the Imperial Valley from attaining sound economic development, based principally on agriculture, as a consequence of U.S. capitalist expansion in the Southwest.

The Municipality of Mexicali is Imperial County's neighbor south of the border. Compared to municipalities of the Spanish colonial period located in central Mexico, Mexicali is relatively young. The first city to be established in the municipality also bears the name Mexicali. It was officially founded on March 14, 1903, although the exact date that settlers first established themselves there is unknown. Today, it is the capital of the State of Baja California. The Municipality of Mexicali borders Imperial County to the north; the Colorado River, which separates it from the State of Sonora, to the east; the Municipality of Tecate to the west; and the Municipality of Ensenada to the south. Mexicali "was born a border municipality and integrated into the U.S. economy, particularly that of California, by means of direct investments by U.S. corporations" (Ortega Villa 1993: 26). Both Imperial County and the Municipality of Mexicali emerged with common roots in agricultural activity.

The Rise of Imperial County, California

Although the Imperial Valley is a desert and arid zone with little rain, it was attractive in the early twentieth century because of the fertility of its lands and the natural slopes that characterize the depression, which allowed for the diversion of Colorado River waters that made agriculture possible in the region. In 1896, the California Land Development Company was founded and presented an irrigation project to the U.S. Congress to bring Colorado River water to the Imperial Valley. It subsequently carried out that plan, assuring irrigation for the cultivation of local lands, thereby favoring the establishment and development of capitalism in the region.

At the end of the nineteenth century, the region was practically devoid of population. To achieve capitalist development in the region a migratory wave was generated from various U.S. states, including Pennsylvania, Illinois, Arizona, and northern California. These migrants were pioneers who colonized the Imperial Valley. One of the reasons for their migration to the region was based on the possibility of acquiring lands for cultivation, an offer that was made by the company in charge of colonizing the valley. Migrants from different parts of the country were transported by railroads that connected the eastern states to those of the West, thereby facilitating the movement of people as well as goods.

Paralleling the California Land Development Company was a colonizing agency called the Imperial Land Company that was in charge of locating settlements, distributing land, and attracting colonizers. By 1905, the two companies had planned and established the populations of Calexico, Imperial, Dixieland, Brawley, El Centro, and Holtville. The residents of the valley proposed to the Board of Supervisors in San Diego that the Imperial Valley be recognized as a county. In August 1907, by official agreement, Imperial County was created and El Centro was named its capital (Estrella Valenzuela 1982: 813). By 1914, the towns of Seeley, Westmorland, Calipatria, and Niland were included as part of the county (Dowd 1956: 24).

Imperial County's economic life has historically been linked to agriculture, an activity that has always demanded large pools of labor. To achieve commercial and agricultural development in the region, one of the most essential factors was the availability of labor, which could not be fully satisfied by local workers. As a strategy to fulfill that need, workers were brought from Asia. Years later, this flow of immigrant workers was interrupted due to nationalist sentiment (Massey et al. 1991: 53).

Imperial Valley farmers resolved the labor shortage problem by hiring the few Mexicans who lived in the City of Mexicali across the border. During those years, the U.S. Colorado River Land Company, known as "La Colorado," held a monopoly over the exploitation of land in the Mexicali Valley and the incorporation of Mexicans into the workplace was minimal since the company employed Chinese, Japanese, and Hindu workers, and totally excluded Mexican workers (Grijalva 1980: 53).

The investment of capital in the Imperial Valley created a labor market whose central premise was based on so-called occasional labor reserves that depended on the demands of agricultural processes. The actual relationship between contracted labor and the farmer was only to last for the period deemed necessary for the harvest periods (Acuña et al. 1983: 100). This type of market was adopted by agricultural businesses to contract immigrant labor, which was largely made possible by the geographical location of the county and the valley (Grijalva 1980: 54).

Imperial County thus became a magnet for Mexican immigrants and economic growth. The actual border was largely fictitious, delimited only by geographic landmarks. Mexican workers could enter the United States to work quite easily. The border crossing was relatively problem-free; there was little vigilance of the border, and there was great demand for labor. Hence, the border during this period was quite permeable to the transit of capital, goods, and Mexican workers. It remained this way for the first four decades of the twentieth century, until about 1942, when the border became less permeable and more selective to the flow of Mexican labor. At this time, the Bracero Program (a guest worker program) had been agreed upon by the United States and Mexico. The program gave Mexican agricultural workers the opportunity to cross legally into the United States during its 22-year duration. The program was developed under Public Law 78 and manifested the magnitude of the requirements of agribusiness: low-cost labor that was available and subject to the seasonal necessities of agriculture and the interests of capital (Acuña et al. 1983: 51).

During its existence, the Bracero Program largely met the demand for seasonal labor in the agricultural sector in the southwestern United States. Imperial County was the most popular destination for Mexican immigrants. The region obtained great benefits from the importation of Mexican labor. During this period, the Imperial Valley reached its highest growth rates and experienced surges in agricultural production (Massey et al. 1991: 189).

Since this period, the successive reforms of immigration law and the economic crisis that emerged in Mexico in the 1970s have increasingly hindered efforts of Mexican workers to migrate to the United States and obtain legal documentation (Massey et al. 1991: 303). Even so, both legal and illegal immigration have continued to increase in the United States and Imperial County has not been an exception.

Regional Population Growth and Origin

Since the early twentieth century, the population of Imperial County has been made up of very diverse immigrant groups, including Anglo-Americans, Europeans, Asians, and Hispanics. Of this last group, the majority is Mexican (see Table 1). Immigration to this region, as previously stated, was caused by the investment of U.S. capital and the need for labor for regional economic growth, which made it one of the most agriculturally productive regions in the country.

Nonetheless, the first years were very difficult for the populations that arrived in the region at the beginning of the century. They faced flooding in the valley by the

Table 1. Population Growth and Origin of
Imperial County, 1910, 1990

Period	Total Population	Population Growth (%)	Anglo-American (%)	Hispanic Origin (%)	Other Ethnicities (%)
1910	13,591	-	75.0	18.2	6.8
1920	43,453	219.7	67.3	14.8	17.9
1930	60,903	40.1	54.4	35.5	10.1
1940	59,740	(2.7)	87.2	10.3	2.5
1950	62,975	5.4	84.5	13.6	1.9
1960	72,105	14.4	58.1	27.3	14.6
1970	74,492	3.9	61.9	30.5	7.6
1980	92,110	23.6	38.4	53.8	7.8
1990	109,303	18.6	34.7	63.6	1.7

SOURCE: U.S. Bureau of the Census (1910, 1920, 1930, 1940, 1950, 1960, 1970, 1980, 1990).

Colorado River. Imperial County residents feared that the Salton Sea, fed by the Colorado River, would eventually flood the entire valley, rendering it useless. Due to this fear, many residents abandoned their land (Estrella Valenzuela 1982: 9). The first official county census was conducted in 1910, reporting 13,591 inhabitants, of whom 75 percent were Anglo-American, 18.2 percent were Mexican, and 6.8 percent belonged to other groups.

On the other side of the border in Mexicali, hydraulic projects had been initiated to take advantage of the Colorado River waters, thereby opening zones to the cultivation of cotton. U.S. companies located in the City of Calexico executed these projects. These events gave way to the establishment of settlements in the Municipality of Mexicali, which had 1,614 inhabitants in 1910 (see Table 2).

The problems caused by the seasonal floods of the Colorado River were solved during the first decade of the twentieth century, giving stability to the development of the region (Estrella Valenzuela 1982: 5). Once again, immigration increased in the Imperial County area, which was reflected in high growth rates. By 1920, there were 43,453 residents in the region, a 219.7 percent increase over the previous decade. This period boasted the population's highest growth rates in the county's history. At that time, Anglo-Americans were 67.3 percent of the population, those of Mexican origin 14.8 percent, and others 17.9 percent. This composition changed through the years and by 1980, the majority of the population was of Mexican origin.

By 1920, the Municipality of Mexicali had grown to 14,599 inhabitants due to two events. The first was the implementation of the Volstead Act in 1918 in the United States, which established the prohibition of the production, sale, and consumption of alcoholic beverages. It triggered tourism and service activities on the

Table 2. Total Populations of Baja California, the Municipality of Mexicali, and the City of Mexicali

Jurisdiction	1910	1920	1930	1940	1950	1960	1970	1980	1990	2000
City of Mexicali	462	6,782	14,842	18,775	64,609	174,540	263,498	349,931	458,877	555,794*
Municipality of Mexicali	1,614	14,599	29,985	44,399	112,436	281,333	396,326	510,664	601,988	764,602
Baja California	9,760	23,537	48,327	78,907	226,965	520,165	870,421	177,886	166,855	2,487,367

*Projection estimated using the City of Mexicali's population growth rate from 1990 to 1995 (1.93%).

SOURCES: Data regarding the populations from 1910 were derived from Ortega Villa (1993); INEGI (2001).

Mexican side of the border in the form of new cantinas and recreation centers, as well as a brewery dedicated to satisfying the demand of the U.S. market (Ortega Villa 1993: 27). The second event was the Mexican Revolution, which affected both rural and urban populations and reached even those Mexican regions that wished to distance themselves from the armed conflict.

Between 1920 and 1930, the population of Imperial County grew by 40.1 percent, to a total of 60,903 inhabitants. Of these, 54.4 percent were Anglo-American and 35.5 percent were of Hispanic origin. By 1940, the population had decreased by 2.7 percent to 59,740. This decrease was caused by the economic crisis of 1929 and the related national economic depression throughout the 1930s. The Anglo-American population in 1940 totaled 87.2 percent, its highest of all periods, while the Hispanic population was only 10.3 percent, the lowest level recorded in the Imperial County. It should also be noted that the decrease in the Hispanic population was partly the result of deportation policies adopted by the U.S. government in the 1930s and supported by state authorities to deport thousands of Hispanic workers from the country, either "voluntarily" or by force (Massey et al. 1991: 55).

Between 1930 and 1960, the population of the Municipality of Mexicali grew considerably due to various events, among them:

- The establishment of a free zone in 1937 to maintain the region's population

- The recuperation of lands owned by U.S. companies that were transferred to Mexican peasants in 1937

- The participation of the United States in World War II, which resulted in the establishment of the Bracero Program and strengthened the migratory flow into the City of Mexicali as an obligatory crossing point

- The start-up of operations for the Sonora-Baja California railroad in 1948, which boosted commercial activities with the interior of Mexico as well as the United States. It also facilitated the arrival of Mexican migrants to the region (Ortega Villa 1993: 28)

- The attraction of Baja California being the state with the highest minimum salaries in the country since 1938 (Acuña et al. 1983: 106)

- The Korean War, which augmented the demand for cotton and almost doubled the area cultivated from 1951 to 1954, requiring greater amounts of labor (CONAPO and CONEPO 1986: 711)

After 1940, the population of Imperial County grew at a moderate rate, notwithstanding the existence of the Bracero Program. By 1950, the population totaled 62,975, of which 84.5 percent were Anglo-American, 13.6 percent were of Mexican origin, and 1.9 percent belonged to other ethnic groups.

In 1960, there were 72,105 people living in the county. Anglo-Americans represented 58.1 percent of that total, Mexicans 27.3 percent, and others 14.6 percent. It should be mentioned that with termination of the Bracero Program in 1964, many of the workers (called *braceros*) were able to legalize their presence in the United States. The immigration laws in force at that time facilitated the process of obtaining proper documentation for legal residence in the United States (Massey et al. 1991: 98).

In the 1960s, the population of the Municipality of Mexicali declined (see Table 2) due to: (1) the end of the Bracero Program, which reduced the number of migrants to the region; (2) problems related to the decline in agricultural activity in the Mexicali Valley resulting from a fall in the international price of cotton; and (3) problems with the salinity of Colorado River water, which reduced the valley's productivity.

By 1970, Imperial County showed a slight growth from 1960 in population, reaching 74,492 inhabitants. Of this total, 61.9 percent were Anglo-American, 30.5 percent were of Mexican origin, and 7.6 percent represented other groups. At the same time, the inhabitants of the Municipality of Mexicali numbered 396,326 in 1970. This growth was due to a great extent to the implementation of the Border Industrialization Program (BIP), beginning in 1965, which promoted the establishment of *maquiladoras* (assembly plants) along the border. Their presence brought new waves of migrants to the municipality with the deportation of Mexican workers from the United States and migration to the area from other parts of Mexico. This program resulted in a change in the border region's economic activities, especially in the Municipality of Mexicali, increasing the volume of activity in the secondary and tertiary sectors and decreasing that in the primary sector. This situation has continued over the last two decades, reflecting state policies that boost activities in the secondary and tertiary sectors and have greatly reduced support programs and investments in primary activities such as agriculture.

The population in Imperial County has experienced important changes in its composition and size over the last two decades, mainly due to increases in the population of Hispanic origin (see Table 1), which has comprised the majority of the population since 1980. The 1980 Census reported that 92,110 people lived in the county, of whom 38.4 percent were Anglo-American, 53.8 percent were of Mexican origin, and 7.8 percent were from other groups. By 1990, the population of Imperial County reached 109,303 inhabitants, showing the same behavior as in the previous decade. The population of Mexican origin had grown to 63.6 percent of the total, while Anglo-Americans were 34.7 percent, and other groups declined to only 1.7 percent of the total population.

The population of Hispanic origin in 2000 was distributed throughout all Imperial County (see Table 3), with the City of Calexico housing the greatest number of Hispanic residents. Of its 27,109 inhabitants, 95.3 percent were Hispanic. Heber was the only locality to have a higher percentage than Calexico; of its 2,988 residents,

Table 3. Total Population and Hispanic Population,
Imperial County, 2000

City	Total Population	Hispanic Population	Hispanic Population (%)
Imperial County	142,361	102,784	72.2
Brawley	22,052	16,274	73.8
Calexico	27,109	25,834	95.3
Calipatria	7,289	4,176	57.3
El Centro	37,835	28,224	74.6
Heber	2,988	2,913	97.5
Holtville	5,612	4,141	73.8
Imperial	7,560	4,619	61.1
Niland	1,143	632	55.3
Seeley	1,624	1,323	81.5
Westmorland	2,131	1,751	82.2

SOURCES: U.S. Bureau of the Census (2000) and author's calculations (2002).

97.5 percent were of Hispanic origin. The Hispanic population of the other cities of the county was more than 50 percent.

The changes in the population's composition are due to a number of features of the county. First, great changes in its economic structure have not been made. The agricultural sector continues to be one of its most important activities. The tertiary sector has increased substantially in commerce and services as a result of population growth in the region. Second, its geographical position favors the out-migration of Anglo-Americans, as nearby counties may offer better opportunities to relate culturally and socially and greater possibilities for employment in more productive branches with higher salaries, as in San Diego and Riverside counties. By contrast, legal Mexican residents often live close to the border so as not to lose sociocultural and familial contacts with their country of origin.

Employment and the Labor Force in Imperial County from 1940 to 1990

The abundant employment opportunities offered in Imperial County in the 1960s had been primarily agricultural. However, changes in cultivation patterns and technological breakthroughs over the last thirty years (regardless of its importance in the productive structure) have caused the labor force to be less concentrated, thereby propelling a phenomenon of labor force displacement to other sectors.

Table 4 shows that the agricultural sector employed the greatest number of workers in 1940 (45.7%). In the following two decades, this percentage dropped, but

Table 4. Civil Employment by Period and Type of Activity, Imperial County, 1940-2000

Activity	1940	1950	1960	1970	1980	1990	2000
Number of Civil Employees	20,783	23,117	28,027	23,479	33,778	36,412	43,100
Agriculture	45.7%	36.9%	38.9%	19.7%	20.3%	20.7%	14.2%
Manufacturing	4.0%	6.2%	5.6%	6.7%	6.4%	6.1%	4.4%
Construction	4.9%	5.3%	3.4%	5.2%	6.0%	5.6%	4.9%
Commerce	18.9%	25.1%	27.0%	27.4%	22.4%	21.8%	24.1%
Finance, Insurance, and Real Estate	1.6%	1.6%	2.0%	3.1%	3.8%	4.6%	2.6%
Services	14.4%	15.0%	12.1%	23.6%	26.5%	22.7%	13.2%
Government	9.6%	8.5%	8.5%	14.3%	14.6%	18.5%	36.0%
Not Specified	0.9%	1.4%	2.5%	-	-	-	-
Total	0.1%	0.1%	0.1%	0.1%	0.1%	0.1%	0.1%

Note: Due to rounding, some numbers may not add up correctly.

SOURCE: U.S. Bureau of the Census (1940, 1950, 1960, 1970, 1980, 1990, 2000).

the sector remained the largest employer in the region. In 1950, it employed 36.9 percent of the workforce; in 1960, it employed 38.9 percent. In 1970, the percentage of workers in the primary sector was only 19.7 percent, which meant a decline of almost 50 percent compared to the number of jobs that it had absorbed in prior decades. The tertiary sector showed the highest level of growth in this period.

Agricultural activities that for 30 years were the number one employer fell to third place as a result of the diversification of crops that was introduced to the valley in the 1970s. In this period, commercial and service activities grew in the county and, as such, jobs in these sectors came to represent a greater percentage of the workforce than those of the primary sector.

In the 1980s and 1990s, the services sector grew to employ the greatest number of workers. In 1980, it included 26.5 percent of the economically active population and in 1990 it was 22.7 percent. Commerce employed 22.4 percent in 1980 and 21.8 percent in 1990. Agriculture employed 20.3 percent of the workforce in 1980, and 20.7 percent in 1990, relegating it to third place.

It is worthy to note that the composition of the civil workforce in 2000 presents several interesting changes. Government jobs rose to 36 percent of total civil employment, a figure that during earlier decades had remained relatively low. Second, the commercial sector, with 24.1 percent of the employed population, also maintained high growth rates, although lagging behind government employment. Third, the agricultural sector employed 14.2 percent of the workforce, demonstrating a decline in the sector's ability to generate employment. In view of this, it may be assumed that many agricultural jobs continue to be performed by commuters, or residents of the City of Mexicali.

Conclusion

Since the early twentieth century, the Imperial-Mexicali region has become a magnet for both U.S. investors and migrants from both sides of the border. Such development and economic growth resulted in binational processes stemming from socioeconomic spatial proximity. Regional binational relationships were established by U.S. investors based in Imperial County as the economic compass that has sustained the economic growth and development of the region and oriented its activities. This development was based on two factors. First, the attraction of new job opportunities for U.S. and Mexican citizens through the recruitment of labor, which facilitated the growth of the agricultural sector, paving the way for other employment sectors. Mexican migration to the region was "… as much the result of the structural relationship of workers with the organization of the forms of production as of the uneven development of the geoeconomic sectors between countries and regions" (Gómez Quiñones 1979: 68). Second, the regulation of the border's permeability arises in the two nation-states' policy spheres in a partial and selective manner and through a complementary relationship that promotes the development of transnational and transborder relations. These relations involve the following elements: capital, in the form of investments or savings; goods or products; and people, either workers or consumers. In practical terms, each of these elements or factors has defined various binational processes, such as migration and commercial exchange.

These changes have accentuated transnational and transborder relationships. The structural differences between the two countries and regions have intensified the power and control each nation-state wields over its territories. Thus, the international boundary is no longer a fictitious border for people and capital (and many goods), constituting a limit to the exercise of sovereignty and control of economic markets. As a result, the border has become a selective check for U.S.-Mexican relations. Despite this, Mexican migration has remained strong since the region's initial formation (Alegría Olazábal 1992: 38–42).

References

Acuña, Guadalupe Beatriz, Frida Espinoza, Gabriel Estrella V., and Pablo González. 1983. *El trabajador agrícola transmigrante de la frontera Municipio de Mexicali-Condado Imperial*. Mexicali: Instituto de Investigaciones Sociales, Universidad Autónoma de Baja California.

Alegría Olazábal, Tito. 1992. *Desarrollo urbano en la frontera México-Estados Unidos. Una interpretación y algunos resultados*. México, D.F.: Consejo Nacional para la Cultura y las Artes.

Consejo Nacional de Población (CONAPO) and Consejo Estatal de Población (CONEPO). 1986. *Encuesta demográfica de Baja California*. Mexicali: CONAPO and CONEPO.

Dowd, M.J. 1956. "History of Imperial Irrigation District and the Development of Imperial Valley." El Centro: Imperial Irrigation District, Community and Special Service.

Estrella Valenzuela, Gabriel. 1982. "El origen de la región de los valles de Mexicali e Imperial, desde la perspectiva de las relaciones sociales." *Cuaderno de Ciencias Sociales* 1.

Gómez Quiñones, Juan. 1979. "La importancia de la exportación de capital e importación de mano de obra." *Historia y Sociedad* 20.

Grijalva, E. Aidé. 1980. "Una aproximación al estudio de una empresa agrícola: la Colorado River Land Company, S.A." *Revista Calafia* 4 (3).

Instituto Nacional de Estadística, Geografía e Informática (INEGI). 2001. "Tabulados básicos 2000" *XII Censo general de población y vivienda, 2000*. Baja California. Aguascalientes: INEGI.

Massey, Douglas, Rafael Alarcón, Jorge Durand, and Humberto González. 1991. *Los ausentes*. México, D.F.: Consejo Nacional para la Cultura y las Artes and Ed. Alianza.

Ortega Villa, Guadalupe 1993. "Localización residencial en la ciudad de Mexicali: una aplicación del modelo de Alonso." Master's thesis, Instituto de Investigaciones Sociales, Universidad Autónoma de Baja California, Mexicali, Baja California, Mexico.

U.S. Bureau of the Census. 1910. *Census of Population, 1910*. Washington, D.C.: U.S. Bureau of the Census.

U.S. Bureau of the Census. 1920. *Census of Population, 1920*. Washington, D.C.: U.S. Bureau of the Census.

U.S. Bureau of the Census. 1930. *Census of Population, 1930*. Washington, D.C.: U.S. Bureau of the Census.

U.S. Bureau of the Census. 1940. *Census of Population, 1940*. Washington, D.C.: U.S. Bureau of the Census.

U.S. Bureau of the Census. 1950. *Census of Population, 1950*. Washington, D.C.: U.S. Bureau of the Census.

U.S. Bureau of the Census. 1960. *Census of Population, 1960*. Washington, D.C.: U.S. Bureau of the Census.

U.S. Bureau of the Census. 1970. *Census of Population, 1970*. Washington, D.C.: U.S. Bureau of the Census.

U.S. Bureau of the Census. 1980a. *Agriculture Census for Imperial County*. Washington, D.C.: U.S. Bureau of the Census.

U.S. Bureau of the Census. 1980b. *Census of Population, 1980*. Washington, D.C.: U.S. Bureau of the Census.

U.S. Bureau of the Census. 1990a. *Agriculture Census for Imperial County*. Washington, D.C.: U.S. Bureau of the Census.

U.S. Bureau of the Census. 1990b. *Census of Population, 1990*. Washington, D.C.: U.S. Bureau of the Census.

U.S. Bureau of the Census. 2000. *Census of Population, 2000*. Washington, D.C.: U.S. Bureau of the Census.

5

Tribal Adaptation:
The Quechan of Imperial County

Jay von Werlhof*

Abstract

Adaptation is among the least understood of cultural processes that initiate or react to change. Adaptations are stressful and sometimes terminal for cultures subjected to external and superior forces of other cultures or nature. The Quechan tribe along the Colorado River in Imperial County successfully thwarted the first phase of Western culture. However, within 75 years it failed excessively to adapt to stronger forced changes and became an ineffective society. One hundred years later, the more humanized United States of America modified its control over native tribes as the tribes themselves began awakening to American processes and, under a coadaptation mode of government and tribe, the Quechan retained essential traditions while moving toward mainstream American culture.

Introduction

There were more tribes in the Imperial County and Northern Baja California region than any other comparable sized area in the far Southwest. Despite the many complexities of each tribe, only two sublanguages were spoken in this large and environmentally diverse territory. In the uppermost northwestern portion of Imperial County are the Cahuilla, Takic, and speakers within the Shoshone-Comanche group of the Uto-Aztecan linguistic family. All others in the westernmost region of the desert are Yuman speakers within the Hokan linguistic family that, at one time, had

*Von Werlhof is Anthropologist and Founder of the Imperial Valley College Desert Museum.

spread throughout the whole of California and Baja California. Today, the Yumans are located in the southwestern corner of Arizona, the southern and northern ends of the Lower Colorado River, in Baja California to the twenty-sixth parallel, and in several enclaves in San Diego County. All of the tribes have been subjected to common detrimental cultural and governmental practices, thus, this paper will focus, as an example, on only one of the border Yuman tribes: the Quechan (often called the Yuma by the sixteenth-century Spaniards).

Human Adaptation and Culture

Every desert person has a story of adaptation to tell. Adaptation gets at the very root of consciousness and the need for adaptation can best be explained as a series of challenges. Major challenges are best couched in terms of environment and culture. Despite many complaints about the climate, most people agree that there is nothing one can do but adapt or move away. The most difficult challenge, however, is culture, an element that can supposedly be modified. After all, culture is a human product that consciousness bred into a system. Culture was already in place when people were born. While the human disposition is naturally inclined to adapt to the cultural system of one's birthplace, the adaptation process becomes stressful when the cultural position that one pursues is itself undergoing change. People once believed that to

Figure 1. Map of Native American Tribes' Lands

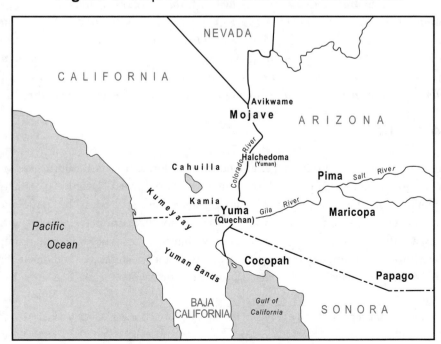

place themselves where they wanted to be in society all they had to do was accept the cultural system, concoct an ideal goal, and work hard (in or out of school) to meet the challenge. Failures have led to a loss of cultural accountability and self-esteem and have given rise to alternative forms of education, a burgeoning of nondirective megabusinesses, an enlarging group of misplaced persons, and governing forces that are out of touch with those they govern. Such sliding changes have re-created challenges that put people back into the original posture of cultural formation and a reawakened consciousness. And now, here are people rethinking themselves, their environment, and how their culture can best be adapted to them rather than the other way around. This is done for a future that people can have a hand in directing before it becomes their past. This, indeed, is a brave new world, disarming outmoded adaptive strategies and mustering new avenues with which to replace them.

Environment and Culture

In this endeavor, attention is placed on two strongly related factors of adaptation: environment and culture. The key to understanding these factors is to recognize that early settlers in the desert modified the border environment through irrigation and adapted a synchronous culture that was based on a supply/distribution system that for a time met the needs of the new agrarian community. Such a single-purpose economy was limited, however, and could not support nor absorb the expanding non-agrarian population seeking employment. Although diversification is sought, options still lag behind the surplus labor force with unemployment currently exceeding 25 percent of the total labor force, creating a cultural stress that has not gone away. Coupled with this is a possible environmental threat. The settlers had turned a sumpish trough into a productive "valley" by diverting Colorado River water. Without that transported water, not a single person would be in the valley today. Currently, there is a powerful political movement to divert this water to mega-urban centers, which in an extreme scenario would return the valley to its former sumpish desert state. In order to maintain the roots of the valley's adapted border culture, a large portion of its hydroenvironment must be preserved. At the same time, if the border culture does not continue to change to enable a growing and diversified population to adapt to the region's economy, the initiative and rationale to preserve the water supply will be lost. This is not a catch-22 situation. History has shown that through cultural as well as environmental adaptation, humanistic values can suppress the stress that challenges breed.

Government and Adaptation of Cultural Diversities

Peoples of diverse cultures have been migrating to Southern California for thousands of years, each requiring adaptation to both environmental factors and a culture already established by earlier migrants. While U.S. society has long been known as a "melting pot," it is also clear that historically the United States has used color, religion, political ideology, gender, age, ethnic background, sexual preference, education, habitation style or place, dress, occupation, economic class, and language for social or political discrimination. While each discriminatory practice historically limited the adaptive process, the movement toward democracy, which neither the Constitution nor the Bill of Rights sanctioned, grew in bits and pieces across the nation's first 190 years. Its stride has since accelerated over the past 35 years. Today, the rise of humanistic values in response to a troubled world has focused on educational opportunities, the rapid growth of well-financed organizations with socially aware agendas, and the proliferation of assistance programs at all government and corporate levels to lessen the challenges to cultural adaptation for women, the underprivileged, the insecure, the specially talented, the migrant, and the Native American. U.S. society has not always been so generous. It was not until the federal government obtained the power to collect income taxes (Amendment XVI, 1913) that the people and the government developed a more direct relationship, rather than maintaining a strictly representative one. This new relationship gradually led to greater cultural awareness on the part of government. In response to the Great Depression, the government took the first major steps toward policies based on cultural accountability. The ideology that the government should even have a cultural conscience was not widely accepted until after World War II, although the degree of responsibility the government should have in responding to cultural problems, or at least the speed for doing so, has remained a basic dividing point in political theories and the basis for contemporary party platforms. Over the last thirty years, there has been a growing trend for the federal government to financially support and monitor programs under the direction of local or regional groups. From the Block Grant concept to the Empowerment plan, the government has cleared the way for local areas to define and resolve issues outside the legislative process. Two border groups still remain beyond this net: the immigrants and native tribes.

Incidentally, these groups have had experiences similar to other participants in U.S. history. Immigrants today have the same courage and faith as early settlers when they moved to the United States. At that time, the United States was someone else's land. The culture of native populations had reached a level of sustenance and governance through the adaptive process. The Southern California Yumans had at least three thousand years of adaptive settlement before Western civilization arrived with Spanish, Mexican, and American immigrants in quick succession. To capitalize on the route that Captain de Anza opened between Sonora and Los Angeles, Spanish priests founded a mission in the southeast corner of Imperial County. Cultural conflicts led the native Yuma (Quechan) to reject forced change, massacre the missionaries and soldiers, and burn the mission (1781). Although the Spanish did not attempt to reestablish their authority there, the Mexican government did so with a fort built along the New River, west of Imperial, in 1825. Though this was ostensibly to protect the proposed reopening of the Anza trail, a cultural conflict between the Mexican cadre and the Kumeyaay (Yuman speakers), who occupied the San Sebastian Marsh eight miles north, led to a similar uprising that ended only when the natives killed three soldiers and drove off the remainder. The fort was never reoccupied and a farmer bulldozed its decaying remains in 1969.

The United States assumed control of the Yuma area in the American West following the war with Mexico (1848). A year later, the California gold rush brought thousands of hopeful prospectors through the Yuma area, some of whom stayed to exploit rumored gold fields along the Colorado River. To prevent cultural clashes among prospectors, settlers, soldiers, and native Quechan in the area, the United States army built Fort Yuma at the juncture of the Colorado and Gila Rivers. The Quechan attempted to repeat their resistance to adaptation with militant force as they had against the Spanish and Mexicans. Even though other Yumans, including the Mohave and Maricopas, joined the Quechan in an armed confrontation, they were not equal to the U.S. forces and were defeated. They then found themselves as subjected people in a foreign land. To reduce the stigma of the Yumans as a conquered people, the United States drew up a land cessation treaty with the Quechan, but the Senate never ratified it. The Indians were "given" reserved lands that amounted to less than 10 percent of their original territory and the Bureau of Indian Affairs monitored their use of it, including Fort Yuma. Fort Yuma contains the oldest-standing buildings in Imperial County (1854–1856) and is currently the seat of tribal government. Although the buildings are suffering from age and neglect, the Quechan are reluctant to restore a symbol of the repressive change that ended their revered past 150 years ago.

Adaptational Defeatism

A core Quechan group still uses the native tongue, tells the creation story, sings and shares traditional lore, and conducts spiritual rites of ancestral times. For this group, as well as for most on the tribal rolls, cultural adaptation has been a defeating process. The clichés about cultural acceptance, idealistic goals, hard work, and education attainment have been more demoralizing for them than for many others. Few have entered the mainstream. For most, identification is rooted in their traditional land where opportunities for Western adaptation are few.

The natives are tribal people who adapted to the environment through cultural modification. Their adaptation was so complete that they identified their creation with this land. Their lore, their rituals and spiritual essence, their art, and their organization are integrated with a conscientious view of the world and their part in it.

Historic accounts help to better comprehend how this native view led first to confrontations over the imposing ways of Spanish, Mexican, and American entrants and then to the demoralizing effect the eventual conquest had among the natives. Native cultural historians know the Yuman creation story, which takes four days to tell, but can be related in a brief account (Cachora and Arrow-weed n.d.). *Mastamho*, the creator and repositor of all energy, formed the universe and all things within it. From his central place at *Avi-Kwami* ("Spirit Mountain" or Newberry Mountain near contemporary Needles, California), he gave his created people knowledge, cultural ways, and their relationships to all things that they were to teach new generations through songs, stories, traditions, and rituals. Central to the passing of one generation to the next was the ceremony, which began with the death of the creator and his spiritual escape through cremation. With the tribal adoption of this funerary practice called the *keruk* ceremony, which encompassed the burning of one's body and all material possessions, each generation began anew with no material possessions for heirs to use, cherish, or squabble over. Through this ceremony and cremation, family and tribe sent the soul of their deceased members to the spirit world of *Mastamho*.

In memory of the original ceremony and their creator, tribal members ideally would annually visit their spiritual center by following the sacred *keruk* trail from their villages to *Avi-Kwami*. In effect, however, the trek has traditionally been made spiritually rather than physically, especially at the time of a creation ceremony. Contact with the spiritual world of the creator has also been traditionally available to tribal members through vision quests, prayers, dreams, or shamanic powers.

Following other directives of the creator, the tribe undertook a major migration to other parts of the country, west and south, though details are scarce in tribal lore. There is ethnographic and archaeologic evidence, however, that the Yumans ventured into Baja California as far south as the twenty-sixth parallel. Linguists trace a large group of Yumans moving out of this location about six thousand years ago, probably in response to the growing aridity of the Holocene, which gradually depleted the carrying capacity of the peninsula. By 3000 B.C., a group had crossed into Coyote Valley in the southwest corner of Imperial County. The Yuha Man, whose remains were unearthed at the eastern edge of Coyote Valley in 1972 and later reburied, was probably in this vanguard. The Yuha Man was dated by the carbon 14 method as 5,000 years before the present. It is also probable that the group divided, one portion going into the In-Ko-Pah Mountains, directly to the east of the Imperial Valley, while others crossed the Yuha Desert to the Colorado River. Pushing west and east, the Yuman occupation pattern was formed that remained fairly intact until the mid-nineteenth century. This constituted a return back to the territory of their cultural origins. The riverine group eventually clustered along a 150-mile front while the western group fanned across the mountains and coastal belt. Each emerging tribe spiritually identified itself with a prominent peak, symbolic of *Avi-Kwami*.

For the next 150 generations, the various tribes of the river and Kumeyaay bands of the mountains and coast relived seasonal rounds, rites, ceremonial dances, and songs and stories for the celebration of initiation, death, and life renewal. Traditions and other sacred possessions gave everyone power and direction for various life encounters. Knowledge came from elders, spiritual leaders, vision quests, prayers, and dreams. Their dreams were not considered dips into subconscious fantasies; they were viewed as events that the soul experiences out of the body to give warnings or advice to a perplexed mind. Natives were taught how to choose subjects of concern or interest for their dreams.

Although receptive, the natives were not passive. Anyone who has lived in the natural world subject to forces other than climate can more easily appreciate the Indians' constant interaction with the total universe, of which they felt a spiritual part rather than victims or contestants. Their spirituality did not evolve into a work ethic or employment drive that the Westerners used to mistake the Indians' ways as evidence that they were indolent and immature adults, careless of self, and absent of purpose. The assumption fortified the intruders' desire to take charge of these wasted lives and land as God or destiny mandated.

U.S. military might, which was more than what the Spanish or Mexican forces could muster against the defiant Yumans, soon commanded the riverine tribes from Needles to Yuma and east to Gila Bend. By 1884, the federal government felt that the Yumans were no longer a threat and turned their control over to the administrative Bureau of Indian Affairs (BIA). The BIA established the 45,000-acre Fort Yuma Reservation that year and attempted to manage its affairs through a resident agent and an appointed "chief" from its headquarters nearly two hundred miles away. The BIA did not offer helpful programs to the tribes and permitted non-Indians to settle the better farmlands where, since A.D. 750, the Yumans had planted corn, squash, beans, and melons. Children were sent to a Catholic boarding school for nine months a year, away from contacts with parents and other relatives. Instead of teaching children and adults vocational skills as the government had promised, they were assigned menial tasks with little compensation.

In 1887, the U.S. Congress passed the Dawes Act, allotting reservation plots to every tribal member on the official roll. It also opened to non-Indians all lands not taken up under the allotment. The plan went into effect in 1890, but it was not until 1893 that the government surveyed the land and presented the plan to the Indians at meetings. Chief Miguel and a group of his supporters opposed the plan; they were consequently arrested under vague charges and sent to Los Angeles County jail. In their absence, the government pressed tribal members to sign the plan and the Quechan still claim that the government forged enough names to indicate that a majority accepted the agreement. The government selected an alternate chief and the police force to put the agreement into effect. It then divided the reservation into tribes that broke down what unity the Indians had earlier mustered.

Except for the 8,000 allotted acres, speculators from the City of Yuma bought at noncompetitive bidding the best lands free of tax assessments and were provided with a government-guaranteed irrigation system. Further discriminations required male Quechans to cut their hair before they could enter Yuma and the tribe had to get BIA permission before holding traditional ceremonies or performing sacred rites. Personal property of the deceased could no longer be burned. At the risk of arrest, many families performed private memorial ceremonies in the desert without permission (several of these sites have been recorded on archaeological surveys by the author). Alcoholism, tuberculosis, diabetes, measles, and depression reduced the number of enrolled Indians from 2,700 in 1900 to 835 by 1910. Those who left the reservation found only menial jobs in towns, although some found good positions on ranches where their ability to work with animals was appreciated. In 1950, a hospital was built on the reservation, reducing the need for the seriously ill to be taken to Phoenix for care.

In 1934, the U.S. Congress passed the Indian Reorganization Act, which ended new allotments and permitted tribes to form constitutions and elect representatives to tribal councils. Yet, the government remained the land trustee under the Secretary of the Interior and denied Indians the right to sell their former allotments. When a landholder died, his allotment was divided equally among his rightful heirs. The power of tribal councils was curtailed when the government failed to respond to council petitions or decisions. Interest in self-government all but disappeared on the Fort Yuma Reservation. The old boarding school became a public day school in 1935, still under BIA direction. Enrollment dropped off as few saw an advantage to education. During the 1940s, non-Indian landholders on the reservation began selling or leasing their lands to the new agricultural corporations that consolidated holdings in large farm operations. Indians were still denied the opportunity to rent or lease their lands and many holders left their lands fallow except for personal gardens.

Policy Changes and the Coadaptational Movement

Following World War II, California assumed responsibility on reservations for education, police, and courts systems. During the Great Society Era of the 1960s, the federal government declared its war against poverty wherever it was found. The American Indians were clearly the nation's most impoverished people, due mostly to governmental policies and regulations. With the passage of Public Law 280 that made social welfare and health services available, the lot of the reservation Indian began to change. Policies affecting housing, education, and employment were put into practice along with new water facilities and agricultural services.

In 1978, the Secretary of the Interior gave back Quechan treaty lands of 1884 that were largely open desert, but have traditionally been considered sacred as a connection between their lands and *Avi-Kwami*, their point of creation and source of power. Just north of this 1884 treaty line is sacred land that Chemgold, a Canadian gold mining company, unsuccessfully sought permission from the Bureau of Land Management to open three sections for a 20-year mining venture. The Tribal Council, reinvigorated in recent years with the enlargement of self-rule and economic/social advancements, made a strong and unified stand against this project.

The advancements include help from the Office of Economic Opportunity to build 150 new homes, a practical training program, a Head Start program, and numerous programs for youth and seniors. The opening of the Paradise Casino, with a manager selected by the Tribal Council, has aided the community in new job creation and support for social programs. The council was successful in a $15 million land settlement over the loss of reservation lands sold to non-Indians. It has since opened a museum, built a new tribal government building, a shopping plaza, a trailer park, a youth center, and social services offices.

The Quechan have been singled out in this paper as an example of Yuman tribal conditions in Southern California. The plight of some groups, such as the Cocopah and Kumeyaay bands in Baja California; the Maricopa, Pima, and Papago of southwestern Arizona; and several of the 13 Kumeyaay bands in San Diego County, have not shared in the growing advancement of the Quechan over the last quarter of the twentieth century. There is, however, renewed awareness and consciousness within U.S. society and government toward coadaptation with Indians, whose lives and traditions have been severely shorn by official policies and distasteful activities over the last 150 years. Today, a movement is also growing within the Indian communities to reinvest in their traditional languages, ceremonies, songs, stories, and spiritual values while seeking avenues to adapt to the American mainstream. This movement toward coadaptation has mutual advantages and can bring people closer to what had long been a historical myth about democracy, liberty, and equality.

References

Bee, Robert. 1981. *Crosscurrents along the Colorado: The Impact of Government Policy on the Quechan Indians*. Tucson: University of Arizona Press.

Bee, Robert. 1989. *The Yuma*. New York and Philadelphia: Chelsea House Publishers.

Cachora, Lorey, and Preston Jefferson Arrow-weed. n.d. "MSS the Creation Story." Ocotillo: Jay von Werlhof Library.

Forbes, Jack. 1965. *Warriors of the Colorado*. Norman: University of Oklahoma Press.

Kroeber, A.L. 1925. *Handbook of the Indians of California*. Washington, D.C.: Smithsonian Institution.

Sturtevant, William, and Alfonso Ortiz. 1983. "Southwest" Pp. 86–112 in *Handbook of North American Indians* 10, Alfonso Ortiz and William Sturtevant, eds. Washington, D.C.: Smithsonian Institution.

Von Werlhof, Jay. n.d. "The Desert Cahuilla and Their Yuman Neighbors." In *Archaeological Survey of Ancient Lake Cahuilla*. Redlands: University of Redlands, forthcoming.

6

Governance in Imperial County, California, and Mexicali, Baja California

Glen Sparrow*

Abstract

The issue of governance and the relationships among the different levels of government in a nation is complex. This essay discusses the specific relationships among the federal, state, and local levels of government in the United States and in Mexico, with a specific focus on the Imperial Valley and Mexicali. It deals with the challenges that are faced in governing a border region and the role that organizations called boundary spanners play in promoting cooperation between the two binational governments.

Introduction

It is through the process of governance that structures of government produce the public policies that determine, to a great extent, the quality of life that people experience. In order to understand the Imperial Valley-Mexicali region, it is necessary to understand the impact of government in all of its dimensions on the region. This essay will deal with the governance of the Imperial Valley (the United States) and Mexicali (Mexico) binational region. In addition to issues such as structures of government within the region, it will also address related issues such as public administration, public finance, politics, transborder governance, and the impact of the North American Free Trade Agreement (NAFTA) on the public service delivery and regulation along this section of the U.S.-Mexican border.

*Sparrow is Professor Emeritus in the Public Administration Department at San Diego State University.

National Governance

Both the United States and Mexico are federal republics that separate governmental power at the national and state levels among legislative, executive, and judicial branches. Additionally, they divide authority through a form of governance that calls for a national government, subnational governments (in the case of the United States and Mexico these are referred to as states), and local governments. The national constitutions of the two nations provide a rather limited description of the relationships between the nation and states and even less regarding the relationships between the national/states and the local governments. In both nations the relationships have been, and are, evolving. Constitutional amendments, acts of the national legislatures, executive actions, court decisions, actions of the state governments, governmental reactions to events that have impacted the nations, and other actions have all contributed to the present condition of federalism in each country. Recently, developments in both nations have produced significant changes in the relationships of the three levels of government.

In the United States, a decentralized federal structure has been further decentralized by decisions of all three branches of the national government to devolve authority for policy and service delivery in some critical areas to the state level and hence through state decisions to the local governments. Delivery of services such as welfare, transportation, and education has become a greater responsibility of the state/local governments in the past decade. In Mexico, a much more centralized federal system has begun to devolve as well. The past decade has seen the amendment of the Mexican Constitution (Article 19), the transformation from a one party to a multiparty political system, the promise of President Vicente Fox to enhance state/local financial transfer payments from the national government, and greater expectations of decision making and service delivery at the local level. All of these events have enhanced expectations for greater devolution of authority and resources to the state/local levels.

In both nations, the expectations for a more developed intergovernmental system have been growing over the last decade as the national governments have devolved (or indicated their intention to devolve) authority and service delivery responsibility to state and local governments. This shift of governing power has placed greater responsibility upon the state/local governments and increased awareness of the role and responsibilities of these levels. In this review of the governance of the Imperial Valley-Mexicali region, these governments will be emphasized.

Intergovernmental Relations

One additional lesson that is learned when one operates in a federal system is that intergovernmental relations become a very complex undertaking. The multiple relationships among and between all of the governments—50 states and 68,000 local governments in the United States and 31 states and 2,420 local governments in Mexico—require substantial rules and regulations; a significant as well as subtle understanding of the system is also required, as is the need for institutions that can operate across and within the levels of government. Getting the various levels of government—national, state, and local—to work in coordination or cooperation with one another often requires an additional type of coordinating mechanism that can span the layers of government. These organizations are referred to as *boundary spanners*, which describes the role they play in producing cooperation or coordination among the various branches, levels, and forms of government. Often, these boundary spanners are not governments, but are extragovernmental agencies whose sole purpose is to bring together the various governments in order to accomplish a particular task. One theme of this explanation of the governance of the Imperial Valley-Mexicali region is that the lessons learned by both nations from centuries of federal governance are being adapted to the governance of the border region. Due to the nature of federalism, transfer of power or authority between layers of government is not always easy. The nation, states, cities, counties, and special districts are not prone to easily alter their influence, control, or prestige.

Thus, in both the United States and Mexico, pragmatic steps are often taken to coordinate, develop cooperation, or even override the individual governments in order to "get something done." For this reason, the agencies that do this are called boundary spanners. Nationally, they perform the function of spanning the boundary between the levels of government or jurisdictions. In the United States, a good example is the Council of Government (CoG). This is an extragovernmental agency whose primary function is to get various local governments—mainly cities and counties—together to accomplish areawide or regional functions. The CoG is not a government but a facilitator of governments. It spans the division between the local governments and coordinates the local region for state and even national governmental functions.

The reason these boundary spanning organizations are described here is because the same type of organization is developing along the U.S.-Mexican border and is seen as playing the same sort or role only in a binational context. Later in this article, this entity and examples will be discussed further.

State Governments

In the United States, local governments are not considered sovereign governments. Local governments receive their power to govern from their states. This assures the control of the State of California over cities, counties, and special districts. Issues of public health care and, recently, welfare are within the purview of state governments, which mainly delegate the administrative function to counties in California. Water quality, transportation—primarily highways—state parks, wildfire suppression, education policy, higher education, and economic development are some of the additional areas of public policy over which the state has primary jurisdiction. Many of these issues are managed by the state's local governments.

Local Government in the Imperial Valley

In California there are three primary local government entities: counties, cities, and special districts. All are involved in the transborder region.

Counties serve in many areas as the administrative agents of the state. The Imperial County Board of Supervisors is the elected policy body that is responsible for carrying out state policy—i.e., health, welfare, air quality, elections, courts, and criminal prosecution—and for making county policy in areas such as land use, transportation, law enforcement (including jails), public works, vital statistics, and tax assessment and collection. The Board is composed of five members selected in nonpartisan elections, representing districts of equal population, for four-year terms. Additionally, the voters of the county also elect at large a district attorney, superintendent of schools, sheriff, treasurer, auditor/controller, tax collector, and county clerk. A chief administrative officer is responsible for the day-to-day operation of the county and is hired by, and is responsible to, the Board. The county began a two-year budget cycle and projected $187 million for fiscal year 2000–2001 and $183 million for fiscal year 2001–2002. The county is divided into incorporated areas (within the boundaries of cities) and unincorporated territory (that area outside the cities for which the county provides municipal services).

Imperial County's seven cities provide municipal-type services: fire, police, water, sewer, parks and recreation, library, public works, streets and roads, land use, and economic development for their residents. All of Imperial County's cities— Brawley (estimated for 2000: population 21,900, budget $10.6 million), Calexico (27,000/$9.6), Calipatria (7,550/$0.7), El Centro (38,300/$10.9), Holtville (5,550/$0.9), Imperial (8,075/$1.3), and Westmorland (1,770/$0.5)—are council-manager municipal governments. Each city elects at large a city council of five members (one of whom is selected as the mayor). The council selects a city manager who is responsible to the council for the day-to-day operation of the city. The Imperial County Local Agency Formation Commission (LAFCo) also uses the classification of "townsites," which it describes as non-incorporated communities that do not have an elected governing body and lack certain municipal services such as sewer, water, paved streets, and so forth. The LAFCo list of Imperial Valley townsites includes Bombay Beach, Desert Shores, Felicity, Heber, Niland, Ocotillo, Palo Verde, Salton City, Salton Sea Beach, Seeley, and Winterhaven. In California, each county is required by the state to have a Local Agency Formation Commission, whose task is to oversee the creation, expansion, and dissolution of cities and special districts.

Special districts are usually single service governments that are found throughout the county. These districts provide all education through school districts; most water, sewer and fire service; and various other services in the unincorporated area of the county (See Table 1).

Table 1. Imperial County Special Districts

General	Educational
Bard Resources Conservation District	Brawley Elementary
Bard Water District	Brawley Union High
Bombay Beach Community Services District	Calexico Unified
Central Valley Cemetery District	Calipatria
Coachella Valley Water District	Central Union High
Heber Public Utility District	El Centro
Heffernan Memorial Hospital District	Heber
Imperial Irrigation District	Holtville Unified
Niland County Service Area No. 1	Imperial Unified
Niland Fire District	Magnolia
Niland Sanitary District	Mccabe
Ocotillo Fire Protection District	Meadows Union
Palo Verde County Water District	Mulberry
Palo Verde Irrigation District	San Pasqual Valley
Palo Verde Resource Conservation District	Seeley Union
Pioneers Memorial Healthcare District	Westmorland Union Elementary
Riverview Cemetery District	
Salton Community Services District	
Seeley County Water District	
Winterhaven County Water District	
Winterhaven Fire District	

SOURCE: Author's analysis (2000).

The one special district that requires additional consideration in Imperial County is the Imperial Irrigation District (IID). A community-owned utility, it provides irrigation water and electric power to the valley. Arguably, it is the most powerful and certainly the wealthiest public entity in the Imperial Valley. According to the IID:

Imperial Irrigation District was formed in 1911 to acquire the properties of the bankrupt California Development Company and its Mexican subsidiary. By 1922, the district had also acquired the 13 mutual water companies, which had developed and operated the distribution canals. By mid 1920, the district was delivering water to nearly 500,000 acres. Since 1942 water has been diverted at Imperial Dam on the Colorado River through the 82-mile long All-American Canal, all of which the district now operates and maintains. IID is the largest irrigation district in the nation and ranks among the top ten agricultural counties in the nation. Of the water IID transports, 98 percent is used for agriculture in the Imperial Valley. The remaining 2 percent is delivered to nine Imperial Valley cities which treat it to safe drinking water standards and sell it to their residents. ... The IID has a present perfected right to 2.6 million acre-feet (MAF) of water annually.[1] (IID 2000)

Additionally, the IID provides electrical power to Imperial Valley customers. IID operates eight gas turbines, eight hydroelectric generation plants, and one generating station. IID has also entered into agreements with Southern California Public Power Authority and Southern California Edison for interests in nuclear and steam generating plants. Of importance to this study is the 1987 agreement signed in Mexico City by IID and Mexico's Federal Energy Commission (Comisión Federal de Electricidad–CFE). The agreement allows the two utilities to purchase and sell low-cost energy from each other when available and also to provide energy in the event of an emergency in either system. In one of the most important water arrangements of the past half century, IID is currently in the process of negotiating an agreement with the San Diego County Water Authority to see excess (conserved) water for residential/urban use. This agreement will also require the agreement of the Municipal Water Districts of Southern California to provide transportation of the water (IID 2000).

Councils of government are local, multijurisdictional coordinating organizations that foster intergovernmental relations within a metropolitan region. They are not governments since they are not empowered by the state with service delivery or regulatory or taxing authority, but they do perform the function of boundary spanning in that they secure cooperation and coordination among various local governments. Imperial County and the seven incorporated cities belong to the Southern California Association of Governments (SCAG) and Imperial Valley Association of Governments (IVAG). Among the tasks SCAG performs are researching and drawing up plans for transportation, growth management, hazardous waste management, and air quality. The following are among the leading activities of SCAG:

- Produces a Regional Transportation Plan and a Regional Transportation Improvement Program

- Develops demographic projections plus integrated land use, housing, employment, transportation programs, measures, and strategies

- Determines conformity projects, plans, and programs under the federal Clean Air Act

- Functions as the authorized regional agency for intergovernmental review of programs proposed for federal financial assistance and direct development activities

- Reviews environmental impact reports for projects that have regional significance for consistency with regional plans

- Functions as the authorized areawide waste treatment management planning agency

- Is responsible under state law for preparation of the Regional Housing Needs Assessment (SCAG 2000)

IVAG is located in El Centro and provides a coordinating role for the Imperial Valley governments.

Transborder Governance: Boundary Spanning

A great challenge to any federal state is the determination of how governing authority is to be divided among the numerous levels of government. A pragmatic solution has evolved in the United States on many occasions when the governments cannot coordinate or cooperate to get the job done. This method is to circumvent the governmental structure through the creation of quasi-governmental regional coordinating entities. Local examples include the following:

- The California Coastal Commission is a regional entity that governs a coastline composed of one state, 15 counties, 58 cities, and numerous special district governments. The CCC was created in 1972 and given authority to make land-use and environmental decisions along the 1,100-mile California coastline.

- The aforementioned Southern California Association of Governments (SCAG). Originally created by the national government, it currently provides for regional planning, interjurisdictional cooperation, and coordination of transportation planning, demographic research, and other tasks mandated by both the national and state governments.

- Imperial Valley Association of Governments (IVAG) performs a similar task for the county and seven city governments.

SCAG and IVAG, like the Coastal Commission, undertake boundary spanning functions that become necessary when too many governments cannot develop plans or policy due to jurisdictional limitations, rivalries, or jealousies.

There are fewer governments in the Mexican context. However, the need for boundary spanning entities still exists. The Mexican model has less flexibility in creating public jurisdictions. In general, instead of integration or coordination, there is a trend to divide public functions among the three levels of government (federal, state, and municipal), coordination among governments is established case by case, and there are very few organisms permanently related to the three levels of government. Those boundary spanners that do exist include: the Planning Committee for the Development of the State (Comité de Planeación para el Desarrollo del Estado–COPLADE), which is integrated by the federal and state governments; and the Planning Committee for the Development of the Municipality of Mexicali (Comité de Planeación para el Desarrollo del Municipio de Mexicali–COPLADEMM), which is mainly integrated by the local government, although federal and state governments are invited to participate. Specifically, COPLADEMM is a weak organism used to articulate intergovernmental relationships, while COPLADE is limited to the task of promoting urban infrastructure such as highways and public services (e.g., water supply and electricity). Intergovernmental coordination in Mexico is a weak institutional practice that remains in its initial stages. As a consequence, most Mexican governmental agencies are in no position to establish relationships with U.S. border governments or boundary spanners. Like many other governmental relationships in this rapidly changing nation, intergovernmental coordination is a growing need that is just now being recognized.

One encouraging action has been the appointment by President Fox of a "border czar." Fox has chosen a popular former governor of Baja California, Ernesto Ruffo Appel, to serve as Northern Border Commissioner. Expectations of greater coordination and cooperation of Mexican governments along the border and more encouragement of boundary spanning are higher than most can remember as the former governor has energetically undertaken his tasks.

Governing the Imperial Valley-Mexicali Border

Border regions throughout a world that is transitioning from one dominated by nation-states to one termed "globalized," present an interesting point of contrasting governance. In the era of the nation-state, when borders, by definition, represented the most distant limits of national sovereignty—the point where competing national sovereignties clashed—the formal treaty was the mechanism that defined the governance process. As the potency of the nation-state declines and new continental trade alliances come to prominence, how can any semblance of border governance or binational regional public policy actually be created and implemented?

Observations along the U.S.-Mexican border can provide some instances of governance and some indications of the future course of border governance. This information will also serve to answer the question: How is the Imperial-Mexicali border region governed?

In order to regulate activities, provide services, and otherwise manage the border region, over the years the U.S.-Mexican border region also has experienced the creation of boundary spanning, quasi-governmental entities that transcend the border in order to accomplish public pursuits. Perhaps the longest-running and best-known example of such an entity is the International Boundary and Water Commission (IBWC) (Comisión Internacional de Límites y Aguas–CILA). Created by treaty in

1889 and reconfigured in 1944, the IBWC/CILA deals with issues ranging from the maintenance of the boundary and its markers and the allocation of surface waters between the two countries, to addressing some surface water sanitation issues, including the construction and maintenance of international sewage treatment plants. The IBWC/CILA works to produce coordination not only between the United States and Mexico, but also between and among their various governments. Thus, for the recent construction of the International Wastewater Treatment Plant in the San Diego-Tijuana area, the IBWC/CILA worked closely with federal, state, and local governments on both sides of the border. Even though an example of the "old style" treaty organization, IBWC/CILA has evolved into a new role as a pragmatic facilitator of border infrastructure that seeks negotiated solutions to disputes or problems among the various parties.

The La Paz Agreement (1983) provided another opportunity for coordination on border environmental matters. This agreement, signed by presidents Ronald Reagan and Miguel de la Madrid eventually produced the Border 2012 Program in 2003 to coordinate local, state, and federal government, as well as other stakeholders, in addressing border environmental issues. Border 2012 was preceded by the Border XXI Program (1996–2001) and the Integrated Environmental Plan for the Mexico-U.S. Border Area (1992–1994) that were both largely federal efforts with some state involvement. While not of treaty status, these agreements are necessary to border environmental cooperation and have grown out of the improved relations under the North American Free Trade Agreement (NAFTA).

A more recent step in binational boundary spanning has been the formalization of previously informal relationships between twin cities. Examples include the agreements of cooperation signed by San Diego and Tijuana (Letter of Agreement, April 1993), and those already existing between El Paso and Ciudad Juárez. These agreements have not created special organisms and usually experience limited efficacy, but they provide examples of city governments in binational regions recognizing the need to move toward greater cooperation in exchanges of information, planning, and coordination.

In the immediate past, the City of Calexico and the Municipality of Mexicali have had a Letter of Agreement between the mayors. This called for joint training, especially public safety, and regular meetings between the department heads and city manager. The City of Calexico has established a Department of International Relations to encourage greater and more formal relationships and closer interactions with Mexicali. As in the San Diego-Tijuana instance, this relationship is based on personal relationships and interactions between the mayors of the two cities. The Board of Supervisors has also had letters of agreement signed with the mayor of Mexicali. Greater "formal" interaction could be anticipated, but the degree of it is legally in doubt since there is some question as to how formally involved local (or state) governments may become with foreign governments.

Binational collaboration and cooperation between the states of California and Baja California are particularly effective in the area of planning and development of transportation projects. On May 6, 1996, a letter of intent created the Bi-State Transportation Technical Advisory Committee (BTTAC). The task of the committee is to coordinate local and state efforts to plan and develop transportation infrastructure for the border region to the year 2020. The letter of intent has increased technical exchange and binational planning and activity coordination among the transportation agencies on both sides of the border. The BTTAC is comprised of representatives from the California Department of Transportation (Caltrans), the San Diego Association of Governments (SANDAG), the Southern California Association of Governments (SCAG), the Imperial Valley Association of Governments (IVAG), and the cities of Calexico and San Diego. Baja California partners in BTTAC include the Secretariat of Human Settlements and Public Works (Secretaría de Asentamientos Humanos y Obras Públicas–SAHOPE) and the municipalities of Mexicali, Tijuana, Ensenada, and Playas de Rosarito.

When discussing binational state relations, note must be made of the much more positive attitude of Governor Gray Davis toward Baja California and Mexico. Visits to Mexico by Davis and return visits by President Fox bode well for furthering these "informal" relationships between elected leaders.

The wisdom of boundary spanning has also been embraced by the North American Free Trade Agreement. NAFTA side agreements between Mexico and the United States produced new binational entities to address the environmental problems that plague the border region: the Border Environment Cooperation Commission (BECC) and the North American Development Bank (NADBank). Their tasks are to identify, coordinate, design, and finance environmental infrastructure projects, particularly in the areas of wastewater treatment, water pollution, and municipal waste problems. BECC is a binational organization that represents states, localities, and the public on both sides of the border. NADBank is the financial arm of the process, providing evaluation of financial feasibility and developing financing packages for BECC projects. As binational institutions, BECC and NADBank have the ability to work with all levels of government on both sides of the border. Examples of BECC-NADBank border environmental infrastructure projects include (Spalding 2000):

- Brawley CA   Water Treatment Plant   Certified 1995 $25.0 m

- Mexicali BC   Wastewater Treatment   Certified 1997 $50.4 m

- Calexico CA   Potable Water Project   Certified 1998 $11.3 m

These institutions (IBWC/CILA, Border XXI, BECC, and NADBank) were designed to be boundary spanning, literally and functionally, to create pragmatic solutions for the shortcomings of federal governance in binational matters and involve all levels of government, nongovernmental organizations, and the public.

An interesting state-level initiative that grew out of the NAFTA activities is the California Border Environment Cooperation Committee (Cal/BECC). Created by the governors of Baja California Sur, Baja California, and California in 1994 at the Forty-eighth General Assembly of the Commission of the Californias, Cal/BECC is charged with identifying mutually agreed upon environmental infrastructure needs along the California-Baja California border and seeking funding for those projects. Specifically, Cal/BECC works to help the projects identified achieve BECC certification and NADBank funding. This three-state organization also serves as a vehicle for environmental planning, technology transfer, and technical assistance programs. Cal/BECC has a tri-state, seven-member board of directors, is scheduled to meet quarterly, and has support staff housed at the State Water Resources Control Board in Sacramento.

The U.S. and Mexican federal governments are coming to the realization that they cannot solve all local transborder problems and that there is a need for local authorities in both countries to interact directly on issues of mutual concern. Accordingly, in 1992 Mexico and the United States created the Border Liaison Mechanism (BLM). Established in the San Diego-Tijuana region in 1993, the BLM enabled the consuls generals of Mexico and the United States in San Diego and Tijuana to convene the three levels of government from both sides of the border to address important issues. For the first time, local governments were enabled to directly work on binational issues. The initial committee of the BLM worked on border crossing issues at the ports of entry and later committees were established for public safety and mutual aid, migration and consular protection, water, and culture and education. It is anticipated that the BLM process will be utilized in the Imperial-Mexicali region in the future.

Conclusion

Governance of border regions presents problems not faced in any other governance situations. Two sovereign nation-states have absolute jurisdiction up to an arbitrary line, but neither has jurisdiction beyond that line. Only in instances where both nations agree is there any governance across the line. Historically, international boundaries have presented barriers or even barricades to movement of people or goods. Many times, however, these barriers have not been able to impede the movement of cultures. Leakage across borders increased during the latter portion of the twentieth century, especially as a byproduct of globalization. Along the U.S.-Mexican border, due to historical, cultural, social, and now economic forces, there is much more interaction across an international boundary that is receding. It is in the area of governance, the last major expression of national sovereignty, that the "hard" boundary continues to exist. It is for issues such as immigration, smuggling, and drug trafficking that governance is a significant issue.

However, in a region bisected by an international boundary and that is faced with many significant and similar problems that require public policy solutions, the question of governance becomes critical. This raises another question that requires an answer in integrated border regions throughout the world, but that is relevant to the Imperial-Mexicali region as well. How can planning for regulation, construction and maintenance of infrastructure, and delivery of services necessary for the health, safety, and welfare of people residing in the border region be accomplished if neither nation-state has any authority in the other's jurisdiction? The answer is to create boundary spanning organizations. These quasi-governmental, regional coordinating organizations have been developed pragmatically by the U.S. and Mexican governments to attend to the externalities that arise from a greater border integration.

These organizations were designed for boundary spanning in both the literal border-related and practical functional senses. While not ordinary, they should not be considered odd. They were devised by two nations that historically have been required to invent pragmatic solutions for the shortcomings of federal governance. In addition, the experience of developing binational solutions and of two different cities/states/nations working together outside the formal or traditional governmental structure, to find—and fund—solutions to needs, problems, and service delivery, provides a prototype of border governance that may become the model for the future. And the Imperial-Mexicali region may look forward to greater involvement with these entities.

Endnote

1. Parts of this article contain excerpts and adaptations from Guillén and Sparrow "Governance and Administrative Boundaries."

References

Calavita, Nico, Tonatiuh Guillén López, and Glen Sparrow. 1998. "Financing Development for Local Governments in the Tijuana River Basin." State of the Environment of the Tijuana River Basin: Working Draft. San Diego: Institute for Regional Studies of the Californias.

Capitol Impact. 2000. http://www.capitolimpact.com/gw/cacty/ca06025.html (August).

Guillén López, Tonatiuh, and Glen Sparrow. 2000. "Governance and Administrative Boundaries." Pp. 41–47 in *Tijuana International Border Area Planning Atlas/Atlas de Planeación del Área Fronteriza Internacional Tijuana-San Diego*, Paul Ganster, ed. San Diego: Institute for Regional Studies of the Californias and San Diego State University Press.

Guillén López, Tonatiuh, and Glen Sparrow. 1998. "Governing the Tijuana River Basin." State of the Environment of the Tijuana River Basin: Working Draft. San Diego: Institute for Regional Studies of the Californias.

Imperial Irrigation District (IID). 2000. http://www.iid.com (December).

Southern California Association of Governments (SCAG). 2000.
    http://www.scag.ca.gov/about/whatdo.htm (December).
Spalding, Mark. 2000. "Addressing Border Environmental Problems Now and in the Future:
    Border XXI and Related Efforts." Pp. 105–37 in *The U.S.-Mexican Border Environment: A
    Road Map to a Sustainable 2020*, Paul Ganster, ed. San Diego: San Diego State University
    Press.

7

Municipal Governance and Management in Mexicali, Baja California

José María Ramos García and
Vicente Sánchez Munguía*

Abstract

The objective of this essay is to present a description of the recent evolution of the government and public management of Mexicali. This municipality has the third largest urban population in the Mexican border. It is also the capital of the State of Baja California and, thus, the seat of the state-level governments. Mexicali is the only capital city of a Mexican border state that is located adjacent to the border and there is no city immediately across the border on the U.S. side of similar population size and political and economic importance. This work intends to provide a general description of the basic characteristics of the government and public administration in the Municipality of Mexicali. An integral approach focusing on the social, economic, and political issues will be used to highlight elements within local administration and public policy (Moore 1995).

Introduction

From a historical perspective, even though the Constitution itself defines municipalities as independent, Mexican municipal institutions have been characterized by their limited political, financial, and administrative autonomy. Subordination has tended to be greater in municipalities that are also the seat of state-level governments. This is due to the different abilities of governments to carry out projects, and also the authority of the

*Ramos García and Sánchez Munguía are Professors at El Colegio de la Frontera Norte, Tijuana, Department of Public Administration Studies.

state government over the municipalities. In addition, within the framework of the law, the state governor is granted specific attributes that provide certain advantages in his or her relationships with municipalities and specifically with the capital city.

The previous information is important since this essay refers to the Municipality of Mexicali, which is also the capital of the State of Baja California and the seat of its public powers. It is the place from which political actions of the state government unfold. This aspect has historically represented an advantage for the inhabitants of the capital because they benefit from public investment in the form of urban infrastructure that is relatively greater than in the rest of the municipalities. However, from a political point of view, housing the state capital also meant greater subordination of the municipality to the state government. The disadvantages were greater when the mayor and governor belonged to different political parties. Regardless, the coexistence of the municipal and state governments has always added a dose of complexity to the municipal administration. This results from the disparity of available resources and the fact that the state government also usually maintains its own social investment programs.

According to population, Mexicali is the third largest border municipality in Mexico's northern region, only behind Tijuana, in the same state, and Juárez, in the State of Chihuahua. Mexicali has a diverse set of economic activities. As the center of activity of the governments' multiple agencies and offices, Mexicali is characterized by the availability of public jobs and the types of services demanded by government-employed populations.

In the past 20 years, the Mexican federal government has carried out different processes and initiatives to decentralize its activities and become more efficient in its performance. The most important changes are related to the reform in 1983 of the Constitution. These changes assigned municipalities their own treasury, thereby establishing a first step toward financial autonomy. At the same time, municipalities were granted a series of powers including public services and urban development. Later, in 1999, the Constitution was again reformed with the intent to accelerate the transfer of responsibilities from the state governments to the municipalities. This action resulted from the state governments' resistance to transfer control of the areas of management to the municipalities, as was stipulated by the Constitution since 1983.

The most important changes that have occurred in Mexican intergovernmental relations have been motivated by the dynamics for change within the context of political representation. As a result, some state institutions have greater political participation, making democracy possible, and have had changes of political parties in power. This alternation between political parties is particularly important for Baja California since it was the first Mexican state to have a different party govern it other than the central party or the Institutional Revolutionary Party (Partido Revolucionario Institucional–PRI).

In 1989, the National Action Party (Partido Acción Nacional–PAN) was able to win the governorship of the State of Baja California, an unprecedented and historical event in Mexico. The alternating rotational process later extended to the municipalities of Baja California and other regions of Mexico; it became a normal part of the country's political life. As part of the same process for change, but in another institutional scenario, parties other than the PRI have been able to gain seats in the state and federal congresses. This change in power has developed a system with counterbalances and support networks which, in turn, has strengthen the country's states and municipalities. In this respect, Mexican municipalities have begun to accept the role that, by law, is theirs to manage their urban and community development.

Municipal Governance in Mexico

Municipal governance is exercised by a city council that is popularly elected for a three-year term without the legal possibility of reelection in the next race. The city council is the maximum authority headed by the municipal president—or mayor—who is responsible for organizing the administration. Therefore, the mayor heads the executive branch of the municipal government. The city council is made up of the party that won the most votes, but also includes members of other parties that ran in the election by formulas of proportional representation. Thus, the city council is comprised of the president, advisors called *regidores* (council members), and the trustee whose duties include the control and supervision of the government's practices and administration.

Trained professionals generally administer the programs and agencies in the municipalities. There is very high personnel turnover at the executive administration level due to the triennial character of the government and the legal impossibility of reelecting the city council. This translates into loss of expertise and lack of continuity in policies and government programs. Each new city council brings its own team of executives that takes on the management of the different areas of responsibility. The turnover of executive leaders also divides public administration according to political affiliations. This inhibits the principle of political neutrality that, in theory, should be the basic feature of a constitutional state. There is more continuity and guaranteed permanent employment at the lower levels of administration. Thus, the administration in major municipalities is a complex organizational unit, given the range of service areas covered, the skills required to meet social demands, and the different classification of government employees.

The development of municipal administrations has been gradual along with decentralization and the transfer of responsibilities to the municipality from the state and federal governments. However, the integration of professional leaders continues to be within the traditional network of interest groups, relatives, and friends. This practice continues even in those municipalities governed by parties that traditionally remained in the political opposition and criticized the patronage practices of the party that previously governed. In some way, this situation shows the existence of traditional political and administrative subcultures that remain and reproduce despite the turnover in the government from one party to another.

Governance and Political Change in Mexicali

With a population of approximately 800,000 inhabitants, Mexicali is the second largest Municipality of Baja California and the third largest in the Mexican northern border. Most inhabitants reside in the City of Mexicali (73%) and the remainder in San Felipe and other localities in the valley of Mexicali. Within the national context, it is a medium-size municipality, but one of the three largest border cities. In addition, the capital of the state is located in Mexicali and this particular aspect is significant within the framework of relations between the municipal and state governments.

The municipality has an economic base that is widely diversified because of the ever-expanding *maquiladora* industry.[1] Agriculture also continues to be among the most important activities in the region, even though the population that depends on this activity is decreasing. Some towns in the valley[2] have even registered reductions in agricultural activities. In this respect, the relative clout of the municipality's rural population has tended to decrease compared to the urban population of the City of Mexicali and that of less populated urban centers in the valley.

The Municipality of Mexicali, then, can be characterized as a very complex entity, but also as having a greater degree of sophistication because of the government's organization and provision of services to the community. In other words, the municipality's public administration is a complicated organization due to its number of divisions and offices, as well as its number of employees. In addition, given the dispersal of about 18 percent of the municipal population located in San Felipe and other centers in the Valley of Mexicali, government management in those areas is conducted through 14 municipal delegations. Although the municipality's population that does not live in the City of Mexicali represents a small percentage, in absolute terms it accounts for more than 140,000 inhabitants. This poses to the municipal administration a challenge of considerable dimensions for the provision of public services. This task is exacerbated by the dispersal of such population centers and the limited resources made available by the municipality for social programs.

As mentioned earlier, in 1989 PAN won the governorship and became very important in the Congress of Baja California (see Table 1). However, the PRI managed to keep governance of the Municipality of Mexicali for the six years that Ernesto Ruffo was governor, until 1995. In that year, the PAN was able to win the elections and has retained continuous control of the municipal government to the present, which means three consecutive administrations.

Table 1. Percentage of Votes by Main Political Parties, Mexicali Municipal Elections of 1995–2000

Party	Year		
	1995	**1998**	**2000**
PRI	43.70	40.20	35.38
PAN	48.10	43.97	50.19*
PRD	2.60	15.13	6.09
Did not vote	34.70	50.92	63.36

*Participated as Alliance for Baja California in coalition with the Green Ecological Party of Mexico (Partido Verde Ecologista de México–PVEM).
**Percentage of registered voters that did not vote.

SOURCES: State Electoral Institute (Instituto Estatal Electoral) (2001); Espinoza Valle (2000).

In some respects, the PRI had based its political hegemony and control on the rural population in the Mexicali Valley. However, the fact that the rural population has decreased in relative terms also meant that it was no longer a determining factor in electoral results. Also, events such as the opening up of trade policies considerably affected the population dedicated to agricultural activities, as did the withdrawal of the government's agricultural assistance. In addition, through more liberal policies, the government dismantled the PRI's corporate links with the *ejidatarios* (holders of a portion of commonly held land, or *ejidos*). The PRI's ideological elements lacked relevance for the social actors (*ejidatario* organizations, unions, bureaucrats, and small business people) in the face of a regime that opted to distance itself from its own past. Thus, the PAN's victory was not surprising, but just a matter of time. It also resulted from the elimination of official control of the electoral process and the agencies that supervised elections.

In 1995, the PAN's candidate, in alliance with the Green Ecological Party of Mexico, won the municipal presidency of Mexicali and displaced PRI from the local government. Eugenio Elorduy Walther, who had also been a candidate in 1983 and whose victory was not recognized then, became the new mayor of the municipality. In 1998, PAN was again victorious at the municipal level with Víctor Hermosillo Celada as the candidate for the municipal presidency. The PAN won Mexicali's municipal presidency for the third successive time in 2000, with its candidate Jaime Rafael Díaz Ochoa. However, the electoral process failed to attract large percentages of voters and the 2000 elections had an electoral absenteeism of 59.5 percent in Mexicali and 63.4 percent statewide for the gubernatorial election. The state's Congress has maintained a balance of political powers since 1989, and there are almost equal numbers from the two parties that generated the most votes: PAN and PRI. Other parties—such as the Party of the Democratic Revolution (Partido de la Revolución Democrática–PRD)—

Table 2. Congress of the State of Baja California:
Representation of Political Parties, 1995-2004

Legislature	Political Party			
	PAN	PRI	PVEM	PRD
XVII	12	10	1	2
XVI	11	11	-	3
XV	13	11	-	1

SOURCE: Instituto Estatal Electoral de Baja California (2002).

had a lower representation, but one quite valuable in the legislative process of state government (see Table 2).

Municipal Governance and Public Administration

The different levels of Mexico's public administration are in the process of administrative and political modernization. The rise of the *panista* governments has favored greater professionalism in public management and, in certain ways, has improved the effectiveness of some decision-making procedures. There is an important difference between just managing a city and doing a good job of governing a city, a situation that applies to some governments with PAN affiliations (Ward 1998: 126). A technocratic administration that does not incorporate elements of strategic and integral public management can be promoted; that is, a traditional management structure has been proposed, one that favors decision-making processes that are separate from political, social, and cultural aspects. This essay provides examples of traditional management through characteristics found in the lack of public safety and in considering the importance of this problem in the Municipality of Mexicali.

In late 1999, the administration of the Municipality of Mexicali had 13 divisions, 13 semi-municipal entities, and 14 delegations. These offices had a total of 4,026 employees; 1,883 were classified as permanent, 1,458 were senior personnel, and 685 were temporary employees. The major problems faced by this municipal administration included the following:

- Lack of financial resources to meet the needs of the community

- Lack of credibility of public officials and their responsibilities

- Insufficient physical spaces that limited the development of internal work and service to the public

- Lack of professional training of public employees

- Excessive internal requirements that delay the acquisition of inputs and that are reflected in the quality of the service delivered

Table 3. Main Problems in Mexicali
(by order of importance)

Focus Area	Percentage
Public safety	22.0
Street maintenance and restoration	17.0
Sewerage and drainage	8.0
Social assistance	6.0
Public lighting	5.0

SOURCE: COPLADEMM (1998).

During the administration of Víctor Hermosillo Celada (1999–2001), some of the administrative-related problems of Mexicali were resolved. However, other public problems emerged or became more acute. Among these was the lack of personal safety, which was related to the significant increase in drug addiction that resulted in increased robberies and delinquency in general. Another problem was the deterioration of the environment from pollution and lack of adequate urban infrastructures.

Despite advances attained in some aspects of administrative management, the municipal government of Mexicali has encountered difficulties in managing and governing public problems that deal with the structural factors associated with the lack of public safety. In this regard, strategic planning designed by the government of Mayor Hermosillo stands out as a major municipal government policy initiative that was implemented through the Planning Committee for the Development of the Municipality of Mexicali (Comité de Planeación para el Desarrollo del Municipio de Mexicali–COPLADEMM). Although COPLADEMM has played an important role in defining objectives and priorities of local public policies, the administration's ineffectiveness in dealing with the complexity of implementing, managing, and evaluating policies is obvious. This situation, for example, makes the problems of the public's lack of safety and social marginalization more apparent in the Municipality of Mexicali.

General Problems of the City of Mexicali

In 1998, COPLADEMM implemented a community survey to identify the main problem areas that the municipal government must first address. These areas are identified in Table 3.

As a result of the public's prioritizing of the problems, COPLADEMM identified important problem areas and the following strategic objectives were established for the municipal development of Mexicali:

1. Improved public safety
2. More public works and services

3. Increased employment and economic development

4. Greater citizenry participation

In order to achieve these objectives, municipal management should have a government with an adequate, honest, and efficient organizational structure. It should also have the necessary infrastructure and resources to provide essential works and services for the development of the community. The main strategies of Mexicali's administrative development were the following:

1. Improve control of municipal finances

    a. Governmental finances: Make sure that government finances are balanced between revenues and expenses

    b. Municipal revenue: Increase municipal revenue through efficient and equitable collection plans

    c. Municipal resources: Manage greater federal and state resources

Traditionally, one of the main problems encountered by local governments has been the lack of adequate financing for development of the municipal government's priorities. This problem has not yet been solved and, in some ways, could even be considered worse as new issues have emerged. One alternative that local governments, such as Mexicali, have put into practice is increasing the levels of public indebtedness as an option for building public infrastructure and promoting urban development. However, it is not clear if this option is the best alternative for addressing public problems without redesigning each sector's policies, especially when such problems are complex and have many dimensions that cannot be limited to financing.

One of the main deficiencies of governments that conduct themselves more like businesses, and have similarities to the business entrepreneurs of the PAN, is that they find it difficult to analyze public problems according to social, cultural, and political dimensions. Additionally, financing is seen as the only solution to reducing these problems. This can be illustrated, for example, by the lack of public safety. During the 1999–2001 administration, it was expected that the budget for municipal public safety would increase, especially for the acquisition of patrol cars, weapons, and equipment. However, this budget increase proved insufficient to address the increasing crime taking place in the Municipality of Mexicali in 1999. What had failed? It is believed that it was the lack of conceptualizing, managing, and implementing the budget, as well broadly evaluating the problem in a way that goes beyond the objectives and missions of institutions and their policies (Agranoff and McGuire 1998).

The process of strategic planning carried out by municipalities such as Mexicali is an important and necessary task for identifying the main characteristics of local public problems (Ramos n.d.). This process, though, is insufficient if the different variables that condition development and its evaluation are not taken into account beforehand. This is particularly important when the management of public problems involves consensus building and management of policies in the different stages of the process, and is not achieved by decree. Herein lies one of the main weaknesses in management and governance at the local level.

2.   Administrative Modernization and Simplification

    a.   Train personnel: Develop training programs for personnel to improve the performance

    b.   Transfer responsibilities and resources: Negotiate and determine new areas of governance that can be transferred by the state government to the municipality, as the local government directly interacts with the community

    c.   Update standards: Update current standards in order to simplify regulations

    d.   Improve administrative structure: Develop an administrative structure that is quick, efficient, and provides improved public services. Provide the tools for administrative modernization by automating and simplifying systems and procedures that effectively and efficiently deliver services

One of the main impacts of administrative modernization is for the change in policies to be institutionalized. However, social and political demands that local governments face in their first year of governance make it difficult to institutionalize any changes generated by the end of the three-year municipal government term. This has limited the number of actual changes in municipalities such as Tijuana, Mexicali, and Ciudad Juárez. Hence, this represents another challenge for these governments to make public policies. Additionally, there is no guarantee that the few changes that do occur in the administrative management will overcome immediate problems, and initiate planning and management geared toward an improved quality of life.

The possibility of redesigning local public policies is set by more professionalization, capacity building, and greater government capability and management at the local level. Capacity-building programs for public officials of the Municipality of Mexicali and, in general, for the state government of Baja California, have been determined by the following factors:

•   The impact of capacity-building programs in promoting the efficacy and efficiency of public officials and staff is conditioned by the level of program updates and innovation, the administrative culture of the workplace, the institutional philosophy, and the political climate prevalent at the municipal and state levels.

- The impact of capacity-building programs in promoting institutional innovation and change depends on the understanding of the programs; an administrative culture that favors and encourages motivation, performance, and decision-making capability; a visionary organization that promotes institutional change and consensus; and a political climate that advances institutional legitimacy based on the leadership, efficacy, and efficiency of its actors.

- The impact of capacity-building programs is limited because program content is not up-to-date and lacks emphasis that promotes strategies and mechanisms for institutional change and innovation.

- The impact of capacity-building programs is basically geared toward technical updating and toward promoting innovation in the role of public management officials and staff.

- Studies of the government's role in the northern Mexican border states have found limited governmental capacity, specifically in public officials' lack of professional training and knowledge to promote cooperation and negotiation of border issues with the United States.[4] In addition, important differences were detected in local government administrations in the United States and Mexico. These were associated to perception variables regarding the public sector, education, expertise level, and work motivation in the public administrations of Mexican northern border municipalities.

3. Dissemination (outreach) and greater interinstitutional coordination

    a. Dissemination of works and services: Disseminate high impact services and works and diversify channels of communication

    b. Linkages with other government levels: Establish linkages with other government levels to address issues of interinstitutional interest

    c. Community outreach: Strengthen the "Civic Wednesday" program and develop other activities that facilitate direct interactions between the mayor and officials and the citizenry

    d. Approval of public works: Submit to the community, for its consensus, public investment plans to be carried out in the municipality

Two aspects stand out in this third general strategy of the municipal government of Mexicali: intergovernmental management and civic participation.

Intergovernmental Management

Traditionally, management of public policies within the different levels of government and the actors had not been part of the analysis and implementation of policies. This was basically due to the centralization of decisions and policies in the federal government in Mexico. The tendency toward centralization was one of the structural components of the relationship among federal, state, and local governments. In recent years, advances in the democratization of Mexico have supported greater administrative and partial political decentralization. As a result, the different levels of government need to coordinate themselves administratively. In a marginal way, they also need to promote cooperative intergovernmental agreements in order to efficiently manage decentralized tasks and public policies.

Within this framework, one fundamental issue is the shared management of public policies under the criteria of efficacy, efficiency, and effectiveness. This issue has not been extensively analyzed from the academic point of view due precisely to the incipient process of national democratization and to the fact that public discussion about governability has had greater emphasis than discussions about management of the decentralization processes. The lack of public safety in the Municipality of Mexicali represents a specific policy that shows the importance of the influence of intergovernmental relations.

From this viewpoint, the redefinition of the role of the federal government within a new democratization framework is an essential task in order to overcome problems, inertia, and political interests among the different actors and government levels. Limitations to an effective coordination among local and state governments of Baja California and the new federal government could be overcome with regard to public safety, migration, and the environment. This can be achieved because an ideological agreement exists and because the importance of the public safety issue is recognized. However, this does not necessarily mean that a substantial change should be expected in the short term. Structural factors that condition the public's lack of safety and other problems identified will continue to be present. Also, a certain readjustment of the groups that have benefited under current conditions can be expected. Here, indicators of social and institutional vulnerability stand out and cannot be reduced in the short term, but are part of medium- and long-term policies.

One of the main contributions of the intergovernmental relations approach is that it goes beyond the regulatory notions that are typical of relationships between government actors and society. It should be pointed out that governmental action in the Municipality of Mexicali has not been able to overcome the legalistic tendency that emphasizes authority and the system of law. Although this tendency is certainly an important part of the process of developing policies, it is insufficient if it does not adapt to new social, cultural, and political processes that adjust government actions in diverse public policies.

The intergovernmental relations approach when applied to local public policies provides the conceptual elements for the development of cooperative and coordinated proposals through the negotiation and definition of different opinions. Its implementation requires the capability of managing and governing, thus creating agreements with different actors regardless of their political differences and bureaucratic interests.

Table 4 presents an overview of some characteristics of relations among the federal, state, and local municipal governments with regard to public safety. The role of the federal government has structural characteristics in that it is part of the traditional way that the lack of safety problems have been perceived. As a result, the institutional role needs to be reconfigured. Otherwise, if it continues with its tendencies, management in the federal government will be ineffective and its policies will lack meaning. The persistence of these problems reflects the inability to reduce them. It also indicates that in the short term it will be difficult to promote effective cooperation between the federal and other levels of government. Cooperation does not result from a decree. It is achieved through agreements, consensuses, and, especially, negotiations. To assume that being respectful of authority is the only means to direct policies reflects a lack of understanding of governance within the context of political and social conflicts, as would be the case of Mexicali.

The role of the Baja California state government in public safety policies has not experienced important changes in comparison to other state governments. This also does not mean that the government has redefined its policies. Changes have been specific and, in this respect, a set of actions that have advanced the policies may be

Table 4. Tendencies of Intergovernmental Relationships and Public Safety

Federal Government	State Government (Baja California)	Local Government (Mexicali)
• Discretion • Inefficiency • Corruption • Conflict • Mistrust • Political interests • Minimal political willpower • Low credibility • Institutional suspicion	• Centralization • Corruption • Mistrust • Political interests • Minimal political willpower • Emphasis on rule of law • Conservatism (law) (values) • Hierarchy • Delegation of responsibilities to other levels of government (migration and drug trafficking) • Institutional suspicion	• Inefficiency • Mistrust • Minimal political willpower • Lack of coordinated intergovernmental public policy on safety

SOURCE: Authors' analysis (2002).

identified. These advances, however, are insufficient in the face of the structural factors that condition the lack of public safety in Baja California.

Changes are shaped, though not structurally, as a result of political, social, and bureaucratic forces. A decrease in structural factors such as drug trafficking, organized crime, and the transborder context, as well as consideration of the surrounding factors, would allow for the reduction and control of the elements of local public insecurity. As the changes have not been structural in the past three years, common and federal crimes have increased in the State of Baja California, particularly in the municipalities of Mexicali and Tijuana.

Using an intergovernmental relations' analysis, among the characteristics that stand out in the role of the state government is its reproduction of the federal government's tendencies, including its centralization characteristics, minimal political willpower, history of corruption, and an emphasis on the rule of law with a rhetorical tone.

The role of Mexicali's municipal government in the system of intergovernmental relations is manifested through the political, administrative, technical, and law enforcement actors. This reflects a level of specificity (which will not be discussed thoroughly in this article). A more modest conclusion is to present the municipality's limitations and potential in its participation in the system through its abilities and priorities. It should be pointed out that the Municipal Development Plan of Mexicali does not explicitly make a formal or informal proposal for intergovernmental management. This indicates that the issue has minor relevance within the municipal scope. Its proposal is limited to the administrative coordination among the three levels of government.

In the case of the Municipal Development Plan of Mexicali, a critical diagnosis is made of its problem of public insecurity and a series of proposals is presented for changes in management and law enforcement officials. It is difficult to implement important changes that fix some of the structural problems that are a part of the lack of public safety, such as corruption and impunity. Additionally, cooperation with the other governmental actors is not perceived as a priority. However, as can be identified in the overview of intergovernmental tendencies, there is a relationship between governmental actors associated with the lack of public safety.

There are several difficulties in establishing intergovernmental cooperation. Those that stand out are the federal and state governments' tendencies toward centralization; corruption; mistrust; lack of political desire to develop common policies among the three levels of government that respond to the efficacy, efficiency, and effectiveness criteria; institutional suspicion because of image and prestige problems; and the role of each federal, state, and municipal agency; all of which translate into ineffective intergovernmental cooperation. One of the main problems of management and governance of the Municipality of Mexicali can be found within this structural framework.

4.   Strengthening of the municipal planning system: Develop a planning system
      that efficiently responds to the requirements presented by the community. Its
      main lines of action are:

   a.   Planning for the future: Plan the development of the municipality with
        long-term vision

   b.   Community participation in municipal planning: Promote involvement
        and participation in municipal planning of the different levels in society

   c.   Management indicators: Establish indicators that facilitate control,
        advancement, results, and interpretation of statistical data that assist in
        adequate decision making

Undoubtedly, planning of public policies with a long-term vision is an essential
task of any government. However, a series of cautions have been included in the
development of the Mexicali municipal planning document. These warnings are
related to the difficulties of Mexicali's management and municipal governance,
specifically in designing, formulating, implementating, and evaluating public policies
that are part of an integral vision. The municipality's vision is based on its redesigned
role and on its limitations to promote efficacy, efficiency, and effectiveness in local
public policies. The absence of these elements produces a general visualization of a
desire for government action during specified time limits. However, it does not
include proposals based on social realities. This is particularly troublesome when
considering the multiple dimensions that condition local public problems.

Management or institutional performance indicators should not be based solely
on quantitative actions, but should also include the social impacts on quality of life.
This is a structural problem that has not been resolved by the governments and public
administrations that derive from a process of democratic switching of political power,
such as is the case of the Municipality of Mexicali.

5.   Follow up, update, and evaluate the municipal development plan,
      1999–2001: Control, follow up, and evaluate municipal management. The
      main lines of action are:

   a.   Follow up on the municipal development plan: Provide continuous
        follow-up with community and government participation regarding
        progress achieved during the administration

   b.   Update development strategies: Establish the bases for continuity to
        the institutional planning that allows directing action toward the
        municipal reality

    c.   Evaluate the municipal development plan: At the end of the administration (2001), evaluate the achievements attained by the administration and disseminate results

The importance of municipal development planning is shown through an integral approach to public policies, which includes a critical and objective assessment of the governments' local achievements and limitations. Within this framework, the evaluation of the role of management, as well as policies, is a fundamental task that has not necessarily taken place in an objective and critical way in the Municipality of Mexicali. The following arguments support this statement:

One key element of public administration is the evaluation process of its policies and organization. The fundamental idea of evaluation is to monitor changes and imbalances that characterize an organization. The purpose is to know if this organization meets its policy objectives and if what they are carrying out makes sense. This becomes a fundamental condition for developing countries that are not quite accustomed to strategic and critical evaluations, especially because it allows for the monitoring of public policy advances, problems, and challenges. In addition, there is a low level of institutional self-criticism about advances and reversals of public policies and, consequently, low institutional capacity for redefining objectives, strategies, and goals, and for reaching these within a context of uncertainty and limited management capabilities.

One objective of evaluations is to generate changes in order to increase an organization's efficacy, efficiency, and effectiveness. One problem is that any change within the administration generates resistance from the actors because, basically, many times they do not identify with or understand the importance of such changes. That is, these actors lack awareness to promote these changes because they are not sufficiently motivated to participate in these changes.

Within a law enforcement context of a municipal scope of Mexicali (which is characterized by structural problems of corruption, inefficiency, and impunity), it is a challenge to redefine the role of law enforcement and administrative players associated with the lack of public safety that characterizes the Municipality of Mexicali. The persistence of the lack of public safety at the local and state levels in Baja California reflects the governments' limitations in reducing its structural problems. Through the years, the complexity of the problem has become more acute because the local, regional, and transborder sociocultural environment has fallen into this problem. Consequently, governmental responses have been insufficient because, generally, they have not been able to solve the structural problems of insecurity, such as drug trafficking, organized crime, and the transborder context. In fact, it could be stated that, in general terms, the policies of former governments are only reproduced, as shown in Table 5.

Table 5. Public Management Tendencies in Baja California:
Public Safety

Regulatory emphasis
Efficiency
Resources control
Efficacy
Limited social communication
Value efforts
Public employees conscience
Legal vision

SOURCE: Authors' analysis (2002).

Endnotes

1. In December 2000, there were 202 *maquiladora* plants in the municipality that employed 64,230 workers; in 1998, there were 182 industries of this type that employed 46,474 workers. See Decimoséptimo Ayuntamiento de Mexicali (2002).

2. The Plan Estatal de Desarrollo Urbano 1996–2001 (state plan for urban development) identifies a population decrease in the *ejidos* (common land) of Guerrero, Veracruz Uno, Veracruz Dos, and Tlaxcala for the 1980–1995 period. This decrease extended into the 1995–2001 period and became present in other *ejido* nucleus of the valley.

3. Data from the State Electoral Institute of Baja California: www.ieebc.org.mx (cited August 3, 2002).

4. This study was limited to government officials of El Paso, Texas, and Ciudad Juárez, Chihuahua (Saint-Germain 1995). In the case of El Paso, 51 municipal officials from 35 public agencies were interviewed. In Ciudad Juárez, 28 municipal officials from 22 public agencies were interviewed. Saint-Germain states that the intent is not to generalize results obtained for the U.S.-Mexican border cities. Interviews were carried out in early 1993. Saint-Germain's study was conducted prior to the development of NAFTA. However, it is considered current in terms of its proposed methodology to analyze the role of public administrations of border states. Also, some of the structural problems addressed in Saint-Germain's article (1995) continue to exist, but with other variations and tendencies in the local and regional border public management (Ramos 1996; n.d.).

References

Agranoff, Robert. 1997. "Las relaciones y la gestión intergubernamentales." In *La nueva Administración Pública*, Rafael Bañón and Ernesto Carrillo, eds. Madrid: Alianza Universidad.

Agranoff, Robert, and Michael McGuire. 1998. "Multi-Network Management: Collaboration and the Hollow State in Local Economy Policy." *Journal of Public Administration Research and Theory* 8 (3): 67–91.

Aguilar Villanueva, Luis F. 1998. "Prólogo." Pp. xiii–xviii in *Desarrollo regional y relación transfronteriza. El caso de México-California*, José María Ramos García, ed. México D.F.: Instituto Nacional de Administración Pública.

Comité de Planeacion para el Desarrollo del Municipio de Mexicali (COPLADEMM). 1998. *Plan Municipal de Desarrollo 1999–2001. Municipio de Mexicali*. Mexicali: COPLADEM.

Décimoquinto Ayuntamiento de Mexicali. 1998. *Tercer informe de gobierno*. Mexicali: XV Ayuntamiento de Mexicali.

Décimoséptimo Ayuntamiento de Mexicali. 2002. "Plan de Desarrollo del Municipio de Mexicali." *Periódico Oficial del Estado de Baja California* 13 (29 March).

Espinoza Valle, Víctor Alejandro. 2000. "El segundo gobierno de oposición en Baja California." Pp. 55–77 in *Alternancia y Transición Política. ¿Cómo gobierna la oposición en México?*, Víctor Alejandro Espinoza Valle, ed. Tijuana: El Colegio de la Frontera Norte/Plaza y Valdez editores.

Gobierno del Estado de Baja California, Secretaría de Asentamientos Humanos y Obras Públicas. 1996. *Plan Estatal de Desarrollo Urbano 1996–2001*. Mexicali: Gobierno del Estado de Baja California, Secretaría de Asentamientos Humanos y Obras Públicas.

Hernández Vicencio, Tania, and José Negrete Mata, eds. 2001. *La experiencia del PAN. Diez años de gobierno en Baja California*. Tijuana: El Colegio de la Frontera Norte/Plaza y Valdez editores.

Instituto Estatal Electoral de Baja California. 2002. (Cited 3 August), www.ieebc.org.mx.

Instituto Nacional de Estadística, Geografía e Informática (INEGI). 2001. *Mexicali, Baja California, Cuaderno Estadístico Municipal*. Aguascalientes: INEGI.

Moore, M.H. 1995. *Creating Public Value. Strategic Management in Government*. Cambridge: Harvard University Press.

Ramos García, José María. n.d. "Seguridad pública fronteriza: gestión, contexto y redefinición de políticas." *Frontera Norte*. Tijuana: COLEF. Forthcoming.

Ramos García, José María. 1996. *Desarrollo regional y relación transfronteriza. El caso de México-California*. Mexico D.F.: Instituto Nacional de Administración Pública.

Rodríguez, Victoria E. 1997. "Decentralization in Mexico." Pp. 25–37 in *Reforma Municipal to Solidaridad to Nuevo Federalismo*. Victoria E. Rodríguez, ed. Boulder, CO: Westview Press.

Saint-Germain, Michelle. 1995. "Similarities and Differences in Perceptions of Public Service among Public Administrators on the U.S.-Mexico Border." *Public Administration Review* 55 (6): 507–16.

Sosa, José. 1999. "Modernizar la administración fronteriza: ¿Una tarea pendiente?" Pp. 119–56 in *Anuario México-Estados Unidos-Canadá*. México D.F.: El Colegio de México.

Ward, Peter. 1998. "Del clientelismo a la tecnocracia: cambios recientes en la gestión municipal en México." *Política y Gobierno* 5 (1).

PART THREE

Economy and Agriculture

8

Explaining Low Income and High Unemployment in Imperial County

James Gerber*

Abstract

According to per capita income, Imperial County is the fifth poorest county in the State of California. Although the county has a large agricultural sector, the role of agriculture is diminishing and is not the sole source of low average incomes, despite the fact that it may generate highly unequal incomes. As a whole, agriculture generates more income per employed person than most other sectors of the economy. Other differences between the economic structures of Imperial County and the state—such as the share of employment in the retail or service sectors—do not account for the differences in income either. Most reasons for low per capita income probably stem from labor market and human capital variables. Among the most important are the high rate of unemployment, the low level of educational attainment, the very high proportion of the population that does not speak English, the relative youth of the population, and the significantly smaller share of the working age population that is part of the labor force.

Introduction

Imperial County is one of the poorest counties in the State of California. According to the U.S. Department of Commerce, its 1998 per capita income placed it fifty-third among the state's 58 counties.[1] Imperial County's per capita income of $17,353 was 64 percent of the U.S. level ($27,203) and 62 percent of the statewide California level ($28,163).

*Gerber is Director of the Center for Latin American Studies and Professor in the Economics Department at San Diego State University.

A key task of any examination of Imperial County's economy is to explain why its per capita income is so low. Low is a relative term, however, so average California levels are used as a benchmark throughout this analysis. The next section provides a look at the income trends over time, followed by a brief digression on the determinants of income and an examination of the structure of Imperial County's economy. Finally, the rate of unemployment and several human capital variables are considered, including the labor force participation rate, the dependency ratio, and the level of educational attainment.

The results of the analysis point to several conclusions. First, while Imperial County is one of the most agriculturally oriented regions of the state, the role of agriculture has been diminishing over time. Agricultural incomes may be highly unequal in their distribution. However, agriculture is not the source of low average incomes, since it generates more income per employed person than most other sectors of the economy. Second, other differences between the economic structures of Imperial County and the state, such as the share of employment in the retail or service sectors, do not appear to account for differences in income. Third, most of the reasons for low per capita income probably stem from labor market and human capital variables. Among the most important are the high rate of unemployment, the low level of educational attainment, the very high proportion of the population that does not speak English, the relative youth of the population, and the significantly smaller share of the working age population that works or is looking for work.

The Time Trend of Income

Over the last two decades, per capita income in Imperial County diverged significantly from the statewide level of per capita income (U.S. Department of Commerce 2001).[2] Divergence occurred in two stages, the first beginning roughly in the mid-1970s and ending in the mid-1980s, and the second beginning in the mid-1980s and extending to the present. Figure 1 divides the years from 1969 to 1998 into three periods. From 1969 to 1975, the average level of per capita income in Imperial County was 84 percent of the state level; from 1976 through 1985, it was 78 percent; and from 1986 to 1998, it was 68 percent. Figure 1 compares state and county per capita income levels and Figure 2 shows the trend in the ratio of county and state income. The trend line in Figure 2 shows the rate of decline.

Some of the divergence between statewide per capita income and that of Imperial County may have been the result of lagging growth rates in employment, particularly between 1976 and 1985. Figure 3 shows the Imperial County average annual percentage change in employment from 1969 to 1998. During the first period, when there was little deterioration in Imperial County's income relative to the state, the average annual rate of employment growth was 3.8 percent per year, which is significantly higher than the statewide rate of 2.2 percent per year (EDD 2001).

Figure 1. Imperial County and California Per Capita Income, 1969–1998

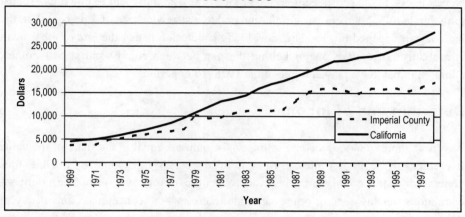

SOURCE: U.S. Department of Commerce (2001).

Figure 2. Ratio of Per Capita Income, Imperial Valley to California, 1969–1998

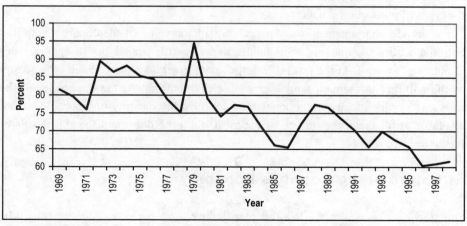

SOURCE: Author's calculations based on data from U.S. Department of Commerce (2001).

During the next period, from 1976 to 1985, the income gap between Imperial County and the state began to widen significantly and job growth was 0.2 percent per year in the county and 3.4 percent statewide. The lack of county-level job creation seems significant because it occurred at the same time that the income gap opened. Nevertheless, in the subsequent period (1986–1998), employment returned to a robust growth rate of 3.2 percent per year, compared to a statewide rate of 2 percent. Yet, the income gap widened further. The most likely conclusion is that the rate of job growth is probably not the key factor behind the gap between county and state incomes, although it may have played a role in the 1976–1985 period.

Determinants of Income

As a first approximation, income in Imperial County is equal to the share of the value it creates in the goods and services it produces.[3] While some of the incomes generated in the county may be paid to people living outside of the county—commuters, landowners, or other corporate interests—the conceptual equivalency of the county's income and the county resident's share of the value of the output produced is a useful tool for beginning an analysis of the causes of the county's relatively low income levels.

The determinants of the value of the output of a firm, region, or nation can be easily broken into two components. The first component consists of the types of goods and services produced. In other words, at the level of a single enterprise, does a farm produce alfalfa or asparagus? At the county level, does the economy generate a large quantity of low-value retail services, or does it produce high-value financial services? These questions take into consideration the structure of the economy and the types of production it undertakes.

A second component of the determinants of the value of the county's output is both the quality and quantity of its inputs, as well as the availability of opportunities to put them to work. At the level of enterprise, a farmer takes into account the quality of the soil and how much land is available for planting. At the county level, the relevant questions focus on the availability of jobs, the quantity of labor and capital available to fill them, the quality of the available technology, and the skill levels of the labor force.

Structure of the County's Economy

One possible explanation for low incomes in the county is that its economy might be concentrated in sectors where output values are relatively low. For example, instead of high-value financial and business services, relatively greater numbers of the county's workforce might be concentrated in low-value retail services or some other relatively low-paying sector. This does not seem to be the case for Imperial County.

Figure 3. Average Annual Rate of Employment Growth in Imperial County, 1970–1998

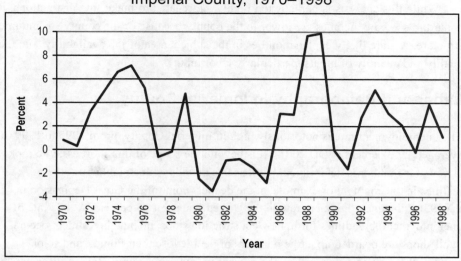

SOURCE: U.S. Department of Commerce (2001).

Perhaps the most dramatic change in the structure of the economy over the last three decades has been the decline in the relative importance of agriculture.[4] Measured in terms of both total income generated and total employment, agriculture is a smaller share of the economy today than it was in 1970, and the trend is downward. Figures 4 and 5 illustrate this point.

At the same time that agriculture was shrinking in relative importance, the county's income gap with the state widened. On the surface, this argues that the presence of a large agricultural sector is not the reason for the income gap. Further evidence is found in agriculture's relative income and employment shares. In general, agriculture has produced a larger share of total county income than its employment share. For example, in 1998, earned income in agriculture was about 30 percent of total earned income, while the labor force in agriculture was about 26 percent of the total labor force. In other words, while agricultural incomes may be unequally distributed (for example, between landowners and farmworkers), income per worker in agriculture is greater than in other sectors of the county economy. This pattern is illustrated in Table 1.

Further analysis of the sectoral pattern of employment shows that the county is not disadvantaged by its economic structure. Table 2 compares the county to the statewide employment pattern. While there are some high wage sectors, such as the manufacturing and financial sectors, that are relatively smaller in Imperial County than in the state, other sectors compensate. In particular, Imperial County has a relatively smaller service sector and a much larger government sector. The latter pays much higher than average wages and more than compensates for the relative lack of manufacturing and financial services.[5]

While this analysis is perhaps too highly aggregated to make fine distinctions, it is hard to see how incomes are lower in the county because of the county's economic structure. A more likely explanation lies in the subject area of job availability, and the quality and quantity of inputs, particularly labor inputs.

Labor and Demography in Imperial County

The unemployment rate is notoriously high in Imperial County. From 1995 to 1999, it averaged 29.6 percent (EDD 2001). It is beyond the scope of this short essay to look at how this number is determined, but it seems at odds with a number of other realities in the county. For example, at the deepest point of the Great Depression in the 1930s, the unemployment rate in the United States hit 25 percent. At this rate of unemployment, breadlines form, new construction stops, no new investment occurs, retail shops are boarded up, large numbers of people lose their homes, and so on. None of these symptoms appear to be present in Imperial County. Rather, it seems likely that the methods used by the U.S. Bureau of Labor Statistics to measure local area unemployment are biased in the case of Imperial County.[6]

Nevertheless, even if the reported unemployment rate is double the actual rate, it is still very high. In 2000, for example, when the state's unemployment rate was 5.2 percent, the estimated county rate was 23.2 percent, more than four times higher. Using the labor and employment figures for 1998 (the most recent year of reported

Figure 4. Agricultural and Nonagricultural Employment, Imperial County, 1969–1998

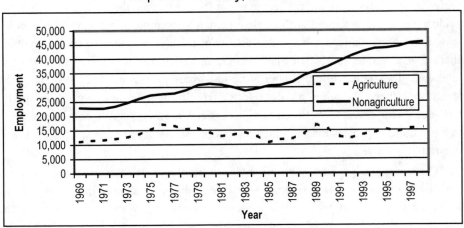

SOURCE: U.S. Department of Commerce (2001).

Figure 5. Agricultural and Nonagricultural Income,
Imperial County, 1969–1998

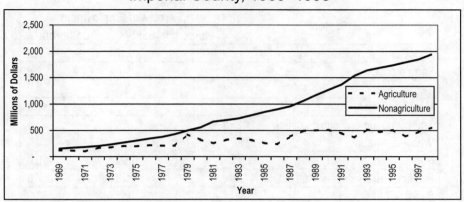

SOURCE: U.S. Department of Commerce (2001).

income for the county), a fall in the reported unemployment rate to 15 percent would generate approximately 8,230 more jobs or about $248 million in annual income. This would be a 10 percent increase in the county's total personal income. Note that this is a conservative estimate of the direct role the county's high unemployment rate plays in the determination of its relatively low income since it only assumes a reduction to 15 percent.

In addition to high unemployment, three characteristics of Imperial County's population are important sources of differences between the county and the state: the

Table 1. Imperial County Income and
Employment by Sector, 1998

Sector	Percent of Employment	Percent of Earned Income
Agricultural services	16.7	7.8
Farm production	9.6	22.6
Construction	3.1	3.1
Manufacturing	3.0	3.2
Transportation and public utilities	4.6	5.4
Wholesale trade	3.3	3.8
Retail trade	16.2	9.1
Finance, insurance, and real estate	1.8	2.1
Services	18.7	12.3
Government and government enterprises	22.9	30.6

SOURCE: U.S. Department of Commerce (2001).

Table 2. Structure of Employment,
Imperial County and California

Sector	Percent of Employment	
	Imperial County	California
Agricultural services	16.7	2.2
Farm production	9.6	1.8
Construction	3.1	4.9
Manufacturing	3.0	11.2
Transportation and public utilities	4.6	4.4
Wholesale trade	3.3	4.7
Retail trade	16.2	15.8
Finance, insurance, and real estate	1.8	7.8
Services	18.7	33.9
Government and government enterprises	22.9	12.8

SOURCE: U.S. Department of Commerce (2001).

human capital of the labor force, the age structure of the population, and the share of the working age population that chooses to work (labor force participation rate). Human capital refers to the qualities of the labor force. It is shorthand for all the characteristics of a worker that determine his/her ability to work, including education and skill levels as well as variables that are more difficult to measure, such as attitudes and energy levels. Table 3 compares the educational attainment of the county population that is age 25 and older with the attainment of the state population. Data were drawn from the 1990 Census since, at the time of writing this essay, the 2000 Census was not yet available except for population counts. Most notable is the 46.8 percent of the population without a high school diploma, nearly double the 23.7 percent at the state level. At the other end of the distribution, 9.6 percent of the county's population has an undergraduate or graduate degree, compared to 23.4 at the state level (U.S. Census Bureau 2001).

These differences in educational attainment are economically significant. In order to illustrate this point, consider how Imperial County incomes might be different if the county population had the same levels of educational attainment as the state, but kept its current structure of production. The 1990 Census estimates of the differences in earnings between people with different levels of education can be used to estimate the income effects of an increase in the average level of educational attainment for Imperial County residents. If education levels in the county were the same as overall state levels, and if incomes rose accordingly, then the average level of income per worker would be the same in the county as it is in the state.[7] In other words, the differences (18%) in output per worker ($30,098 in Imperial County and $36,538 statewide) would disappear and nothing would be left to be explained by the county's large retail sector or small manufacturing sector.

Of course, reality is more complicated than this and while education causes income, it is equally true that income causes education in a complex feedback through the economy and the family. The purpose of this simple and rather crude calculation is not to make the unrealistic claim that a change in the educational attainment of valley residents would automatically lead to higher incomes with no changes in occupations or employment. Rather, it is to give some sense of the economic penalty of low levels of education. Undoubtedly, an increase over time in the educational attainment of valley residents would create new kinds of jobs and occupations as a more educated labor force would attract different types of businesses to the region and create a different set of opportunities for businesses already located there. None of this will happen automatically, but the point remains that higher levels of educational attainment are necessary for higher incomes, even though they do not guarantee them.

Another variable of human capital influencing the rewards of labor is the share of the population that does not speak English or speaks it poorly. According to the 1990 Census, 10.8 percent of Californians speak no English or speak it poorly; in Imperial County, that percentage is 25.5. The lack of language skills contributes to the linguistic isolation of large segments of the population and severely limits their economic potential. While the 1990 figure is out of date at this point, the differences between the state and county are likely to have widened during the 1990s, based on the fact that Imperial County received a relatively larger share of the immigrant pool than any other county in the state. During the 1990s, international immigrants to the State of California raised the population by 7.6 percent; in Imperial County this number rose by 17.5 percent. Consequently, the share of the county's population that is linguistically isolated has probably grown since 1990.

Table 3. Educational Attainment, Imperial County and California, 1990 Census

Educational Attainment	Imperial County	California
Less than 9th grade	29.2	11.1
9th to 12th grade, no diploma	17.6	12.6
High school graduate (includes equivalency)	20.1	22.3
Some college, no degree	16.4	22.6
Associate degree	6.9	7.9
Bachelor's degree	6.2	15.3
Graduate or professional degree	3.4	8.1

SOURCE: U.S. Department of Commerce (2001).

Even if income per worker in the county were equal to the state average, a gap would remain between the county and the state in income per person. That is, while income per worker in 1998 was 18 percent lower in the county, income per person was almost 40 percent less.[8] Changing the educational attainment of the population puts a dent in this number, but does not eliminate it. Two other characteristics of the county population are also relevant: the dependency ratio and the labor force participation rate. The dependency ratio is measured as the share of the population too young or too old to work:

(population under 16 + population over 65) / (total population)

Imperial County's dependency ratio is 39 percent, compared to the statewide ratio of 35 percent. Imperial County has a smaller share of its population age 65 and over, however, and quite a larger share under age 16 (29% versus 25%). Consequently, since many men and women 65 and older still work, the dependency ratio probably understates the county's disadvantage. If the county had five percentage points less of its population under 16, and if that 5 percent chose to work, it would add another 6.4 percent to the county's per capita income.[9]

In addition to educational attainment and the dependency ratio, a third important characteristic of the population is its labor force participation rate. The labor force participation rate is a percentage that measures the share of the working age population that is either working or seeking work. It is calculated as:

(population working + population seeking work) / (population ages 16–65)

In 1999, the statewide labor force participation rate for California was 66.4 percent, while Imperial County's was 59.6 percent (U.S. Census Bureau 2001; EDD 2001). In other words, approximately 40 percent of the working age population is out of the labor force in Imperial County, while the statewide figure is 34 percent. Generally, people choose not to work or look for work because they are discouraged about their prospects of finding a job (due to a lack of skills, racial discrimination, physical disabilities, economic recession, or some other barrier) or because they simply do not want to work (homemakers, students, retirees). To some extent, the high unemployment rate may be a causal factor in determining the labor force participation rate since a region that lacks an adequate number of jobs also discourages potential workers from looking for work. Nevertheless, if the share of the working age population looking for work or working was equivalent to the rest of the state, it would add about 6,360 workers to the labor force. Assuming that three in four could find jobs at the average level of earnings per worker, this adds another 5.8 percent to the county's income.

Each of these three characteristics of the labor force—its educational attainment, the dependency ratio, and the labor force participation rate—interact with the unemployment rate in negative ways. For example, increases in educational attainment do little good if there is an inadequate supply of jobs.[10] Similarly, high unemployment rates mean that even if a larger share of the population enters the labor force to look for work, a depressingly large number will not be able to find a job in a reasonable amount of time.

Conclusion

Table 4 summarizes the effects discussed previously. Taken as a whole, they conservatively account for almost two-thirds of the difference in per capita income between the county and the state. That is, per capita income would rise from $17,353 to approximately $24,190, compared to the state level of $28,163 in 1998. Given the assumptions of the calculations and that the cost of living in Imperial County is probably less than the statewide average, the real gap between the county and the state would probably be less than the remaining 14 percent difference estimated here.

Not all of the changes examined are subject to control through policy changes. Dependency ratios, for example, or the share of the population that cannot speak English, can be influenced by policy, but they are largely outside the control of local policymakers. As long as population growth is fed by large numbers of international migrants, even variables such as educational attainment are outside the control of the current county residents. While it is undoubtedly the case that international immigrants add dynamism to the economy and create new sources of energy and opportunity, it is also true that many arrive from nonindustrial societies where they

Table 4. Sources of Divergence between
Statewide and County Incomes

Sources of Additional Income	Estimated Increase in Total County Income (%)
Unemployment rate reduced from 25 to 15 percent	10.0
Labor force participation rate rises to state level	5.8
Educational attainment equal to state level	13.6
Dependency ratio equal to state ratio	6.4
Interaction between unemployment rate and:	
Education	2.0
Labor force participation rate	0.8
Dependency ratio	0.8
Total increase in county income	39.4

SOURCE: Author's calculations.

have not had the opportunity to prepare themselves for the industrial economy of the United States.

It is important to note that there is another way to look at these numbers, particularly with regard to international migration. Since the majority of immigrants come from Mexico, where per capita and per worker incomes are significantly lower, there is an obvious improvement in their living standards. California has been the benchmark used to assess Imperial County incomes, but perhaps Baja California is a better standard. If so, the task at hand is to explain why Imperial County is so much better off in terms of per capita income than the average resident of the Mexicali Valley, just across the border.

Endnotes

1. Glenn County was ranked fifty-fourth, followed by Lassen, Yuba, Del Norte, and Kings (Newman et al. 2000).
2. Income data from the Department of Commerce's Regional Economic Information System is made available online by the Geospatial and Statistical Data Center at the University of Virginia.
3. This follows from the fact that every good and service produced generates incomes of equal value. It also follows from the fact that the price for a good or service can be broken into wages, rents, interest, profits, and dividends, plus the cost of intermediate inputs used to produce the output. Tracing the flow of money, the share of the price that goes to pay for intermediate inputs can be broken into the intermediate input producer's labor costs, profits, and so on. In this way, each dollar of output is associated with a dollar of income.
4. The U.S. Department of Commerce separates the farm sector, which is direct farm production, from a sector labeled, "agricultural services, forestry, fishing and other." In Imperial County, the latter sector is dominated by agriculturally related production. Consequently, both sectors should be included when using the term "agriculture."
5. Unlike manufacturing, service sectors produce intangibles. The production of a haircut, banking services, education, or prison guard services may entail jobs with different levels of social status, but all of these activities are valued by the economy to the extent that people pay for them. In the sense of income and output, services are no different from manufacturing, construction, or agriculture, regardless of whether they are produced in the public sector or the private sector.
6. Nationally, the unemployment rate is determined by telephone interviews with approximately 60,000 randomly selected households. Local unemployment rates are inferred through an entirely different methodology. First, state employment department (EDD in California) personnel estimate the local rate based on the number of new claims for unemployment insurance and other relevant data. Second, the state labor office uses a statistical model to estimate the state's unemployment rate. Third, the local (county) and state estimates are reconciled through a process that divides the state estimate into its county components in proportion to each county's share of the sum of all counties. It is this last step that often ends up doubling Imperial County's unemployment rate over the local estimate. There are several potential points of bias in this methodology (local estimate, state estimate, reconciliation of the two) and it is uncertain at what point the bias enters. It is also uncertain why the same bias does not occur in other California counties with similar demographic and economic characteristics.

7. According to the U.S. Census Bureau, if a worker with no high school education is taken as the base, someone with a diploma earns 25 percent more and someone with a college degree earns 2.15 times more. In order for the county to have the same educational attainment distribution as the state, it would have to move its college degree category from about 13 percent to 27.3 percent (this divides the associate degree in two: one down, one up), its high school category from about 40 percent to 48.9 percent, and in the less than high school category down from 47 to 23.7 percent. Given the implied changes in income, this would add about 18 percent to earned income ($338,764,000) and completely eliminate the difference between the county and state levels of income per worker.

8. Income per person is (total income)/(total population) while income per worker is (total income)/(total number of workers). Since the share of the population that works is different in different regions, even if income per worker is the same in the county and the state, income per person will be different.

9. This assumes that one in four would be unemployed and unable to earn any income.

10. Although it is also the case that people with more education are less likely to be unemployed, if they do lose a job they tend to stay unemployed for shorter periods of time. Education, apparently, aids people in dealing with the uncertainties of unemployment.

References

Employment Development Department (EDD). 2001. "Labor Market Information: Employment by Industry Data." http://www.calmis.cahwnet.gov/htmlfile/subject/indtable.htm.

Newman, Jeffrey, Kathy Albetski, Robert Brown, and Adrienne Pilot. 2000. "Comprehensive Revision of Local Area Personal Income." *Survey of Current Business* 80:7.

U.S. Census Bureau. 2001. http://www.census.gov.

U.S. Department of Commerce. 2001. "Regional Economic Information System." http://fisher.lib.virginia.edu.

9

Economic Overview: Employment Patterns in the Municipality of Mexicali

Sergio Noriega-Verdugo*

Abstract

This essay deals with recent economic history and focuses on economic growth mainly from 1970 to 2000. It covers employment within the major productive sectors: agriculture, manufacturing, and trade and services. However, regional growth on the international border is seen as mostly a consequence of outside forces, namely the Mexican and the United States national politics and economies. While both systems have become more integrated because of the North American Free Trade Agreement (NAFTA), this transition is not without regional problems. Nonetheless, instead of looking for past mistakes, this essay calls on Mexicali's population to shoulder greater responsibility for its future development. More specifically, the study points to the need for greater investment. Underlying the challenge of regional development is the belief that mutual understanding between border neighbors is not only common sense but particularly appropriate, given the present trend toward globalization.

Introduction

The Mexicali and Imperial valleys are contiguous parts of the Colorado River Delta. The delta is an alluvial plain that runs northwest to southeast. It extends from just

*Noriega-Verdugo is Professor of Economics at the Universidad Autónoma de Baja California in Mexicali, the Center for Technical and Higher Education, and San Diego State University's Imperial Valley Campus.

beyond the Salton Sea to the mouth of the river at the Gulf of California. The arid landscape, along with scorching temperatures during the long summer months, made this area impossible to settle until the beginning of the twentieth century, when Colorado River water was diverted to the valleys to allow irrigated farming.

Mexicali is the capital of the State of Baja California and the name of the county or *municipio* that borders Imperial County to the north. This municipality covers approximately 5,300 square miles of the northeast corner of the Baja California Peninsula. It also borders to the east with Yuma County in Arizona, San Luis Río Colorado in Sonora, and the Gulf of California, or Sea of Cortez, to the southeast. It also borders the Municipality of of Tecate to the west and the Municipality of of Ensenada to the southwest. Mexicali is one of five municipalities in the State of Baja California.

The Municipality of Mexicali, like any other in Mexico, is run by an elected official for a three-year term who cannot be reelected in successive terms. This elected official is called the *presidente municipal* (president) and acts as mayor of the city where the seat of the county government lies *(cabecera municipal)*. Although the municipality is considered to be the smallest government unit, the municipal president designates his representatives for smaller areas within the municipality called *delegaciones* (delegations). There are presently 14 such delegations in the Municipality of Mexicali. Most of these delegations are centered in small cities or towns scattered throughout the municipality. Half of these are included in Table 1. One more delegation, González Ortega, also called Palaco, is now a suburb of the City of Mexicali.

According to the 2000 population census, 658,159 were living in locations with 2,500 inhabitants or more. This urban population represented 86.1 percent of the

Table 1. Population of Urban Localities in the Municipality of Mexicali, 1990

(City of) Mexicali	549,873
Santa Isabel	18,041
Guadalupe Victoria (Km. 43)	15,561
San Felipe	13,123
Puebla	7,421
Ciudad Morelos (Cuervos)	7,234
Alberto Oviedo Mota (Reacomodo)	6,878
Estación Coahuila (Km. 57)	6,479
Ejido Hermosillo	5,458
Delta (Estación Delta)	4,860
Progreso	4,462
Vicente Guerrero (Algodones)	4,157

SOURCE: INEGI (2000a).

municipality's total (764,602). The largest of these localities is the City of Mexicali. According to the State Council on Population (Consejo Estatal de Población–CONEPO) estimates, in 2002 it had 585,340 of the municipality's 813,853 total inhabitants (71.9% of the total municipal population).

One way to acquire a general picture of Mexicali is to look at its economic growth. Unfortunately, a broad range of statistical information is lacking, but changes in employment are a good indicator of how Mexicali's growth has come about over the last thirty to forty years. Population census data are also relied upon for this effort. One must also look beyond the municipality's borders to find other major factors involved in such an open economy, including its role as a border city.

Historical Background

When the border was redrawn after the U.S.-Mexican War (1846–1848), the present Municipality of Mexicali did not exist. During this period, the entire peninsula was governed from La Paz (present-day capital of Baja California Sur). Population along the border was sparse and most of its inhabitants were Cucapá (Cocopah) Indians without permanent settlements in the area. The new border led to land surveying not only near the international demarcation, but also throughout the rest of the peninsula. California's 1848–1849 gold rush brought travelers across the Mexicali-Imperial valleys and with them, more attention from both the United States and Mexico.

From this point, the Mexican central government began to display more interest in land settlements in the northern part of the country. One important reason for doing so was to avert further "Yankee" expansionism. The first settlement in the Mexicali Valley was established on September 16, 1874. Colonia Lerdo was founded along the Colorado River by the Mexican Agricultural, Industrial, and Colonizing Company of the Colorado River (Compañía Mexicana, Agrícola, Industrial y Colonizadora del Río Colorado), which was headed by Guillermo Andrade (c. 1829–1905). Andrade was able to secure government land in return for promised settlements and colonization. Colonia Lerdo eventually failed as the result of flooding from the Colorado River (Hendricks 1996: 62–63).

The next major step in Mexicali's development came with the diversion of water from the Colorado River. The idea to irrigate the desert valley was first conceived by Dr. Oliver M. Wozencraft, who began the project in 1849 (Tout 1931: 25–26). In order to bypass the sand dunes near the border with Arizona, water was channeled through the Alamo River on the Mexican side of the border. The project was realized by the California Development Company, whose major participants included Charles Rockwood, George Chaffey, and Anthony H. Heber. The irrigation of the Mexicali Valley became the undertaking of the Colorado River Land Company and the Land and Water Company of Baja California (Compañía de Terrenos y Aguas de la Baja California). Both firms were owned by U.S. citizens.

The role of foreign capital in Mexicali's early development was quite significant. No single company was more influential than the Colorado River Land Company, which acquired most of the Mexicali Valley from Andrade, and whose business associates were based in Los Angeles. It was responsible for most of the region's infrastructure, including hydraulics, transportation, and finance, from the beginning of the century to about 1940 (see Kerig 2001). The United States was also influential on Mexicali's economic history with Prohibition (1920–1933), the Great Depression (1929–1940), two World Wars (1914–1918, 1939–1945), and the Korean War (1950–1953).

The role the central Mexican government played in the region reflects the changing conditions of the country. With the beginning of the Mexican Revolution in 1910, a group of followers of radical leader Ricardo Flores Magón invaded Mexicali from the United States and seized the Baja California border briefly in 1911. While the Mexican Revolution did not involve Baja California directly, it influenced Mexicali's development through migration and its political leaders.

Although the national economy and the centralized government were weakened by World War I, Baja California and Mexicali in particular grew prosperous during most of the period extending from 1915 to 1929. This growth was spurred by the expansion of the cotton industry (acreage, the cotton gin, and cottonseed oil), the beer industry, construction, and casinos. The Prohibition period in the United States drove many U.S. citizens across the border to drink and partake in gaming activities. The regional government was responsible for creating infrastructure, particularly in the areas of education and communications to meet the needs of a growing population.

The Great Depression (1929–1940) led to a dramatic fall in cotton prices and reduced planting of most crops. Mexican workers in California were forced to return to Mexico due to a shortage of jobs and anti-immigrant sentiment north of the border. Some of them presumably stayed in Mexicali. The repeal of Prohibition in 1933 and the end of legalized gambling in Mexico under President Lázaro Cárdenas' attempt to clean up the image of the border brought a drop in regional employment and income.

After many years of controversy, land reform was finally, although abruptly, accomplished in Mexicali in 1937. Land redistribution deprived the U.S. Colorado River Land Company of most of its holdings. Mexican farmers who had leased farmland from the company were also hurt by the reform. Collective farms, or *ejidos*, were created for the purpose of land redistribution, setting them apart from private farms. Individual plots in Mexicali measured 20 hectares (much larger than land reform elsewhere in Mexico) and thus helped farmers grow cotton for the international market (see Sánchez Ramírez 1990: Chapter 8). Land reform led to a greater inflow of farmers from elsewhere in Mexico and helped secure the border area from the threat of annexation or invasion by the United States.

Population

Practically uninhabited except for a few Cucapá Indians at the turn of the century, the Municipality of Mexicali became one of the fastest growing areas in Mexico from 1910 to 1960. Mexicali is a land of immigrants, most of them from Mexico's interior. In the early part of the century, most immigrants came from neighboring Baja California Sur and Sonora due to both proximity and the lack of communication with other areas. However, as land was opened to cultivation, people from other lands also began to settle in the area. Among them were Chinese, Japanese, Indians (from India), some Europeans, and U.S. citizens. The greatest number came from China as contracted laborers, beginning in 1910 or 1911 (Kerig 2001: 136). According to the state's 1930 Census, the majority of foreigners in Baja California were Chinese, followed by Japanese and U.S. citizens (Dirección General de Estadística 1933).

Because national birth and death rates have not differed drastically from those in Baja California, it may be inferred that immigration is easily detected when the region's total population grows faster than the national average. Using this model, immigration was particularly immense in the 1940s, when the population of Mexicali grew at an annual rate of 10.8 percent, while the country grew at a much slower rate of 2.7 percent. Total population in Mexicali grew faster than in the rest of the country until around 1970. However, beginning about 1990, Mexicali's annual growth rate surpassed that of the nation as a whole.

Migratory flows can be detected by place of birth as reported by the census each 10 years. According to the 1960 Census, only 36.7 percent of the total population was born in Baja California; 2.6 percent were born in foreign countries; and 60.7 percent were born elsewhere in Mexico.

Employment opportunities in farming dropped as the water supply became insufficient to expand land cultivation. Immigrants were thus forced to seek employment elsewhere. Farm labor's share in overall employment declined from 61.9 percent in 1950 to 54.6 percent in 1960. Nonetheless, farming remained the main source of employment for several more years. In the 20 years from 1940 to 1960, urban population within the municipality increased from 42.3 percent to 63.8 percent of the total. During that time, the City of Mexicali grew from 18,775 to 179,539 residents.

The national rate of population growth peaked during the 1960s. By then, the annual rate in Mexico was 3.4 percent, one of the highest in the world. This impressive rate was attributed to a sustained high birth rate and a declining death rate (Centro de Estudios Económicos y Demográficos 1970: 6–8). Since then, both birth and death rates have decreased steadily as the national government has fostered policies encouraging responsible parenthood and smaller families. The national population grew at a rate of only 1.8 percent per annum between 1990 and 2000, almost half the rate four decades earlier.[1]

Economics and demographics are interrelated. Population change influences both the supply and demand for goods and services in the form of production and consumption. Economic change can attract populations to a region; likewise, in its absence, it can drive people away from the area. Population size can change based on any of three factors: (1) births, (2) deaths, and (3) migration. Although each factor can be influenced by economic conditions, migration will be focused on here.

Over a long period of time, people will usually move to live in a particular area while others leave that area. A net gain or loss in population through migration usually reflects the prevailing economic conditions in the area. That is to say, if there is a net gain in the number of migrants, chances are that there has been some degree of prosperity in the area in question; however, if there were a net loss of migrants, it would suggest economic stagnation.

It is difficult to imagine that any region, including the Municipality of Mexicali, can increase its population for any prolonged period of time unless opportunities for gainful employment exist. If the regional production of goods and services becomes stagnant, some residents will soon have to move to work and live elsewhere. Therefore, it is believed that population and economic growth are positively correlated. Thus stated, the changes in population over the last thirty years in Mexico, the State of Baja California, and Mexicali will be examined.

Although the national population continues to grow, it does so at a lower rate than Baja California or Mexicali. Table 2 shows that the national annual growth rate has consistently declined over the last three decades. Mexico's population decline is mainly due to a decreasing birth rate. Births per 1,000 inhabitants have dropped from 44.2 in 1970 to 24.1 in 1996. This drop has helped the economy grow because there are fewer children per household. Fewer children per family implies a lower dependency ratio; thus, on the average, Mexican workers now face a smaller load than before (other things being equal). Children under the age of 15 have dropped from 46.2 percent of the total population in 1970 to 34 percent in 2000. Since children are consumers rather than producers, this reduction can mean greater savings and therefore greater capital formation.

In Mexicali, children under the age of 15 years reached a high of 47.6 percent of the total population in 1970. Thus, the working (economically active) population declined as a percent of the total. The working population dropped to 25.1 percent from 32 percent 10 years earlier. This meant an increased dependency on the workforce. With a smaller proportion of workers available, family income in Mexicali must have dropped.

Population growth rates suggest that economic growth in the Municipality of Mexicali was already slowing down by 1970 and continued to do so until around 1990. After decades of attracting thousands of people from other states, Mexicali's population annual growth rate declined to 2.4 percent, below the national rate of 3.2 percent, from 1970 to 1980. This rate was not only lower than any previous decade,

Table 2. Total Population and Average Annual
Growth Rates in Mexico, Baja California, and
the Municipality of Mexicali, 1970–2000

Year(s)	Mexico	Baja California	Mexicali
1970	48,225,238	870,421	396,324
1970–1980	3.20%	2.90%	2.40%
1980	66,846,833	1,177,886	510,664
1980–1990	2.00%	3.60%	1.70%
1990	81,249,645	1,660,855	601,938
1990–2000	1.80%	4.10%	2.40%
2000	97,483,412	2,487,770	764,602

SOURCE: Based on INEGI (1983, 1991, 1996); Dirección General de Estadística (1971).

but also even lower than the national rate for the first time. Although population
growth rates continued to decline throughout most of the country over the next ten
years, Mexicali's rate still remained below the national level. Table 2 shows that
Mexicali's rate dropped to less than half of Baja California's rate for 1980–1990.
Natural growth rates (births minus deaths per 1,000 inhabitants) for the country and
the region are assumed to be approximately the same.[2]

Net outbound migration from 1970 to 1990 is a reflection of the municipality's low
rate of economic growth. Although there were some improvements in living standards,
it appears that employment growth and real wages dropped during this period.

Agriculture

Measuring regional economic growth for extended periods continues to be a difficult
task because of the lack of relevant statistical information. Nonetheless, a
comparison of input-output tables for Mexicali suggests that the gross regional
product (GRP) had increased from 1965 to 1970 at the annual rate of 3.2 percent,
while the nation had grown at 10.7 percent.[3] Once adjusted to the period's inflation,
the real rate of economic growth of Mexicali was down to only 0.5 percent. With the
total population growing at the rate of 3.6 percent per annum during the 1960s, gross
income per capita was actually dropping in Mexicali during this period (Noriega-
Verdugo 1984: 26–27).

But the bad times were only beginning. Mexicali's economy was largely
dependent on agriculture, particularly cotton. Beginning in late 1961, Mexicali's
share of Colorado River water became polluted because of drainage from Arizona's
Wellton-Mohawk project. The salt content of river water increased to three and a half
times the normal level (Hundley 1966: 175). The water salinity damaged soils in the

Mexicali and San Luis valleys and resulted in high crop losses for many years. Farm employment dropped from 47,427 in 1960 to 32,820 in 1969.[4]

Although a comparison of the 1960 and 1970 censuses suggests an improvement in unemployment rates, this may not have really happened. The rate of unemployment in 1969 stood at 5.3 percent, down from the 1960 level of 6.3 percent. This apparent improvement is belied by the fact that the census undercounted the number of workers, particularly those who were unemployed in 1969.

The census data show a drop in the number of workers (economically active population) as a percent of the total population from 1960 to 1970, from 32 percent to 25.1 percent. Correspondingly, the inactive population—which includes housewives, students, the disabled, and the retired—increased dramatically from 13.9 percent to an unprecedented 35.8 percent of the total population. Some of the unemployed (economically active population) were wrongly classified as inactive because they were not working in the reference period. This appears to be a case of disguised unemployment. Therefore, it is quite possible that unemployment not only did not improve, but also likely became worse during that decade.

The 1980 Census data hardly showed an improvement. Unemployment went unreported. The census was also unable to classify as much as one-third of the total workforce according to the sector of employment.[5]

Although farm labor and related production are a declining part of the regional Mexicali economy, the actual number of Mexicali residents who are employed in this sector may be increasing. There were 32,820 people recorded in the agricultural sector in 1970. In 2000, this number had decreased to 32,300. Yet, it is very probable that this is due to the fact that not all of the working population covered by the census is actually employed in the Mexican municipality. This is particularly true of the farm sector, where many Mexican residents work in the United States. According to research on border crossers in March 1998, "[t]here were 16,200 people employed

Table 3. Percent Distribution of Sectoral Employment in the Municipality of Mexicali, 1969–2000

Sectors	1969	1980	1990	2000
Agriculture*	35.7	20.2	18.6	11.9
Industry**	22.3	26.5	27.2	35.0
Trade and Services***	42.0	53.3	54.2	53.1
Total	100.0	100.0	100.0	100.0

*Agriculture includes cattle raising and fishing.
**Industry includes mining, manufacturing, construction, and utilities.
***Trade includes retail and wholesale.

SOURCES: Based on INEGI (1983, 1991, 1996); INEGI and Gobierno del Estado de Baja California (2000b); Dirección General de Estadística (1971).

in agriculture in Imperial County and 14,300 or 88% were residents of Mexicali" (Cox 1998: 8).

With more synthetic fibers in the market, the international price of cotton took a dive and the cost of growing cotton increased progressively. Inflation rose rapidly after 1971, as President Luis Echeverría (1970–1976) dramatically increased deficit spending. Consumer prices rose 80.5 percent in Mexico—compared to 38.7 percent in the United States—during the first half of the 1970s; yet, the Mexican peso maintained its 12.50 parity with the U.S. dollar. This suggests that Mexicali cotton exports brought in less money during the early 1970s.

On the evening of August 31, 1976, the Banco de México, Mexico's central bank, withdrew its support of the peso and the Mexican currency plunged. This became the first devaluation with regard to the dollar in 22 years. This measure shook the nation generally, and the border area particularly. By January 1977, the peso had stabilized at 22 to the dollar, a 76 percent loss in value.

Although cotton acreage increased a year or two after the devaluation, never again did it reach its previous prominence in farming or in the regional economy. Not only did agriculture lose profitability, but the industry that it was linked to (cotton gins and seed oil) never recovered.

The second major crop in Mexico is wheat. Wheat farmers are far from optimistic. With NAFTA in operation since 1994, farm subsidies have been curtailed. Guaranteed price supports by the Mexican federal government have disappeared. Wheat prices in the valley are now tied to quotations in the Chicago commodities market and Mexican wheat buyers frequently purchase certain varieties from the United States. With demand for local wheat production far beyond regional needs, farmers frequently demand support to cover shipping charges.

Confronted with more competition, Mexican farmers have either abandoned agriculture or have regrouped into larger units in search of economies of scale. With infrastructure and farm equipment either insufficient or largely deteriorated, it is no wonder that farming is undergoing a transition. Many small farmers, including *ejidatarios*, have rented their land, and some have sold their farms. It appears that farming is progressively becoming less labor intensive, with the exception of truck crops like asparagus, onions, radishes, and other vegetables and fruits.

Manufacturing

Industrial employment in Mexicali was impacted by the downfall of cotton, which began in the mid-1960s. Cottonseed oil decreased and the agricultural processing industry resorted to importing safflower and soybeans to cover its raw material needs. From 1970 to 1980, the manufacturing sector's share of total employment dropped from 15.4 percent to 11.3 percent. Even urban growth did not help much in the way of industrial employment since income per capita was falling in 1970. Food processing was then responsible for a large part of the industrial employment. This segment included tortilla shops, bakeries, bottled water, soft drinks, dairy products, fruit and vegetable products, wheat flour, and so on.

Employment was not made any easier from the cost side either. Minimum wages in Baja California were the highest in the country and real minimum wages increased during the 1970s into the early 1980s. In 1970–1971, the urban daily minimum wage in Mexicali was 46 pesos; 10 years later it was 210 pesos. The U.S. dollar equivalent rose from $3.68 to $8.58.

Fortunately, an entirely new source of manufacturing employment came into existence in the form of the *maquiladora* industry. This labor-intensive in-bond assembly industry was born in the mid-1960s in Tijuana and Mexicali in part due to the establishment of a free zone that made Baja California imports practically tax free. As *maquiladoras* became incorporated into a federal Border Industrialization Program in 1966, they were allowed to be entirely foreign owned. This was an exception from the norm, considering the import substitution industrial policy of the time. Originally confined to the border area, *maquiladoras* were supposed to provide employment and increase foreign revenue. They hired young, unskilled women to work mostly with electric and electronic parts and garments in foreign-owned businesses. Hence, the 1970 Census reported an unprecedented increase in female employment in manufacturing. In Mexicali, female workers jumped from 13.2 percent in 1960 to 35.2 percent of the total labor force in 1970.[6]

Despite impressive growth in employment, the *maquiladora* industry experienced some difficulties from the start. The newly formed businesses resorted to improvisation and operated with low budgets. Most plants were created within residential or commercial zones in abandoned stores and warehouses, without proper sanitary facilities or appropriate spaces for waste removal and loading or unloading operations. Some of the companies in Mexicali did not comply with the country's labor laws. For example, some employers did not pay the daily minimum wage until the workers were "sufficiently" trained. Other companies disappeared overnight, leaving their employees stranded without any severance pay. In addition, in some cases, female employees were abused by their male co-workers.

Employment growth in the *maquiladora* industry has not been constant, at least not in Mexicali. From 1974 to 1983, *maquiladora* employment actually declined from 7,888 to 7,392. One possible explanation for this change is that real minimum wages increased during the 1970s and early 1980s. Moreover, *maquiladora* employment as a percentage of manufacturing actually dropped from 43.1 percent in 1969 to 37.1 percent in 1980.[7]

Jobs in Mexicali *maquiladoras* grew from 7,147 in 1980 to 20,729 in 1990, making the industry's share of manufacturing employment jump from 37.1 percent to 56.1 percent and, more recently, to 82.9 percent in 2000.[8] *Maquiladora* employment

Table 4. *Maquiladora* Industry's Share of Manufacturing Employment in Mexicali, 1969–2000

Year	Manufacturing	*Maquiladora*	Percentage
1969	15,193	6,551	43.1
1980	19,283	7,147	37.1
1990	36,920	20,729	56.1
2000	72,481	60,063	82.9

Note: *Maquiladoras* are primarily, but not limited to, manufacturing units.

SOURCES: Based on INEGI (1983, 1991); INEGI and Gobierno del Estado de Baja California (2000b); Dirección General de Estadística (1971).

has surged at the impressive average annual rate of 11.2 percent from 1980 to 2000. This is much faster than the manufacturing industry, which grew at a rate just above 6.8 percent during the same period. This suggests that the *maquiladora* industry is responsible for practically the entire increase in manufacturing jobs since 1980.

Two factors are largely responsible for this impressive growth: low wages and the North American Free Trade Agreement. Devaluations of the Mexican peso, particularly since 1982, have favored foreign investment by lowering the cost of labor and other expenditures in dollar terms. NAFTA has further attracted manufacturing companies from other countries, particularly from Asia, that seek to avoid more taxes and acquire easy access to the U.S. and Canadian markets. Japanese and Korean companies have created particularly large industrial plants, suggesting that the industrial processes involve more manufacturing and value added than before. These two factors, however, are not likely to repeat themselves in the future.

Maquiladora employment in Mexicali has not only changed in quantitative terms, but also in qualitative terms. Originally, most of its personnel were women. By 1975, women made up 77.1 percent of its assembly workers. However, as the industry became larger and more complex, female participation in assembly lines decreased to 56.4 percent in the year 2000. It appears that as plants have become larger and industrial processes more complex, job opportunities for men have increased. Although job requirements have been lowered during this period of expansion, more training now goes into personnel and arrangements have been made for employees to continue their education. Day care centers have grown to accommodate the children of female employees. Also, in 1975, 87.8 percent of the *maquiladora* employees were assembly line workers; by 2000, this number decreased to 78.7 percent, meaning that there are also more technicians and administrative jobs than ever before.

With respect to earnings, it should be noted that labor suffered a serious blow from the peso devaluation that began on December 20, 1994. In the *maquiladora* industry, the devaluation helped its shareholders and hurt its employees. Average earnings per worker in U.S. dollars dropped by approximately 35 percent from 1994 to 1995. It took five years, until 1999, for average earnings per employee in the industry to surpass the level set in 1994. Fortunately for the employees, their earnings continued to increase in the year 2000, partly because of the peso appreciation.

Although *maquiladoras* use few, if any, Mexican inputs (such as raw materials), the industry's contribution to society is more than the wages paid to the employees involved. Also included in the economic impact of *maquiladoras* are packaging, rent of private buildings (such as industrial parks), electricity, water, telephones, transportation, taxes, and profits. Value-added figures for the *maquiladora* industry in Mexicali show significant growth from 1995 to 2000. The annual value added contributed by the *maquiladora* industry rose from $226 million in 1995 to approximately $800 million in the year 2000.

Value-added statistics of the *maquiladora* industry in Mexicali reveal continued expansion from 1995 to 2000, particularly in value added per worker. This appears to mean that productivity per worker has enabled the industry to increase real wages. If this were so, then it would suggest that their work involves more manufacturing— which perhaps is better paid—and that workers have more capital at their disposal in the form of more equipment and machinery, and therefore produce more.

Trade and Services

In no other group is employment greater than in the combined categories of trade and services, also known as the tertiary sector. In the year 2000, there were 144,247

Figure 1. Value Added of the *Maquiladora* Industry and Value Added per Worker in the *Maquiladora* Industry, Mexicali, 1990–2000

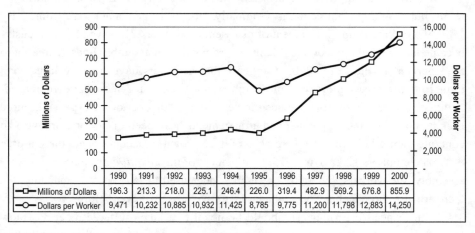

	1990	1991	1992	1993	1994	1995	1996	1997	1998	1999	2000
Millions of Dollars	196.3	213.3	218.0	225.1	246.4	226.0	319.4	482.9	569.2	676.8	855.9
Dollars per Worker	9,471	10,232	10,885	10,932	11,425	8,785	9,775	11,200	11,798	12,883	14,250

SOURCE: Author's calculations based on INEGI (2000).

workers in this sector in Baja California; 53.1 percent were employed in Mexicali. Job growth in this sector has generally been faster than total employment since 1969. While total employment nearly tripled over the last 31 years, workers employed by trade and services increased by 3.7 times the number in 1969.

Trade and services represent a heterogeneous group made up of many different activities, particularly in the services part, where many are difficult to classify. The 2000 Census identified no less than 11 subclassifications, among which are the following: mass media information, financial services and insurance, real estate and furniture for rent, business support services, and so on. It should also be noted that under the same classification there are such important categories as tourism and government activities, including public education, health, and security.

In the past, some analysts of economic underdevelopment have pointed to the trade and services group's growth as a reflection of workers who cannot find jobs elsewhere. Many are thought to be part of the informal or underground economy and work without paying taxes and have no form of social security. One reason for this suspicion is that this group has more people who are self-employed than in any other sector.[9] According to the 2000 Census, the trade and services sector counted 26,133 self-employed workers, representing 69.4 percent of total employment of the self-employed workers in the municipality. They were concentrated in trade, presumably in retail trade. In 2000, there were 11,232 self-employed workers that represented one out of every four persons employed in trade.

It is also important to note that, even though there has been vigorous employment growth in trade, data from the Mexican Institute for Social Security (Instituto Mexicano del Seguro Social–IMSS) and the census are considerably different. According to IMSS data, there were only 27,103 people insured in February 2000 (IMSS n.d.). Census data, however, point to 44,135 people in the area of trade. Therefore, it may be deduced that there were over 17,000 people working in trade that were not registered as insured with the IMSS.

The informal economy is also present in the services subsector; however, the many different types of services make it somewhat more difficult to detect. Services cover a wide array of persons, from those with little or no skills—such as maids and gardeners—to those who have earned higher education degrees—such as lawyers and doctors. According to the 2000 Census, 2,453 persons who were self-employed worked in hotels and restaurants. Many of them depend on tips and therefore do not have any kind of medical insurance.

Although this trade and services sector includes people with low incomes, it also includes some of the higher wages in the region. This is seen particularly in the self-employed (formal and informal) portion of this sector, in which income wages are the lowest and highest. At the low end of income distribution, those who worked for less than the minimum wage were more than double the municipality's average. Likewise, those who worked for themselves and earned from three to more than ten times the minimum wage were also above average.

Notwithstanding its employment potential, trade and services are seldom seen as a key to economic growth or development. Agriculture and industry are generally preferred to trade and services. Similarly, economic base studies—which regard a community's "exports" as the major element in economic growth—suggest that trade and services follow rather than lead the growth process (Tiebout 1962: 9).

One of the main advantages that border trade has in Mexicali is also one of its greatest problems. The supply of foreign goods is characteristic of the area's development. Ever since Mexicali's inception at the turn of the twentieth century, its merchants and service providers have relied on imports. To help this sector, the Mexican government created the free zone in the midst of the Great Depression, which did away with most import taxes. Now it has done away with them in accord with the North American Free Trade Agreement, but the area still warrants special treatment in its trade relationship.

Imports are indispensable for regional growth and also contribute to the quality of life of border residents. However, Mexicali's trade and services sector competes directly with its U.S. counterparts in Southern California, particularly Calexico. Therefore, while competition has helped improve Mexicali's stores, its retail potential is severely restricted. U.S. merchants usually compete in price, quality, and product diversity. Moreover, they sell used goods, such as cars and trucks, domestic appliances, and clothing, which play an important role in border activity. According to a recent study, "[t]he most important reason for crossing the border at the two ports of entry between Calexico and Mexicali is to shop in the U.S. (34% of the crossings)" (Cox 1998: 4).

An important fact about the tertiary sector is that any changes that take place affect the rest of the economy's real income. One needs only to remember that the level of income is influential not only on how much consumers spend, but also the kind of goods and services they purchase. Presumably, families with low incomes purchase necessities such as food and clothing, while those with higher incomes buy more durable goods. Also present in border sales is the marginal propensity to import. That is, whenever real income increases, Mexicali residents purchase greater amounts of imports. At no time is this more evident than during the Christmas season when most employees receive a bonus.

Unfortunately, income figures for Mexicali are rather scarce. Therefore, it is not possible to relate income to sales, except in very general terms. Since wages play an important role in personal income, minimum wages perhaps can serve as a proxy. However, instead of using Mexican currency, which has suffered so much in terms of inflation and devaluation, U.S. dollars are used. In 1970, the daily minimum wage in Baja California and, hence, in Mexicali, was $3.68. Ten years later, in 1980, it had more than doubled to $7.85. With devaluation and inflation, the daily minimum wage

Figure 2. Daily Minimum Wages in Mexican Pesos and U.S. Dollars in Baja California, 1990–2000

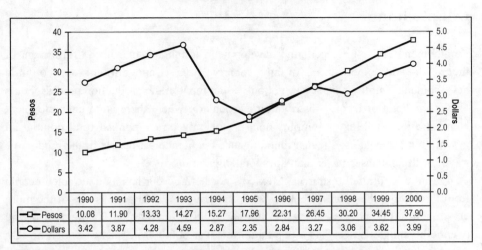

	1990	1991	1992	1993	1994	1995	1996	1997	1998	1999	2000
Pesos	10.08	11.90	13.33	14.27	15.27	17.96	22.31	26.45	30.20	34.45	37.90
Dollars	3.42	3.87	4.28	4.59	2.87	2.35	2.84	3.27	3.06	3.62	3.99

SOURCE: Author's calculations based on INEGI and Gobierno del Estado (1995, 2000b).

decreased to only $3.42 in 1990. By 2000, the dollar equivalent to the daily minimum wage was $3.99. It should be noted that since the dollar has lost purchasing power on its own account, real minimum wages in Mexicali are somewhat more depressed. Figure 2 helps demonstrate the year-to-year changes in daily minimum wage in Mexicali over the last decade.

The devaluation of the Mexican peso in 1994 and the government policy that sought to contain its inflationary effects both had devastating consequences on real minimum wages. Figure 2 shows how the daily minimum wage in Baja California rose from 14.27 pesos in 1993 to 17.96 pesos in 1995. In dollar terms, minimum wages fell from $4.59 to $2.35 per day. Despite later increases, the level held in the year 2000 remained below that of 1993. Therefore, it should come as no surprise that minimum wages in Mexicali have not protected employees from monetary instability.

Nonetheless, from 1995 to 2000, the dollar equivalent of minimum wages rose due in part to the appreciation of the Mexican peso in 1999 and 2000. More important is the fact that actual wages rose in Mexicali because industrial labor demand grew rapidly during the late 1990s. Thus, the daily minimum wage is no longer representative of actual wages. A comparison of the last two censuses shows that earnings in current pesos have made a change for the better. At the low end are those whose earnings were less than one minimum wage. This number dropped from 10.2 percent in 1990 to only 3.2 percent in 2000 of the total number of people who reported income. At the other end are those who earned from two to more than ten times the minimum wage. That number increased from 54 percent in 1990 to 75.8

percent in 2000. This, plus the fact that there are more people employed per household, means that Mexicali's family income has probably improved.

Conclusions

Employment, as well as economic development, is fundamental in the fulfillment of the needs and expectations of any society. It is a concomitant of economic development. Employment serves not only as an input in the production process, but is also at the heart of income distribution, particularly where there is no unemployment compensation. In Mexico, employment is not only a race against total population growth, but also against age distribution, since the number of people in the productive stages of life increases faster than does total population.

Despite its limited resources, Mexico's northern border has long attracted people from throughout the country seeking work opportunities. Mexicali is one of the more developed municipalities along the border. Almost uninhabited at the turn of the twentieth century, it now has a population of over 800,000 people, of which no less than 30 percent were born elsewhere in Mexico.

During the century's last thirty years, Mexicali experienced uneven employment growth. After a multifaceted crisis that struck farming during the sixties and early seventies, farm employment in Mexicali was cut in half. However, total employment was able to increase. Not surprisingly, most new jobs during the same period were created in the trade and services sector, which requires less capital investment. Moreover, it appears that most of the jobs that belong to the informal or underground economy belong to this sector. Industry—which according to the population census classification includes mining, manufacturing, construction, and electricity—increased throughout the period. Largely responsible for this growth was the *maquiladora* industry, whose share of manufacturing increased to over 80 percent by the end of the century.

Although most of the period was beset by macroeconomic turbulence, such as inflation, devaluation, and recession, population census indicators suggest that basic living standards were constantly improving. Not only did health, education, and housing increase through the last 30 years of the century, but their coverage in Mexicali remained above the national average.

Endnotes

1. This rate does not account for those who emigrated during the last decade on a permanent basis to a foreign country, mainly the United States.

2. Crude birth and death rate series for Mexico and Mexicali, in particular, are notoriously incomplete. For unexplained reasons, INEGI has not continuously published these data. At the national level, figures appear to have been revised. See Secretaría de Gobernación and Consejo Nacional de Población 1996: 2.

3. The first regional matrices were completed by the Bank of Mexico. Alfredo Vargas Piñera, Mexicali's first economist, contributed and later promoted these tables. Thereafter, the office of Gustavo Martínez Cabañas created others, including one in the study "El municipio de Mexicali: diagnóstico económico y social y planes para su desarrollo" (1971).

4. Farm employment census data includes those who work with livestock and fish. Economically active population is presented partly for the year of 1969 and 1970.

5. The unclassified workers in the 1980 General Census are for the entire country. For some unexplained reason, figures belonging to this census are omitted in historical time series.

6. Some observers state that the *maquiladora* industry was set up to counter unemployment created by the conclusion of the Bracero Program; this was not the case in Mexicali. Braceros (seasonal workers) were not residents of the border and the employment created benefitted women who had worked as servants or had no previous work experience and were not unemployed. See Fulton Freeman's foreword in Baerresen (1971) and Noriega-Verdugo (1968: 52–55).

7. It should be noted that not all *maquiladoras* are manufacturing units; therefore, the percentages may be overstated.

8. It should be noted that the dates for both figures, the census data for employment in the manufacturing industry and employment in the *maquiladora* industry, do not match exactly.

9. To be self-employed does not necessarily mean that those involved do not pay taxes or have no kind of social security, but it is easy to understand why this category of workers is more difficult for the government to track.

References

Aguirre Bernal, Celso. 1966. *Compendio histórico-biográfico de Mexicali 1539–1966*. Mexicali, Baja California.

Amaya Brondo, Guillermo, and Miguel Ramos Galván. 1977. *Monografía de un distrito de riego: el Río Colorado y el distrito de riego número 14*. México, D.F.: Secretaría de Agricultura y Recursos Hidráulicos.

Baerresen, Donald W. 1971. *The Border Industrialization Program of Mexico*. Lexington: D.C. Heath and Company.

Centro de Estudios Económicos y Demográficos. 1970. *Dinámica de la Población de México*. México, D.F.: El Colegio de México.

Comité de Planeación para el Desarrollo del Estado de Baja California and Instituto Nacional de Estadística, Geografía e Informática (INEGI). 1991. *Anuario estadístico del estado de Baja California*.

Consejo de Planeación. 1958. *Tesis económica y social sobre el estado de Baja California*. México, D.F.: Consejo de Planeación.

Cox, Millicent. 1998. "Survey of Border Crossers: Imperial/Mexicali Valleys." Paper produced for San Diego Dialogue and the Centro de Estudios Económicos del Sector Empresarial de Mexicali, with the assistence of the Autonomous University of Baja California (March).

Decimoséptimo Ayuntamiento de Mexicali. 2002. *I Informe de Gobierno*. Mexicali: XVII Ayuntamiento de Mexicali.

Dirección de Bioestadística. 1965. *Estadísticas vitales en Baja California Norte*. México, D.F.: Secretaría de Salubridad y Asistencia.

Dirección General de Estadística. 1933. *Quinto censo de población, 15 de mayo de 1930, Baja California, Distrito Norte*. México, D.F.: Secretaría de la Economía Nacional.

Dirección General de Estadística. 1952. *Séptimo censo general, 6 de junio de 1950, Baja California Territorio Norte*. México, D.F.: Secretaría de Economía Nacional.

Dirección General de Estadística. 1963. *VII Censo general de población. 1960, 8 de junio de 1960, Estado de Baja California*. México, D.F.: Secretaría de Industria y Comercio.

Dirección General de Estadística. 1971. *IX Censo general de población. 1970, 28 de enero de 1970, Estado de Baja California*. México, D.F.: Secretaría de Industria y Comercio.

Dirección General de Estadística. 1975. *Estadísticas vitales, imagen demográfica, 1960–1973*. México, D.F.: Secretaría de Industria y Comercio.

Hendricks, William O. 1996. *Guillermo Andrade y el desarrollo del delta mexicano del Río Colorado 1874–1905*. Mexicali: Universidad Autónoma de Baja California.

Hundley, Norris, Jr. 1966. *Dividing the Waters: A Century of Controversy between the United States and Mexico*. Berkeley and Los Angeles: University of California Press.

Instituto Mexicano del Seguro Social (IMSS). n.d. "Asegurados Totales por Actividad Económica." Delegación Regional en Baja California, Jefatura Delegacional de Servicios de Finanzas, Oficina de Información y Análisis Financiero.

Instituto Nacional de Estadística, Geografía e Informática (INEGI). 1983. *X Censo general de población y vivienda, 1980, Estado de Baja California*, Vols. 1 and 2. México, D.F.: Secretaría de Programación y Presupuesto.

Instituto Nacional de Estadística, Geografía e Informática (INEGI). 1991. *XI Censo general de población y vivienda, 1990, Baja California: resultados definitivos, tabulados básicos*. Aguascalientes: INEGI.

Instituto Nacional de Estadística, Geografía e Informática (INEGI). 1996. *Baja California, conteo de población y vivienda, 1995, resultados definitivos, tabulados básicos*. Aguascalientes: INEGI.

Instituto Nacional de Estadística, Geografía e Informática (INEGI) and Gobierno del Estado de Baja California. n.d. *Anuario estadístico del Estado de Baja California*. Aguascalientes: INEGI.

Instituto Nacional de Estadística, Geografía e Informática (INEGI) and Gobierno del Estado de Baja California. 1993. *Anuario estadístico del Estado de Baja California*. Aguascalientes: INEGI.

Instituto Nacional de Estadística, Geografía e Informática (INEGI) and Gobierno del Estado de Baja California. 1994. *Anuario estadístico del estado de Baja California*. Aguascalientes: INEGI.

Instituto Nacional de Estadística, Geografía e Informática (INEGI) and Gobierno del Estado de Baja California. 1995. *Anuario estadístico del estado de Baja California*. Aguascalientes: INEGI.

Instituto Nacional de Estadística, Geografía e Informática (INEGI). 2000a. *XII Censo General de Población y Vivienda 2000*. http://www.inegi.gob.mx.

Instituto Nacional de Estadística, Geografía e Informática (INEGI) and Gobierno del Estado de Baja California. 2000b. *Anuario estadístico del estado de Baja California*. Aguascalientes: INEGI.

Kerig, Dorothy P. 2001. *El valle de Mexicali y la Colorado River Land Company 1902–1946*. Mexicali: Universidad Autónoma de Baja California.

Ladman, Jerry R. 1975. *The Development of the Mexicali Regional Economy: An Example of Export Propelled Growth*. Tempe: Arizona State University.

Martínez Cabañas, Gustavo. 1971. *El municipio de Mexicali: diagnóstico económico y social y planes para su desarrollo*. Mexicali: VI Ayuntamiento de Mexicali.

Noriega-Verdugo, Sergio. 1968. *Estado de Baja California*. México, D.F.: Banco de Comercio, S.A.

Noriega-Verdugo, Sergio. 1984. *Diagnóstico económico regional*. Mexicali: Centro de Estudios Económicos del Sector Empresarial de Mexicali. Unpublished.

Poder Ejecutivo Federal. 1996. *Programa Nacional de Población, 1995–2000*. México, D.F.: Secretaría de Gobernación and Consejo Nacional de Población.

Sánchez Ramírez, Oscar. 1990. *Crónica agrícola del valle de Mexicali*. Mexicali: Universidad Autónoma de Baja California.

Tiebout, Charles M. 1962. *The Community Economic Base Study*. New York: Committe for Economic Development.

Tout, Otis B. 1931. *The First Thirty Years*. San Diego: Arts and Crafts Press.

Villareal Z., Humberto J. 1971. *El Valle de Mexicali*. México, D.F.: Secretaría de Recursos Hidráulicos.

Walther Meade, Adalberto. 1983. *Origen de Mexicali*. Mexicali: Universidad Autónoma de Baja California.

10

The Economy of Yuma County, Arizona, and San Luis Río Colorado, Sonora

Gerald L. Schmaedick and Vanessa Owen*

Abstract

The lower Colorado River region is a unique area. From the Yuma Valley of Arizona and the Imperial Valley of California to the mouth of the Colorado River in Mexico, the region is indelibly marked by the influence of the river. During the past thirty-some years, there have been five primary forces driving the delta economy. The agricultural sector has been buoyed by the shift from cotton and forage crops to higher value vegetables, grains, and citrus. A whole new manufacturing sector has been created around the "twin plant" or the maquiladora *program of Mexico. Both the vegetable and* maquiladora *sectors have been boosted by the passages of the North American Free Trade Agreement (NAFTA) and the peso devaluation of 1994–1995. These events have propelled the expansion of these sectors to unexpectedly high levels. Finally, the dynamic growth in seasonal tourism has added significantly to the forces that have produced economic growth rates surpassed by very few other regions in the United States.*

Introduction: An Overview of the Economy of the Yuma County and San Luis Río Colorado (SLRC) Area

The southern reaches of the Colorado River form the boundary dividing Arizona and California. South of the U.S.-Mexican border, it is the boundary between the Mexican states of Sonora and Baja California. But the river unifies more than it divides. Historically, the annual floods of the Colorado River Delta supported agriculture.

*Schmaedick is Senior Lecturer at Northern Arizona University in Yuma; Owen is Vice President of Investor Relations at the Greater Yuma Economic Development Corporation.

Today, water from the river is the lifeblood of an economy dominated by irrigated agricultural production. However, agriculture is not the whole story of the dynamism of the lower Colorado River Delta economy.

The Agricultural Sector

The annual agricultural output of Yuma County reached $692.5 million in 1998. Imperial County typically produces just over $1 billion of agricultural products each year. In neighboring Mexico, explosive growth in the manufacturing sector has far outpaced the growth of agriculture in recent years. Nevertheless, agricultural production still represents an important component of the economic output of the municipalities[1] of both San Luis Río Colorado (SLRC) and Mexicali. The annual value of crops (excluding livestock) of SLRC is estimated at $23.7 million.

The Maquiladora Manufacturing Sector

In the mid-1960s, the Mexican government implemented a program to stimulate the creation of jobs along the border with the United States. This program, known as the Border Industrialization Program, exempted producers of goods for export from duties on the importation of machinery, raw materials, and other inputs required in the production of the exports. This exemption, combined with the relatively low labor costs in Mexico, spawned a dynamic and sometimes controversial manufacturing industry along the border. Because many companies establish complementary plants on each side of the U.S.-Mexican border, the industry is also know as the "twin plant" industry. San Luis Río Colorado has participated in the growth of this industry along with the major *maquiladora* center that has developed in Mexicali. The manufacturing operations of these plants in SLRC have been complemented by supply, warehousing, and distribution activities in Yuma. Thus, the industry bridges the border and fuels economic growth throughout the region.

The North American Free Trade Agreement and the 1994–1995 Peso Devaluation

The North American Free Trade Agreement went into effect on January 1, 1994, reducing trade barriers among the United States, Canada, and Mexico. In December 1994, the Mexican government ended controls on the value of the peso and allowed its value to be determined in the open market. These events have significantly impacted the entire U.S.-Mexican border region. Specifically, the surge in trade between the countries and the fall in the value of the peso created powerful forces at once depressing Mexican purchasing power and reducing the cost of Mexican labor. While retail businesses in both Yuma County and SLRC suffered profound dips in revenues, the *maquiladora* and vegetable production industries enjoyed a windfall reduction in their cost of production and responded by rapid expansion. By 2000, employment in the SLRC *maquiladora* industry rose by about 150 percent from its 1994 level of 4,700. This generated substantial cross-border economic impacts and has increased the interdependence of the economies of Yuma and SLRC.

Winter Visitors from the North

Throughout the past decade, a yearly boost to the delta economy has been the growing number of tourists from the north residing in the region during the winter months. The influx of these consumers begins in October and their impact on revenues of area businesses is enjoyed through April. Their numbers peak in January. A survey in February 2000 estimated that about 89,900 people were added to the Yuma area population during the peak period of visitation in the 1999–2000 period (AWC/NAU Partnership 2000c: 1). The visitor to the Yuma area is a budget-conscious spender who takes advantage of opportunities to economize by making many purchases in Mexico. Algodones, a small Mexican town in Baja California bordering Yuma, is the preferred shopping destination of these visitors, although significant purchases are made in SLRC as well.

These five forces have driven the delta economy to new levels of growth, but the forces themselves are not entirely new. They build on foundations laid over many decades. For example, agriculture depends on the extensive irrigation system begun with the completion of the Hoover Dam on the Colorado River in 1935. The following sections provide a closer look at the foundations and interaction on which the delta economy is built.

The Yuma County Economy

There are four main sources of economic output in Yuma County. The main productive sectors are: agriculture, tourism and senior living, military and government, and the combined impact of these on the services and retail and wholesale trade sectors. In addition, the economy is driven by unusually large transfer payments that greatly enhance the purchasing power of the population. The relative importance of these sectors is illustrated in Table 1. It presents the income generated in the various sectors of the Yuma economy.

An emerging force in the regional economy is the role of the Native American communities. As their gaming revenues rise, investments by the Cocopah and Quechan tribes are playing an important role in key economic development projects. The impact and interaction of all of these economic forces is described below. Before analyzing the economic activities, however, a description of the population and workforce of the county is in order.

Table 1. Yuma County Personal Income by Sector Source*

Sector	1998 Income ($1,000)	1997 Income ($1,000)
Ag. services, forestry, fishing, other	177,960	159,426
Mining	nd	1,038
Construction	92,291	81,900
Manufacturing	66,885	57,850
Transportation & public utilities	73,436	67,588
Wholesale trade	92,115	92,494
Retail trade	157,109	144,520
Finance, insurance, and real estate	nd	46,416
Services	300,974	285,138
Government and government enterprises	503,526	489,324
Subtotal	**1,464,296**	**1,425,694**
Plus: undisclosed sectors	48,429	–
Subtotal	**1,512,725**	**1,425,694**
Plus: farm earnings	258,762	175,958
Earnings by place of work	**1,771,487**	**1,601,652**
Less: personal contrib. SS	(84,089)	(79,792)
Less: adjustment for residence	(68,784)	(68,779)
Net earnings by place of residence	**1,618,614**	**1,453,081**
Plus: dividends, interest, and rent	367,367	339,854
Plus: transfer payments	424,730	407,378
Total income by place of residence	**2,410,711**	**2,200,313**

*Derived from BEA/DOC #CA05.
SOURCE: BEA/DOC (2001b).

Demographics

The permanent population of the City of Yuma is currently estimated at 77,515, with the county total at 165,000 (U.S. Census Bureau 2002). However, a factor must be added to reflect the added population that lives in Yuma from October to April. The previously mentioned survey of these visitors estimated their number at 89,900 (AWC/NAU Partnership 2000c: 1). Since 1975, there has been a fourfold increase in this annual visitation.

The interaction of the populations of Yuma and SLRC is a factor that deeply affects the Yuma economy. There is a daily flow of people in both directions across the border. This movement includes workers, shoppers, tourists, and students. Managerial and technical employees of *maquiladoras* live in Yuma and commute daily to their jobs in SLRC. During the harvest season, as many as a few thousand

Mexican workers may cross the border daily to work in the vegetable fields of Yuma. Shoppers move in both directions. Many young Mexican students go to schools in Yuma. Therefore, the economically relevant population of Yuma must include the population of SLRC and vice versa.

Workforce

The Arizona Department of Economic Security (DES) estimated the total average monthly civilian labor force of Yuma County in 1999 to be 66,700. Average nonfarm employment that year was 38,275, of which 33,325 were employed in "service-producing" activities. Only 4,950 were in "goods-producing" jobs. This is in sharp contrast with SLRC, where manufacturing employs a much higher percentage of the workforce. In August 1999, the DES estimated that there were 74,925 members in the Yuma workforce, about 12 percent greater than the average for the year (DES 1999). This variation reveals that the seasonality seen in the population statistics carries over into the labor force, but it is just the opposite of the population as a whole. The labor force numbers peak when the population numbers are at their lowest (during July and August). High seasonal unemployment also occurs in the Imperial Valley, making an analysis of the area workforce difficult.

Unemployment is high throughout the year in Yuma. By DES estimates, it varies from a low of about 20 percent in January and February to a high of about 40 percent in July and August, with an average for the year of 30 percent. The number of employed people, however, is quite stable throughout the year at an average of 46,825 (DES 1999). This suggests that the peaks in unemployment are primarily a result of an influx of people in the summer months who are unable to find work. Nonfarm employment does not vary a great deal through the seasons of the year, averaging 38,275 (DES 1999). Comparing the average total employment to the average, nonfarm employment suggests that there is an average of about eight thousand people employed in Yuma County agriculture on a permanent basis. Other sectors accounting for a large number of jobs are the government (11,000), trade (10,925), and service (8,775) sectors. The full breakdown of the Yuma County employed workforce is shown in Figure 1.

The low number of people employed by the manufacturing sector in Yuma is in sharp contrast to the profile of SLRC, where manufacturing is a major employer. A similar phenomenon occurs in the Imperial-Mexicali Valley.

Economic Activity in Yuma County

The Agricultural Sector: The Core of the Yuma-SLRC Economy

Agriculture is the largest single source of economic output from Yuma County. As Figure 2 illustrates, in 1998 total cash receipts from all farm commodities produced in

Figure 1. Yuma County Workforce Pie Chart
Based on DES 1999 Figures

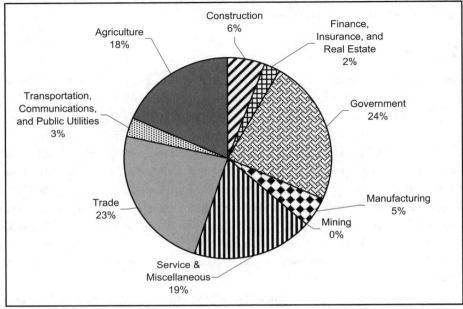

SOURCE: DES (1999).

Figure 2. Yuma County Agriculture Production: Cash Receipts

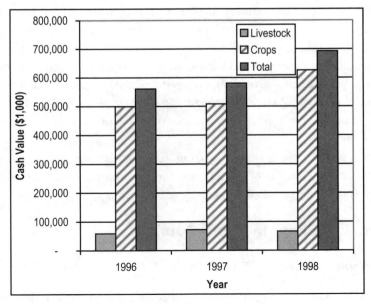

SOURCE: Arizona Agricultural Statistics Service (2000).

Yuma County were $692.5 million. This figure includes crops and livestock. When only the receipts from crops were considered, the 1998 total was $625.9 million, which places Yuma first among Arizona counties by value of crop production. Similarly to Imperial County, vegetables are Yuma's principal crops. Specifically, Yuma is Arizona's leading producer of western head lettuce, as well as leaf and romaine lettuce, broccoli, and cauliflower (Arizona Agricultural Statistics Service 2000). Yuma also leads Arizona in production of citrus (primarily lemons) and durum wheat.

All agricultural production in Yuma depends on irrigation. An extensive irrigation system distributes water from the Colorado River to all of the agricultural areas of the county.

Farm Income

The economic value produced by the agricultural sector of Yuma County is the largest of any single sector, as suggested by the cash receipts from farm commodities cited previously. U.S. Department of Commerce (BEA/DOC 2001a) data place total farm income in Yuma County at $258.7 million in 1998. To this total must be added the $177.96 million from the "agricultural services, forestry, fishing, and other" category. The estimated total income from the agricultural sector then rises to $436.7 million. In terms of income generation, the agricultural sector accounts for about 18 percent of total personal income ($2.4 billion) received by Yuma residents (BEA/DOC 2001b).

Farm Labor

The agricultural labor force of Yuma County is highly seasonal, peaking in January and February and hitting its low in July. As in Imperial County, labor commuting from Mexico is another important characteristic in Yuma County. Based on DES figures, it can be estimated that there is a core of about eight thousand permanent agricultural jobs. According to the DOC data, Yuma farms spent $163.7 million in 1998 on hired farm labor (BEA/DOC 2001a). The workers that stream across the border daily to work in the fields are extremely important to the viability of this industry. A rough estimate of their contribution can be inferred from the adjustment for residence entry that appears in the DOC Yuma personal income table. According to this adjustment, $68.8 million were paid to nonresidents of Yuma County in 1998. The 1998 Yuma figure is typical of recent years, suggesting that farming operations in Yuma County depend on Mexican workers for about 42 percent of their labor needs. For Imperial County, this figure was $68 million, remarkably similar to Yuma. Total expenditure on hired farm labor, however, was $200.3 million. Therefore, the imported component of labor represents only about 34 percent of the total in the case of the Imperial Valley.

Tourism and Senior Living

Much about the tourism and senior living sector can be inferred from the simple fact that almost ninety thousand winter visitors increase the Yuma economy four to six months of the year. The main attraction to the region is its mild weather. The senior living industry is also supported by the climate. The emergence of Yuma as a permanent retirement destination is at least in part due to the experience seniors have during their winter visits. However, tourism dollars are also generated by two other visiting groups. A significant number of Mexicans go to Yuma County for recreation. They attend movies, sports, and cultural events, play golf, eat at Yuma restaurants, and recreate on Yuma area waterways. Another group of visitors is comprised of military personnel and contractors, U.S. and other, who go to Yuma on training and testing missions at the two military/government facilities: the Yuma Proving Grounds (YPG) and the Marine Corps Air Station (MCAS).

The overall economic impact of tourism activities is estimated by the *Lower Colorado River Economic Report* based on its biannual survey (AWC/NAU Partnership 2000a: 4). According to this report, the gross dollar impact on the Yuma economy from tourism in the 1999–2000 season was $501.5 million. The largest portion of this, about 43 percent, is generated by the winter visitors and permanent retired residents. The impact of the visitors from Mexico is a close second with 42 percent.

Military and Government

The government sector consists of federal, state, and local activities. Table 1 reports that the government sector, including the military, was the source of $503 million of income to Yuma County residents. This represents 20.8 percent of Yuma County's personal income. The largest government activities by employment and income are the Marine Corps Air Station, the County School Districts, Yuma Proving Grounds, and the U.S. Immigration Service and Border Patrol.

The MCAS had a civilian and military payroll of $120.8 million in 1999. In addition, a steady stream of personnel from other bases visits each year for training, amounting to about seven to eight thousand annually (MCAS 1999). The combined characteristics of facilities, geography, and weather provide an aviation complex of unmatched utility.

The U.S. Army Yuma Proving Grounds enjoys similar advantages of large protected spaces and excellent weather. The Proving Grounds employs 1,900 people, including military personnel, federal civilian, and contract workers. The expenditures of these people and their families contribute significantly to Yuma's economy. Local and state government is also an important component of Yuma's economy. The educational establishment is a significant part of this sector. Taken as a unit, educational institutions employ even more people than MCAS.

Services and Retail and Wholesale Trade

In an economy that reaps such a large percentage of its value added from tourism and retirement services as well as its provision of a large military establishment, it is no surprise that services and retail and wholesale trade are important. These activities cut across many sectors. As Table 2 indicates, 38 percent of the jobs in Yuma County can be placed in one of these three sectors. The service sector alone accounts for 19 percent of the jobs.

When the income earned by the employees in these sectors of services and retail and wholesale trade is evaluated in relation to the number of jobs, the impact of the heavy reliance of the Yuma economy on these sectors is clear. While 38 percent of Yuma jobs are in these sectors, only 23 percent of the county's earnings are generated by them. Services account for the largest percentage with 19 percent, followed closely by retail trade with 15 percent and wholesale trade accounts for 4 percent.

Total taxable sales (food is not taxed in Arizona) in Yuma County reached $1.4 billion in 1999 (AWC/NAU Partnership 2000a: 6). Retail sales are very seasonal, reaching their peak during the height of the winter visitors season in January and February each year. Annual total sales are boosted by these visitors and by significant retail and wholesale businesses from across the border. For the period May 1999 to

Table 2. Earnings and Employment in Services and Retail and Wholesale Trade, 1994–1998

Earnings by Industry: 1994, 1996, 1998 ($1,000)					
Industry	1994	1996	1998	% Change 1994–1998	% of Total County 1998
Services	235,306	271,507	300,974	28.0	12.0
Retail trade	130,415	139,001	157,109	20.0	7.0
Wholesale trade	70,952	92,600	92,115	30.0	4.0
Other	1,427,442	1,568,131	1,860,513		
Total county earnings	**1,864,115**	**2,071,239**	**2,410,711**		
Employment by Industry: 1994, 1996, 1998					
Industry	1994	1996	1998	% Change 1994–1998	% of Total County 1998
Services	10,859	12,100	12,682	17.0	19.0
Retail trade	9,744	9,883	10,141	4.0	15.0
Wholesale trade	2,941	3,569	2,971	1.0	4.0
Other	34,233	38,351	41,711		
Total county employment	**57,777**	**63,903**	**67,505**		

SOURCE: BEA/DOC (2001b).

April 2000, estimates indicated that Mexican shoppers spent $210 million in Yuma County (AWC/NAU Partnership 2000c: 3). Overall taxable sales increased by 6.6 percent from 1998 to 1999 (AWC/NAU Partnership 2000b: 2).

Construction, Manufacturing, and Transportation and Public Utilities

These normally important sectors contribute a relatively minor portion of value added in the Yuma economy. The data are summarized in Table 3. The aggregate contribution of these sectors represents only 10 percent of total county earnings. About 11 percent of the jobs in the county are found in these sectors. Construction has been the fastest growing of the three sectors in recent years. The case of manufacturing is especially noteworthy when compared to the same sector in San Luis Río Colorado, where it has been the most powerful engine of growth in recent decades. Yuma manufacturing in 1998 accounted for only 2,147 jobs and just 3

Table 3. Earnings and Employment in Construction, Manufacturing, and Transportation and Public Utilities, 1994–1998

Earnings by Industry: 1994, 1996, 1998 ($1,000)					
Industry	1994	1996	1998	% Change 1994–1998	% of Total County 1998
Construction	63,807	72,168	92,291	45.0	4.0
Manufacturing	64,680	51,871	66,885	3.0	3.0
Transportation and public utilities	57,742	64,294	73,436	27.0	3.0
Other	1,677,886	1,882,906	2,178,099		
Total county earnings	**1,864,115**	**2,071,239**	**2,410,711**		
Employment by Industry: 1994, 1996, 1998					
Industry	1994	1996	1998	% Change 1994–1998	% of Total County 1998
Construction	2,325	2,556	3,236	39.0	5.0
Manufacturing	1,994	1,716	2,147	8.0	3.0
Transportation and public utilities	1,923	2,159	2,101	9.0	3.0
Other	51,535	57,472	60,021		
Total county employment	**57,777**	**63,903**	**67,505**		

SOURCE: BEA/DOC (2001b).

percent of total county personal earnings. By 1998, there were approximately nine thousand manufacturing jobs in SLRC, mostly in the *maquiladora* sector.

Native American Economic Activities and Impact

The two Native American tribes that contribute to the economic vitality of the greater Yuma area are the Fort Yuma Quechan and Cocopah nations. The population of the Quechan tribe is estimated at more than 2,900 members, while the Cocopah tribe has 904 tribal members. Historically, agriculture has been the principal economic activity of both tribes, but gaming operations now employ an almost equal number.

The economic sectors in Yuma County most influenced by the Quechan and Cocopah nations are clearly tourism and services. Combined employment for both tribes is nearly 900 persons, of which 457 are nontribal members. The combined payroll for tribal administration and casino enterprises is just over $19 million, not including taxes and benefits. In addition, it is estimated that more than $27 million of goods and services were purchased by both tribes in 1998 and contributions of almost $350,000 were made to nonprofit organizations based in greater Yuma.

The revenue generated by gaming operations has allowed the tribes to become investors in commercial enterprises beyond their traditional scope. Although more than 75 percent of the Quechan nation is actually located in Imperial County, its economy is more closely tied to that of Yuma County. In 2000, the Quechan nation made significant strides toward partnering with the City of Yuma to revive the downtown area. The first was a gift of $193,000 to the city for the purpose of restoring the ocean-to-ocean bridge, allowing easier access across the Colorado River. The second venture was investing in a faltering movie theater project that is expected to anchor future retail development along Yuma's historic Main Street. The latest project to be announced by the Quechan is a combination truck stop, fuel depot, and RV resort proposed along Interstate 8 at the Algodones exit. Future developments that will impact greater Yuma's economy also include an expansion of the current commercial border crossing and port of entry at Algodones.

The Cocopah nation has long been active in transportation planning for Yuma County through their participation in the Yuma Metropolitan Planning Organization (YMPO). They are now also part of the Greater Yuma Port Authority that will manage the proposed new commercial port of entry in San Luis. In addition to the Cocopah casino, the tribe manages a golf and RV resort that caters primarily to the area's winter visitors.

Transfer Payments

Transfer payments, such as Social Security payments, pension benefits, disability payouts, and so on, are important to the Yuma economy. In 1998, these payments totaled $424.7 million and accounted for almost 18 percent of total income enjoyed by Yuma residents. The reason for this high amount is the presence of many retirees in Yuma, especially those retired from the military. Many winter visitors decide to make Yuma their home after they begin permanent retirement, injecting a healthy amount of resources into the Yuma economy.

The San Luis Río Colorado Economy

Introduction: A Common Economic Base Divided by an International Border

San Luis Río Colorado is a municipality of the State of Sonora that borders Yuma County on the south. Mexican municipalities are roughly equivalent to U.S. counties. The territory of SLRC extends south from the international border to the mouth of the Colorado River. The fishing village of Santa Clara is the southernmost center of population in the municipality. It is bordered on the west by the Colorado River, which separates it from the State of Baja California.

Most of SLRC is encompassed by the Sonoran Desert. It has this desert and the Colorado River in common with Yuma County. The desert and the river have been the defining factors of the economy of both Yuma and SLRC. Historically, the annual spring floods dictated the agricultural patterns of the area. Now, the dry, uniform climate—combined with rich delta soils and irrigation water from the river—provides the foundation for highly productive vegetable and citrus industries. The five economic forces described in the introduction to this chapter are apparent in SLRC as well as in Yuma. They differ only in relative importance. The most significant contrast is the dynamic, rapidly growing manufacturing sector of SLRC compared to its slow growth in Yuma.

Another contrast found between the two is that Yuma's agricultural sector has pumped millions of dollars into its economy, while SLRC has lagged in agricultural output and technological innovation. While the impact of NAFTA has generally been positive in Yuma, the devaluation of the Mexican peso that followed its implementation caused a serious depression throughout Mexico. This precipitated violent crosscurrents in the SLRC economy. The devaluation resulted in a severe inflation of prices and consequent loss of purchasing power for the people. At the same time, the lower labor costs in terms of U.S. dollars sparked an acceleration of investment in the *maquiladoras* and a surge of new hiring to fill the new and expanded plants. This, in part, counteracted the negative impacts of the depression. As a consequence, recovery from the Mexican depression was relatively rapid in border cities such as SLRC. The growing numbers of winter visitors to the area have also contributed to the recovery.

Figure 3. Population Growth in SLRC, 1970–1995

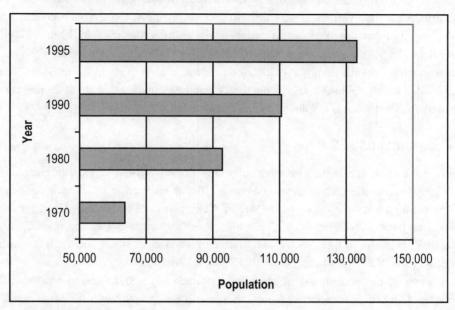

SOURCE: INEGI (2001).

The Population and Workforce of San Luis Río Colorado

Compared to Yuma, the population of SLRC is much more heavily concentrated in the City of San Luis Río Colorado. In fact, few official statistics distinguish the city population that lives in the urban area along the border from the outlying rural and costal areas to the south and east. Data from Mexico's 2000 Census indicate that the total population of the municipality is 145,000, including even the most distant clusters (INEGI 2001). While this figure is contested by some, it is the best estimate available and suggests a population remarkably similar to that of Yuma County (139,650). Figure 3 illustrates how the population of SLRC has grown.

From 1990 to 1995, the municipality grew at a rapid annual rate of 3.8 percent, reaching 133,000 at mid-decade. Population growth slowed in the second half of the 1990s to just 1.8 percent per year. This probably had to do with the economic contraction that occurred in 1995 and continued depressed conditions throughout Mexico during all of 1996. San Luis is the fourth largest city in the State of Sonora; Hermosillo is the largest with 609,829 in 2000 (INEGI 2001b).

Unfortunately, at the time of the authors' writing, detailed data from the 2000 Mexican Census were not yet available. Therefore, the most recent workforce data available are from the 1990 collection. According to that data, there were 34,713 people in the SLRC workforce in 1990, up from 27,935 in 1980. Considering that there has been a population increase of 32 percent between 1990 and 2000, the current workforce must be about 45,000. Figure 4 summarizes how the SLRC workforce was distributed among various sectors in 1990. Not surprisingly, the sectors accounting for the largest proportion of the workforce were: agriculture, forestry, and fishing (27.8%); services (25.9%); and manufacturing (16.9%). It is unlikely, however, that the same distribution prevails today. As described below, the *maquiladoras* in SLRC have expanded rapidly in both size and number. It can be estimated that about 26 percent of the SLRC workforce is employed in that sector today.

The Agricultural Sector

There are great similarities between the Yuma County agricultural sector and that of its neighbor to the south. There is also significant interaction and interdependence. According to a study by the Mexican Center for Research on Nutrition and Development (CIAD 1997: 16): "...a high level of integration exists in production, inputs, financing, technology transfer, marketing, and labor supply between the valley of San Luis Río Colorado and the Yuma Valley of Arizona."

Historic patterns of agriculture in the Colorado River Delta region transcend the border. The SLRC economy was more dependent on agriculture in the mid-twentieth century than Yuma. Yuma had the Marine Corps Air Station, the Yuma Proving Grounds, and a growing winter visitor population to help boost its economy. In SLRC, cotton was supreme. The transition away from cotton and forage crops that occurred in Yuma County during the 1970s has also since occurred in SLRC. In fact, it can be said that this transition is still under way. Investment and the introduction of advanced crop management technologies from the north have been important in propelling SLRC agriculture toward this new model emphasizing vegetables and citrus. Meanwhile, Yuma agriculture has increased its use of Mexican labor and Yuma agricultural marketing companies are increasing their purchases of produce from Mexico.

Land tenure is one aspect of Mexican agriculture that is distinctly different from that of Arizona. In SLRC, 50.7 percent of the land is farmed under the *ejido* system. This is a communal form of ownership similar to cooperative ownership. Until the change of the Mexican Constitution in 1993, ultimate ownership of the land resided with the federal government. This system undoubtedly influenced the development of SLRC agriculture. Even after the passage of the constitutional amendment giving *ejido* members effective ownership of *ejido* land, sale of these lands has often been encumbered by legal challenges.

Principal Crops and Production

The transition in crop patterns that has occurred in SLRC is revealed in Figure 5. Industrial oilseeds, predominantly cotton, accounted for over 50 percent of the land harvested between 1970 and 1980. This percentage dropped to about 23 percent in the

Figure 4. SLRC Employment by Industry, 1980 and 1990

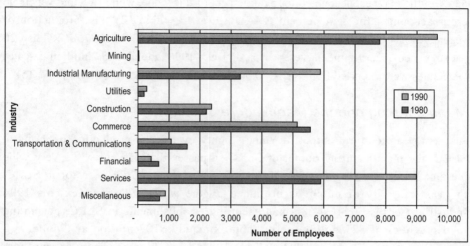

SOURCE: CIAD (1997).

Figure 5. Area Planted by Crop Type

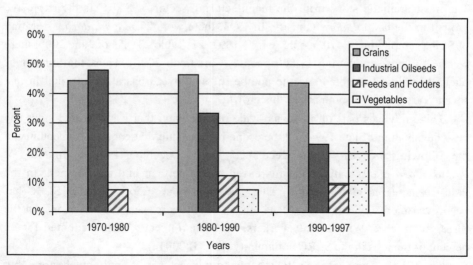

SOURCE: CIAD (1997).

late 1990s. Meanwhile, basic grain production, mostly wheat, maintained its place on about 44 percent of the land. The other shift has been to fruits and vegetables. By the late 1990s, these accounted for 23.6 percent of the land planted. During the 1995–1996 crop year, total value of the principal crops harvested in SLRC was approximately $23.7 million. Wheat accounted for 57.4 percent of this value, while fruit and vegetable crops accounted for 32.4 percent (CIAD 1997: 14, Table 12). The production of vegetables has given rise to a small packing industry in SLRC. In 1997, SLRC had 20 packing sheds. During the harvest season of 1995–1996, a total of 6.7 million cases of vegetables were exported from SLRC to buyers in the United States (CIAD 1997: 15).

Manufacturing and the Maquiladora Sector

Just as the agricultural output of Yuma County dwarfs the production of farms in SLRC, the manufacturing output of SLRC surpasses that of Yuma by a very wide margin. While there is manufacturing outside of the *maquiladora* sector in SLRC, the vast majority of output is produced by the *maquiladoras*. Mexico's 1994 Industrial Census reported 285 manufacturing establishments in SLRC, generating total revenues of 321 million pesos (approximately $107 million at 1 dollar = 3 pesos, the rate for most of 1993) (CIAD 1997: 17, Table 18). There are no more recent data showing the combined revenues of both *maquila* and non-*maquila* businesses of SLRC.

The Maquiladora Sector

The most dramatic story from the manufacturing sector of SLRC is the explosive growth in the *maquiladora* industry. In 1993, there were 23 *maquiladoras* operating in SLRC, employing 4,410 people (CIAD 1997: 21, Table 23). As of June 2000, there were 38 plants, employing 11,800 people (Christman 2000). Thus, the number of plants has almost doubled and the number of employees has almost tripled in just seven years. Figure 6 summarizes this growth.

This growth is part of a Mexico-wide phenomenon that has occurred since the peso devaluation of late 1994 and the economic hardship that engulfed the country in the following two years. From December 1995 to December 1999, the number of *maquiladora* plants nationwide increased by 52 percent and employment in the industry increased by 76 percent. Thus, the industry's rate of growth in SLRC has been even more rapid than in the nation. In 2000, there were 54,425 people in the SLRC workforce. With 11,800 workers, the *maquila* sector then accounted for 22 percent of the jobs in the SLRC community (INEGI 2001c).

Compared to Yuma, the SLRC manufacturing sector is not only much larger, but it also generates very different products. The *maquila*s of SLRC are concentrated in two sectors: (1) garments and textiles, and (2) electronics, especially audio and video equipment. According to the 1999 directory of the SLRC *maquiladora* association, 11

Figure 6. Growth of Maquiladora Plants and Employment in SLRC, 1989–1997

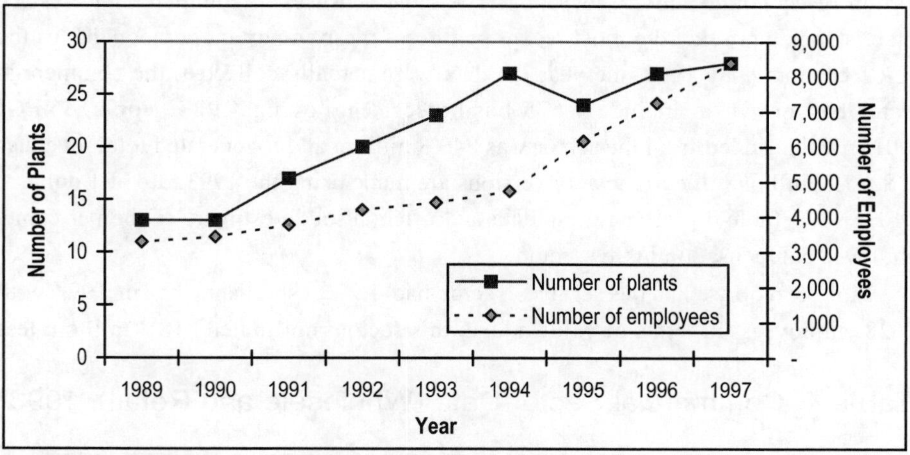

SOURCE: CIAD (1997).

of its member plants employed 4,700 people in the production of garments and textiles. With 9,280 employees, these two sectors accounted for 79 percent of the employment in the SLRC *maquiladora* industry (Asociación de Maquiladoras de San Luis Río Colorado, A.C. 1999).

The *maquiladoras* of SLRC do not follow the "twin plant" model. Only two of them actually have any manufacturing operations in Yuma County. Nevertheless, the interaction and interdependence of this sector and the Yuma economy are significant. All of the plants receive inputs through Yuma. Some inputs are purchased in Yuma; others are simply transported through Yuma. More significantly, part of the output of the *maquila*s is warehoused and distributed in Yuma. These are underexploited opportunities for Yuma businesses.

The industry's greatest impact on Yuma is the purchasing power *maquiladoras* generate for their employees. A serious study of this is needed, but even a casual observer surveying the parking lots of major Yuma retail outlets on any weekend will see a high number of cars from neighboring Mexican communities. The local Wal-Mart store estimates about 30 percent of cars parked in their lot on Sundays are from Mexico.[2] When the peso was devalued in 1994–1995, the negative impact was felt by virtually all Yuma retailers. Previous levels of purchases have now recovered. The AWC/NAU Partnership survey (2000) previously cited estimated that Mexicans spent $210 million in Yuma in the 1999–2000 period.

Services and Retail and Wholesale Trade

The retail and wholesale trade and services sectors account for a very important portion of economic activity in SLRC. The 1994 censuses of commerce and service establishments provide the most recent picture of these important components of the SLRC economy. By 1993, the year the data were actually collected, the commercial sector had grown to include 1,675 businesses, employing 4,927 people (INEGI 2001a). Value added from the sector was $40.8 million and it generated total revenues of $207.3 million (all currency conversions are made using the 1993 rate of 1 dollar = 3.40 pesos). Table 4 presents these data and offers a rough estimate of the per capita employee compensation in this sector.

Table 5 reports that the services sector had 1,273 establishments in 1993 with 3,628 employees. In terms of value added, this sector contributed $18.3 million, less

Table 4. Commercial Sector Data (Wholesale and Retail), 1993

Item	Pesos (1,000)	US$* ($1,000)
Total revenues	704,991.7	207,305.5
Value added	138,694.3	40,792.4
Total employee remuneration	38,254.4	11,251.2
Remuneration/capita per hour	7.764	2.284
No. of establishments		1,675
Total employment		**4,297**

*US$1 = 3.40 pesos.
SOURCE: INEGI (2001a).

Table 5. Services Sector Data (Wholesale and Retail), 1993

Item	Pesos (1,000)	US$* ($1,000)
Total revenues	115,507.3	33,972.7
Value added	62,137.0	18,275.6
Total employee remuneration	24,297.6	7,146.4
Remuneration/capita per hour	6.697	1.97
No. of establishments		1,273
Total employment		**3,628**

*US$1 = 3.40 pesos.
SOURCE: INEGI (2001a)

than half of the commercial sector. Total revenues generated were also significantly less than those of the commercial sector, only about $34 million. Table 5 also suggests that, on average, employees are paid at a lower rate than those in the commercial sector.

Conclusion: Evidence of Interaction and Interdependence

This description of the San Luis Río Colorado and Yuma economies reveals that there are not two economies (one on each side of the border), but one economy bridging the border. In the introduction, five forces were identified that drive the regional economy: the transition in agriculture, dynamic growth in manufacturing, the implementation of NAFTA, the 1994 peso devaluation, and the growing influx of winter visitors. Each of these forces is usually viewed as a dominant force on one side of the border or the other. For example, the boom in agriculture is described as the driving force in Yuma County, while the rapid expansion of the manufacturing sector is identified as the force propelling SLRC. As suggested throughout this essay, however, there is a great deal of interdependence in all five of these areas. Much more work is needed to fully appreciate their degree of integration, but in concluding this essay, a few indications will have to suffice (see Schmaedick 2001).

In the Yuma agricultural sector, labor from Mexico is an indispensable component driving the growth of vegetable production. During the peak of the season (November to March), from three to five thousand workers cross the border each morning to work in the fields, on the tractors, and in the packing sheds of Yuma County. These workers are an essential component to the success of this sector. The income earned by these workers, in turn, supports the retail sector on both sides of the border. The dynamism of the SLRC *maquiladora* sector also depends on human capital and services from Yuma. Several hundred executives and middle managers commute daily from their homes in Yuma to their jobs in the *maquiladoras*. In this case, incomes earned on SLRC-based jobs are spent in Yuma, boosting the sales of all kinds of local businesses. The business sector in Yuma also realizes significant sales to the *maquiladoras* themselves in the form of inputs and supplies. As previously mentioned, a growing warehousing and distribution business is emerging in Yuma to fulfill the needs of *maquiladoras* just across the border.

The forces unleashed by the passage of NAFTA and the devaluation of the peso that followed shortly thereafter have greatly impacted the entire regional economy. The benefits of NAFTA have also attracted businesses from non-NAFTA countries that seek access to the huge North American market. By locating their facilities in Mexico, they can meet the requirements for duty-free access to the U.S. and Canadian markets.

The impact of the 1994 peso devaluation and subsequent inflation greatly undermined the purchasing power of the Mexican consumer, including the *maquiladora* employees who are paid in pesos. The significance of this to Yuma's economy was seen in a sharp drop in retail sales, especially for businesses nearest to the border. As economic conditions in Mexico have improved and as the *maquiladora* sector has expanded so rapidly, the demand for labor has pushed wages up in the manufacturing sector. This has had a beneficial impact on the Yuma retail sector as purchases by Mexican consumers have climbed. This is another demonstration of the important interaction and interdependence that exist between the Yuma and SLRC economies.

Finally, the influx of winter visitors has its greatest impact on Yuma County, but those same budget-minded tourists are also frequent visitors to Mexico. They make regular purchases of pharmaceuticals and cosmetics and obtain services such as dental work and optical care. Thus, SLRC and neighboring Mexican communities also benefit from the numerous visitors to the Yuma area. These examples of interdependence are important indicators for policymakers. They demonstrate that the border does not divide or isolate the two communities. Just as contrasting economic dimensions, policy environments, and socioeconomic conditions on either side of the border create obstacles, they also create opportunities for mutual prosperity. These opportunities will bear fruit and obstacles will be overcome only to the extent that the real basis for interaction and interdependence is recognized and understood. This essay is only a first step in fostering such understanding.

Endnotes

1. In Mexico, a *municipio* is roughly equivalent to a county in the United States. Thus, output is considered here from both urban and rural areas of San Luis Río Colorado, Sonora, and Mexicali, Baja California.

2. Information from author's interview with Wal-Mart manager, April 5, 2001.

References

Arizona Agricultural Statistics Service. 2000. "1999 Arizona Agricultural Statistics." (July)
    http://www.de.state.az.us/links/economic/webpage/eaweb/cescty99.html.
Arizona Department of Economic Security (DES). 1999. (Cited October 2000).
    http://www.de.state.az.us/links/economic/webpage/eaweb/cescty99.html.
Arizona Western College/Northern Arizona University (AWC/NAU) Partnership. 2000a. *Lower Colorado River Economic Report* 10 (1). Yuma: Northern Arizona University-Arizona Western College Partnership.
Arizona Western College/Northern Arizona University (AWC/NAU) Partnership. 2000b. *Lower Colorado River Economic Report* 14 (3). Yuma: Northern Arizona University-Arizona Western College Partnership.
Arizona Western College/Northern Arizona University (AWC/NAU) Partnership. 2000c. *Lower Colorado River Economic Report* 14 (6). Yuma: Northern Arizona University-Arizona Western College Partnership.

Asociación de Maquiladoras de San Luis Río Colorado, A.C. 1999. *Directorio de Empresas Maquiladoras Locales-1999*. San Luis Río Colorado: Asociación de Maquiladoras de San Luis Río Colorado, A.C.

Bureau of Economic Analysis, U.S. Department of Commerce (BEA/DOC). 2001a. "Farm Income and Expenses: Yuma, Arizona (Table CA45)." (October 2000). http://www.bea.doc.gov/bea/regional/reis/ca05/04/ca05_04027.htm.

Bureau of Economic Analysis, U.S. Department of Commerce (BEA/DOC). 2001b. "Personal Income by Major Source and Earnings by Industry (Table CA05)." (Cited October 2000). http://www.bea.doc.gov/bea/regional/reis/Ca05/04/ca05_04027.htm.

Centro de Investigación en Alimentación y Desarrollo, A.C. (CIAD). 1997. *Estudio de factibilidad para una nueva puerta fronteriza en San Luis Río Colorado, Sonora, México*. Hermosillo: CIAD.

Christman, John H. 2000. "The Maquiladora Industry Outlook: 2000–2005." Paper presented at the 39th Maquiladora Industry Meeting, 29 September, Mexicali, Baja California, Mexico.

Instituto Nacional de Estadística, Geografía e Informática (INEGI). 2000. "Preliminary Results, XII Censo 2000." http://www.inegi.gob.mx.

Instituto Nacional de Estadística, Geografía e Informática (INEGI). 2001a. "Censo Commercial y Censo de Servicios, 1994." http://www.inegi.gob.mx.

Instituto Nacional de Estadística, Geografía e Informática (INEGI). 2001b. "XII Censo General de Población y Vivienda, 2000." (Cited 17 January 2003) http://www.inegi.gob.mx.

Instituto Nacional de Estadística, Geografía e Informática (INEGI). 2001c. "XII Censo General de Población y Vivienda, 2000." (Cited 16 May 2003) http://www.inegi.gob.mx.

Marine Corps Air Station (MCAS). 1999. *Statistical Summary: 1999*. Yuma: MCAS.

Schmaedick, Gerald L. 2001. "Integration of Cross-Border Communities: The Case of San Luis Río Colorado, Sonora and Yuma County, Arizona." Paper presented at the meeting of the Association for Borderlands Studies, 20 April, Reno, Nevada.

U.S. Census Bureau. 2002. "State and County Quick Facts." (Cited 19 September 2002) http://www.census.gov.

11

Imperial County Employment Profile

Cheryl Mason*

Abstract

This essay analyzes employment trends in Imperial County, as well as its population, the civilian labor force, industry, and occupational employment. In 2000, Imperial County's population was 142,361 and its unemployment rate averaged 26.3 percent—the highest of all 58 California counties. Approximately 50,400 payroll jobs existed in the county and its two largest industries were government and agriculture. Although the county's population represents only 0.5 percent of the total population of California, its agricultural employment accounts for almost 3.0 percent of the state's agricultural employment. The local labor market is comprised of many small firms. In 1999, of all private-sector firms, 92.4 percent had 30 or fewer employees. The county's employment base is expected to expand over the next few years as economic conditions improve.

Introduction

This document presents an employment profile for Imperial County. It describes the county's population, civilian labor force, and industry and occupational employment. The essay is divided into three sections. The first section describes the county's population and civilian labor force characteristics. The second section discusses industry employment trends and outlook for 2004. The final section examines the projected job increase from an occupational perspective, including an analysis of job growth by wage category.

*Mason is Labor Market Consultant for the Employment Development Department (EDD), where she maintains employment and unemployment estimates for San Diego and Imperial counties.

Population and Civilian Labor Force

Imperial County is a large county in terms of geography, but relatively small in terms of population. As of 2000, it had a population of 142,361 people, representing less than 0.5 percent of California's population. The county has seven incorporated cities, of which the largest is El Centro, followed by Calexico and then Brawley. These three cities made up 61.1 percent of the county's population in 2000. Only 18 of California's 58 counties have a population smaller than that of Imperial County. Its neighboring counties are San Diego to the west (population 2,813,833) and Riverside to the north (population 1,545,387) (Department of Finance 2001). Yuma County, in Arizona, is the county's eastern neighbor with a population of 160,026 (Arizona Department of Economic Security 2001). Its neighbor to the south is Mexicali, Mexico, with a population of 764,100 (Almaraz 2001).

The Employment Development Department (EDD) estimated Imperial County's civilian labor force (defined as those individuals age 16 years or older who are either employed or unemployed and actively seeking work) at 58,200 in 2000. Of these, 42,900 were employed and 15,300 were unemployed, resulting in a 26.3 percent unemployment rate for the year. As shown in Table 1, the number of employed residents has been steadily increasing over the last few years, while the number of unemployed residents has been steadily declining. However, in 2000, the number of unemployed actually increased, likely due to the loss of agricultural jobs that year. Despite this downturn, these data indicate that Imperial County reached a new record in 2000; never before have so many residents participated and held jobs in the labor market. But, at the

Table 1. Civilian Labor Force Data, Imperial County, 1990–2000

Year	Labor Force	Employment	Unemployment	Unemployment Rate (%)
1990	47,500	35,400	12,100	25.5
1991	48,800	36,200	12,600	25.8
1992	54,100	37,500	16,600	30.7
1993	55,300	39,200	16,100	29.1
1994	58,000	42,800	15,200	26.2
1995	58,400	41,300	17,100	29.3
1996	57,400	40,500	16,900	29.4
1997	56,400	41,400	15,000	26.6
1998	56,200	41,600	14,600	26.0
1999	55,500	42,500	13,000	23.4
2000	58,200	42,900	15,300	26.3

SOURCES: EDD (2001). Benchmark March 2002.

same time, Imperial County continues to hold the state's highest annual average unemployment rate, as it has done for at least two decades (EDD 2001).

Employment Characteristics

The EDD estimated Imperial County's total industry employment in 2000 at 50,400 jobs. Industry employment is an estimate of the number of payroll jobs, excluding the self-employed.[1] Figure 1 displays the industrial distribution of the 50,400 jobs. The two largest industries were government and agriculture. Government accounted for 15,500 jobs, or 30.8 percent, of all payroll jobs in Imperial County in 2000. Approximately one-third of the government jobs were concentrated in local education. Agriculture accounted for nearly as many jobs as government, 12,300 jobs or 24.4 percent. Imperial County is a leading producer of row crops and livestock and is often referred to as the state's "winter salad bowl" because of the quantity of vegetables and lettuce that is harvested at that time of year. Imperial County's combined concentration in government and agriculture was higher than most California counties. Only three counties—Lassen, Modoc, and Colusa—had

Figure 1. Distribution of Total Industry
Employment in Imperial County, 2000
(Total Annual Average Employment = 50,400)

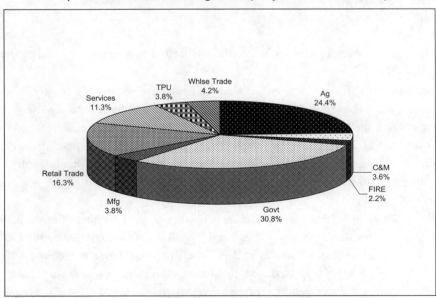

Notes: C&M = construction and mining; Mfg = manufacturing; TPU = transportation and public utilities; and FIRE = finance, insurance, and real estate. Figures may not add up to 100 percent due to rounding.

SOURCE: EDD (2001).

Figure 2. Projections of Nonfarm Industry Employment,
Imperial County, 1997–2004

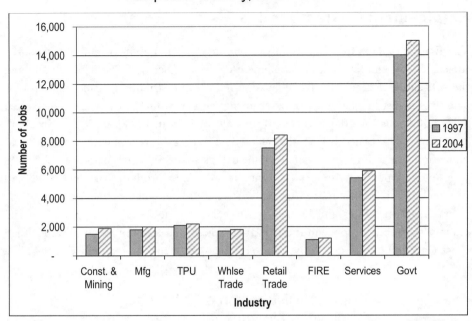

Notes: Mfg = manufacturing; TPU = transportation and public utilities; and FIRE = finance, insurance, and real estate.
SOURCE: EDD (2000b).

slightly higher concentrations, although their labor markets are much smaller than Imperial County's.

The retail trade industry, which includes general merchandise stores, food stores, and restaurants, accounted for 8,200 jobs, or 16.3 percent of all payroll jobs. The services industry, which includes hotels, business services, and health services, accounted for 5,700 jobs, or 11.3 percent of all employment in the county. The remaining 17.2 percent of the jobs was divided among construction and mining; manufacturing; transportation and public utilities; wholesale trade; and finance, insurance, and real estate (EDD 2001).

Imperial County's labor market is characterized principally by small firms. This is consistent with many California counties and with Mexicali. According to the EDD (2000a), 3,072 private-sector firms existed in Imperial County in the second quarter of 1999.[2] Of these, 2,839, or 92.4 percent, had between one and 30 employees. Table 2 illustrates that, while the majority of employers fall into this 1–30 size category, collectively they represent only 33.0 percent of all private-sector employment. Two-thirds of all private-sector employees find work in firms that have more than thirty employees. However, these findings vary among the major industry divisions. For instance, in 1999,

Table 2. Firm Size by Industry Division, Private Sector, Imperial County, 1995 and 1999

	1995 Quarter 2			1999 Quarter 2		
	No. Firms	No. Emp	Total Qtrly Payroll	No. Firms	No. Emp	Total Qtrly Payroll
Agriculture						
1–30	344	2,873	15,489,914	316	2,778	16,527,788
31–100	40	2,109	9,350,616	38	1,824	10,721,735
101–300	9	1,684	3,905,241	19	3,412	10,733,498
301+	14	7,804	13,715,406	14	9,944	13,857,494
Mining/Construction						
1–30	119	806	4,006,589	109	756	4,892,682
31–100	15	693	4,609,205	9	405	2,234,165
101–300	*	*	*	*	*	*
Manufacturing						
1–30	46	434	2,226,766	45	366	2,104,215
31–100	8	387	2,394,794	15	816	5,636,900
101–300	3	520	3,567,863	*	*	*
301+	*	*	*	*	*	*
Transportation & Public Utilities						
1–30	144	1,082	5,743,210	148	897	5,349,859
31–100	12	549	3,671,382	19	784	4,635,033
101–300	*	*	*	*	*	*
Wholesale Trade						
1–30	194	1,153	7,267,019	169	1,090	7,988,338
31–100	15	627	4,114,795	16	766	5,812,110
Retail Trade						
1–30	461	2,709	8,077,020	426	2,856	9,877,311
31–100	45	2,398	8,765,595	45	2,374	9,754,582
101–300	12	1,813	6,359,765	13	2,117	8,989,477
301+	*	*	*	*	*	*
Finance, Insurance & Real Estate						
1–30	139	583	2,948,422	135	645	3,121,119
31–100	7	383	1,823,002	4	167	844,070
101–300	*	*	*	*	*	*
Services						
1–30	1,405	3,752	16,283,879	1,491	4,142	19,266,877
31–100	21	867	3,378,850	26	1,342	6,005,641
101–300	9	1,331	6,572,841	7	1,316	7,024,285
Total, Private Sector						
Total	3,067	37,124	144,141,611	3,072	40,901	169,729,780
1–30	2,852	13,392	62,042,819	2,839	13,530	69,128,189
31–100	163	8,805	38,108,239	172	8,478	45,053,705
101–300	33–35	5,766	25,220,719	44	7,638	33,505,744
301+	14–17	9,161	18,769,834	17	11,255	22,042,142

*Indicates supressed data. Size class 1–30 = number of firms with 1 to 30 employees; 31–100 = number of firms with 31 to 100 employees; 101–300 = number of firms with 101 to 300 employees; 301+ = number of firms with more than 301 employees.
SOURCE: EDD (2000a).

of all the firms in the services industry, 97.8 percent had between one and 30 employees and these firms employed 60.9 percent of all the employees in that industry.

The 1995 data, also shown in Table 2, present a similar picture. Between 1995 and 1999, the total number of private-sector firms increased only slightly, from 3,067 to 3,072. The distribution of the employer size remained fairly constant over both years.

Often, small firms do not have the resources to offer formal training to their employees. Therefore, one implication of the concentration of small firms in the labor market is that the workforce development and training organizations need to coordinate closely with employers to create the right mix of training programs that will meet their needs.

Another characteristic of the Imperial County labor market is the role of border crossers from Mexicali. According to a 1998 survey of border crossers, approximately 2.9 million crossings occurred at the three ports of entry from Mexico to Imperial County during the month of March 1998. The study estimated that 22 percent of all the crossings were to work in the United States. Like many border cities, Mexicali and Imperial County have a history of a cross-border labor force. The study estimated that, while Mexicali border crossers work in many industries in Imperial County, they are concentrated in the agricultural industry where approximately 88 percent of the workers are Mexicali residents (San Diego Dialogue and Centro de Estudios Económicos 1998). These data confirm the important role that commuters from Mexicali play in the Imperial County workforce.

Industry Employment Trends and Outlook

As shown in Tables 3 and 4, industry employment in Imperial County expanded from 44,900 jobs in 1990 to 50,400 jobs in 2000. This represents an expansion of 5,500 jobs, or 12.2 percent. The industry divisions that added the most jobs during this period were government, retail trade, and transportation and public utilities. Government employment increased by 6,000 jobs, or 63.2 percent, between 1990 and 2000. At the local government level, growth in local public education fueled job expansion; at the state level, the expansion of Calipatria State Prison in 1992 and the opening of Centinela State Prison in 1993 fueled this growth. The next largest increase occurred in the retail trade industry division. This industry—which expanded by 1,600 jobs or 24.2 percent—continues to benefit from Mexicali residents who cross the border to shop in Imperial County. Transportation and public utilities have benefited from increased trade between the United States and Mexico, and have thus added 800 jobs, or 72.7 percent. Other industry divisions to gain jobs over the time period included manufacturing (up 300 jobs); finance, insurance, and real estate (up 200 jobs); and services (up 100 jobs).

Three industries recorded fewer jobs in 2000 than in 1990. The largest decline occurred in agriculture. This industry fell by 2,700 jobs between 1990 and 2000. The

Table 3. Imperial County Average Annual Employment by Major Industry Division, 1990–2000

Title	1990	1991	1992	1993	1994	1995	1996	1997	1998	1999	2000	1990–2000 Emp Change	1990–2000 % Change
Total, All Industries	44,900	44,600	44,100	46,200	48,400	48,500	47,900	48,800	49,700	51,000	50,400	5,500	12.2
Agriculture	15,000	13,800	12,000	12,700	13,800	14,500	13,800	13,900	14,300	14,400	12,300	-2,700	-18.0
Total, Nonfarm	29,900	30,700	32,200	33,400	34,700	34,200	34,200	35,100	35,400	36,600	38,100	8,200	27.4
Construction & Mining	2,400	2,500	2,200	2,000	1,800	1,700	1,600	1,500	1,400	1,400	1,800	-600	-25.0
Manufacturing	1,600	1,700	1,700	1,700	1,900	1,800	1,700	1,800	1,700	1,800	1,900	300	18.8
Transportation & Public Utilities	1,100	1,000	1,400	1,600	1,600	1,900	2,100	2,100	2,000	1,900	1,900	800	72.7
Wholesale Trade	2,200	2,300	1,900	1,800	1,800	1,700	1,700	1,700	1,700	1,900	2,100	-100	-4.5
Retail Trade	6,600	6,700	7,500	7,900	8,100	7,500	7,300	7,500	7,700	7,900	8,200	1,600	24.2
Finance, Insurance & Real Estate	900	900	1,000	1,100	1,200	1,200	1,100	1,100	1,100	1,200	1,100	200	22.2
Services	5,600	6,500	5,700	5,600	5,500	5,100	5,200	5,400	5,500	5,800	5,700	100	1.8
Government	9,500	9,100	10,800	11,700	12,800	13,300	13,500	14,000	14,400	14,800	15,500	6,000	63.2

Note: Employment Development Department's projections of employment exclude the agricultural industry.

SOURCES: EDD (2000b, 2001). Benchmark March 2000.

industry follows a seasonal pattern of higher employment during the winter months followed by lower employment during the hot summer months. This pattern is exactly opposite seasonal agriculture patterns elsewhere in the state. Employment in the agricultural industry fluctuates annually due in part to external factors such as commodity prices and weather or pest-related conditions. Other industries that declined over the 10-year period were construction and mining (down 600 jobs) and wholesale trade (down 100 jobs) (EDD 2001).

According to the EDD (2000b), the Imperial County labor market should expand from 34,900 jobs in 1997 to 38,600 jobs in 2004, representing an increase of 3,700 jobs, or 10.6 percent. About one-third of the growth should occur in the government industry, with the remaining balance scattered among the other industries.

Construction and mining are expected to grow by 400 jobs, or 26.7 percent, over the 1997–2004 projection period. Employment in construction and mining peaked in 1991 with 2,500 jobs, but has slowed throughout most of the 1990s. Employment picked up significantly in 2000 and should continue to expand as economic conditions improve and the demand for residential housing continues.

Employment in manufacturing is projected to increase by 200 jobs, or 11.1 percent, over the projection period. This industry represents 3.8 percent of all Imperial County jobs. Manufacturing employment peaked in 1994 with 1,900 jobs and then dropped slightly in subsequent years. Its 2000 employment level is back up to the 1994 peak. Improved economic conditions and economic incentives, such as the manufacturing enhancement areas in Brawley and Calexico, should help boost employment in this industry.

Table 4. Imperial County Employment Outlook, 1997–2004

	1997	2004	Emp Change	% Change
Agriculture	*	*	*	*
Total, Nonfarm	34,900	38,600	3,700	10.6
Construction & Mining	1,500	1,900	400	26.7
Manufacturing	1,800	2,000	200	11.1
Transportation & Public Utilities	2,100	2,200	100	4.8
Wholesale Trade	1,700	1,800	100	5.9
Retail Trade	7,500	8,400	900	12.0
Finance, Insurance & Real Estate	1,100	1,200	100	9.1
Services	5,400	5,900	500	9.3
Government	14,000	15,100	1,100	7.9

*EDD's projections of employment exclude the agricultural industry.
SOURCE: EDD (2000b, 2001).

Transportation and public utilities are expected to increase by 100 jobs, or 4.8 percent, between 1997 and 2004. This industry experienced steady annual increases in payroll employment until 1997 and then declined slightly, primarily in the communications and public utilities categories. It is expected to expand over the projection period, especially in the warehousing and transportation arena as the region benefits from increased trade along the border.

Wholesale trade and retail trade are expected to grow by 2004 by 100 and 900 jobs, respectively. Wholesale trade had experienced relatively flat growth between 1995 and 1998, but increased in 1999 and 2000. The projection calls for 5.9 percent growth between 1997 and 2004. Retail trade is the second largest nonfarm industry in Imperial County. It is expected to grow by 12.0 percent over the projection period. This industry peaked in 1994 with 8,100 jobs and then fell after the Mexican peso devaluated and goods became more expensive for Mexicali Valley residents who shop in Imperial County. It has regained some of its strength in recent years.

Finance, insurance, and real estate is not expected to grow measurably over the projection period, advancing by 100 jobs, or 9.1 percent. This industry showed steady employment gains since 1990, but has leveled out in recent years.

Services industry payrolls should grow by 500 jobs, or 9.3 percent, over the projection period. This industry peaked in 1991 and then fell during the subsequent economic slowdown. It has shown steady improvement since 1995 and, as the population of Imperial County continues to grow, demand for more services will lead to an expansion of firms in the industry. Job growth is expected to spread fairly evenly over all of the services subcategories.

Government industry employment is projected to grow by 1,100 jobs, or 7.9 percent, during the seven-year projection period. This industry, which is the largest in the county, expanded its payrolls by 6,000 jobs between 1990 and 2000, mostly due to the hiring in local education and the completion of two state correctional facilities.

By 2002, Imperial County had already realized most of the 2004 projected job growth. This was due to job growth in the late 1990s that was much faster than the EDD estimates indicated.

Occupational Employment Trends and Outlook

In addition to producing employment estimates by industry, the EDD also produces employment estimates by occupation. The previous section described the distribution of the projected 3,700 new jobs by industry. This section examines the distribution by occupation (EDD 2000c).

Figure 3 displays the distribution of occupational employment in Imperial County by type of work (data are estimated for 1997 and exclude the agricultural industry). As shown, the largest group is the professional, paraprofessional, and

Figure 3. Distribution of Nonfarm Employment by
Type of Work, Imperial County, 1997 (Employment = 34,900)

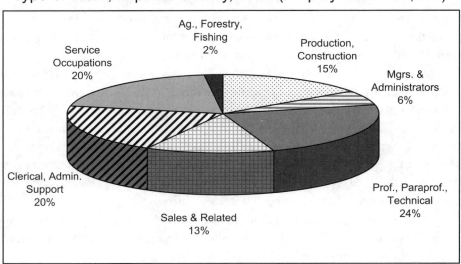

Note: Figures may not add up to 100 percent due to rounding.
SOURCE: EDD (2000c).

technical occupational category, which comprises 23.3 percent of all jobs in the
county. The largest occupations in this group are teachers and registered nurses. The
EDD projects this occupational group will add the greatest number of new jobs
between 1997 and 2004 (870 new jobs).

The next largest occupational groups are the production and construction
occupations and the service occupations categories, with 20.3 percent and 19.7
percent of the jobs, respectively. The production group includes a variety of
construction occupations, as well as maintenance repairers, general utility, automotive
mechanics, truck drivers, and miscellaneous laborers. It is expected to grow by 830
jobs between 1997 and 2004. The services occupational group includes correctional
officers, janitors, waiters and waitresses, cooks, and other food preparation workers.
It is expected to expand by 690 new jobs over the projection period.

Approximately 15.4 percent of all jobs in Imperial County are in the clerical and
administrative support group. The EDD expects this occupational group to expand by
340 new jobs by 2004. Approximately 13.4 percent of total nonfarm employment is
classified in the sales group and 5.9 percent in the managerial and administrative
group. These groups should expand by 720 and 180 jobs, respectively.

The smallest occupational group is the agricultural, forestry, and fishing group,
representing 1.9 percent of the jobs. This grouping appears to be much smaller than
one would think. The reason for this is that the EDD does not produce estimates of

Figure 4. Distribution of Nonfarm Employment by
Education and Training Category, Imperial County, 1997
(Employment = 34,900)

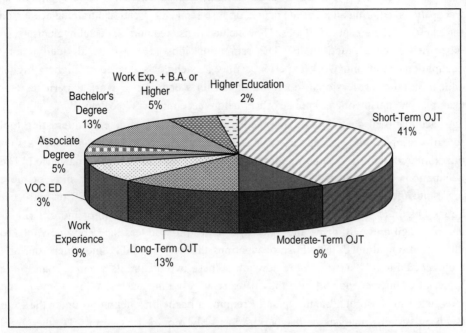

SOURCE: Author's analysis based on EDD's Occupational Employment Projections (1997–2004).

occupational employment for the agricultural industry. Therefore, this occupational group only includes occupations such as landscaper and conservation workers that are found in nonfarm industries. It is expected to add 70 new jobs between 1997 and 2004.

Another way to view occupational employment is to distribute it by education and training. As shown in Figure 4, the vast majority of occupations found in Imperial County require short-term on-the-job training (OJT) to enter the career field. These are jobs that typically take one month or less to learn. They include waiters and waitresses, food servers, truck drivers, general office clerks, sales persons, and cashiers. The occupations in this group accounted for 14,260 jobs, or 40.9 percent, of nonfarm employment in Imperial County in 1997.

The next largest group contains those occupations that usually require a bachelor's degree, such as teachers and general managers. Employment in this group accounted for 4,550 jobs, or 13.0 percent of total nonfarm employment. Occupations that usually require long-term OJT training accounted for 4,460, or 12.8 percent of employment, and those requiring moderate-term OJT accounted for 3,150, or 9.0 percent. The long-term OJT category includes occupations that usually require more than twelve months of OJT or combined work experience and formal classroom instruction, such as apprenticeships and employer-sponsored trainings. Occupations in this category include correctional officers and firefighters. Workers in occupations that typically require moderate-term OJT develop skills they need in less than twelve months of combined on-the-job experience and informal training. They include sales, clerical, and production-related occupations. Occupations requiring an associate degree or postsecondary vocational training accounted for 2,860, or 8.2 percent, of all jobs. They include registered nurses, dental hygienists, and other health care practitioners. The remaining jobs (16.1%) are divided among occupations requiring work experience plus a bachelor's degree or higher; higher education (first professional, doctoral, or master's degree); or work experience (for example, one must work as a police officer before becoming a police detective).

Occupational data can be combined with wage data to create an interesting tool for allocating training resources or making career decisions. Table 5 displays four quadrants containing occupational data from the 1997–2004 projection period. The occupations are arranged by new job growth (less than sixty jobs or sixty or more jobs) and median wage category (less than $10.00 per hour or $10.00 or more per hour). Quadrant 1 lists those occupations that typically pay $10.00 or more per hour and although they will grow, they are expected to provide less than sixty new jobs to the region. Quadrant 2 lists those occupations that pay $10.00 or more per hour and are expected to add sixty or more new jobs. These two quadrants are important to the Imperial County economy since they offer relatively high wages. While some of the jobs listed in those quadrants typically require a bachelor's degree to enter the field (such as systems analysts or teachers), most only require long-term OJT; therefore, they are attainable for residents who do not hold a four-year degree.

Quadrant 3 lists those occupations that pay less than $10.00 per hour and are expected to add fewer than sixty new jobs. Quadrant 4 lists those occupations that pay less than $10.00/hour and are expected to add 60 or more new jobs. Many of the jobs listed in these quadrants require short-term OJT to enter the field; however, applicants still need a good command of the English language, customer service skills, and good work ethics.

Conclusion

This document has analyzed employment trends in Imperial County, including population, civilian labor force, industry, and occupational employment. In 2000, Imperial County's population was 142,361 and its civilian labor force totaled 58,400. Its unemployment rate averaged 26.3 percent—the highest of all 58 California counties. Approximately 50,400 payroll jobs existed in the county and its two largest industries were government and agriculture. The Imperial County labor market is comprised of many small firms. In 1999, of all private-sector firms, 92.4 percent had 30 or fewer employees. Many of the occupations that exist in the labor market do not require a bachelor's degree. In fact, about two-thirds of the occupations in the county

Table 5. Analysis of 1997–2004 Occupational Projections for Imperial County by Job Growth and Wage Category

		NEW JOB GROWTH < 60 JOBS		NEW JOB GROWTH = or > 60 JOBS
	QUAD 1:		**QUAD 2:**	
$10.00/HR OR MORE	79999	Ag, Forestry, Fishing–Nec	87102	Carpenters
	85302	Automotive Mechanics	63017	Correctional Officers, Jailers
	25104	Computer Support Specialists	19005	General Managers, Top Executives
	87311	Concrete and Terrazzo Finishers	79041	Laborers, Landscaping/Groundskeeping
	15017	Construction Managers	85132	Maint Repairers, General Utility
	63008	Firefighters	39999	Other Prof., Paraprof, Technical
	87502	Plumbers, Pipefitters, Steamfitters	63014	Police Patrol Officers
	32502	Registered Nurses	31308	Teachers–Secondary School
	49008	Sales Reps, Non-Scientific–Excl Retail	31311	Teachers–Special Education
	49005	Sales Reps, Scientific–Excl Retail	97102	Truck Drivers, Heavy
	25102	Systems Analysts–Elec Data Proc		
	31314	Teachers–Voc Ed and Training		
	95002	Water Treatment Plant Operators		
	QUAD 3:		**QUAD 4:**	
LESS THAN $10.00/HR	65041	Combined Food Prep and Service	49023	Cashiers
	65026	Cooks–Restaurant	55347	General Office Clerks
	49017	Counter and Rental Clerks	67005	Janitors, Cleaners–Except Maids
	65017	Counter Attendants–Food	98999	Misc Helpers, Laborers–Hand, Nec
	65038	Food Preparation Workers	49011	Salespersons, Retail
	98902	Hand Packers and Packagers	31521	Teacher Aides, Paraprofessional
	27308	Human Services Workers		
	31321	Instructors and Coaches–Sports		
	66005	Medical Assistants		
	66008	Nurse Aides, Orderlies & Attendants		
	27311	Recreation Workers		
	49999	Sales and Related Workers, Nec		
	49014	Salespersons–Parts		
	58023	Stock Clerks–Stockroom, Warehouse		
	53905	Teacher Aides & Educ Assts, Clerical		
	31505	Technical Assistants–Library		
	53102	Tellers		
	58028	Traffic, Shipping, Receiving Clerks		
	97105	Truck Drivers, Light		
	65008	Waiters and Waitresses		

Note: Only those occupations projected to grow by 20 or more new jobs during projection period are included in the analysis. Excludes the additional job openings that occur due to replacement. Nec = Not elsewhere classified.

SOURCE: Author's analysis based on EDD's Occupational Employment Statistics Employment and Wages by Occupation, 1997, and Occupational Employment Projections, 1997–2004.

require only on-the-job training to enter the field. Commuters from Mexicali play an important role in the Imperial County economy. Many cross into the United States to shop, helping to boost retail sales, while others cross to visit family and friends or to work in the Imperial Valley. While the majority of Mexicali residents who work in Imperial County are employed in the agricultural industry, many are hired in other industries and some hold technical and professional positions. This cross-border workforce illustrates an important linkage between the two regions.

Although the number of jobs in Imperial County is expected to increase over the next few years, the quality of the workforce is a challenge for the community. The 2000 Census revealed that 41.0 percent of the population age 25 and older does not have a high school diploma. Although this is an improvement over the 1990 Census estimate of 46.8 percent, this characteristic influences the quality of the labor force and could create some challenges for attracting high paying, high skilled jobs to the county (U.S. Census Bureau 1990, 2000). Local officials and economic and workforce developers need to continue exploring methods to improve the workforce skills while at the same time expand the number of well-paying jobs in the community. Since Imperial County is home to many small employers who may not have the resources to conduct their own formal training, workforce development agencies need to coordinate closely with these employers to create a mix of training programs that will meet employers' needs. Close coordination, information sharing, and an increased understanding of the economy and workforce will help foster successful economic and workforce development efforts.

Endnotes

1. Employment estimates are derived from combining unemployment insurance tax records filed by employers and a monthly survey of firms. Industry employment does not include the self-employed, unpaid family workers, household domestic workers, or workers on strike.

2. The EDD typically uses third-quarter data to analyze size of firm characteristics because, for many counties, it is a time with little seasonal employment fluctuations. However, in Imperial County, the third quarter represents a seasonally low employment time for agriculture. Second-quarter data was used in this analysis because it represents a truer picture of employment levels in the county.

3. The EDD's Labor Market Information Division (LMID) has developed industrial and occupational employment projections since the 1970s. The projections are for a seven-year time period and are revised every two years to incorporate economic changes that occur in the counties and the state. The current projections cover the 1997–2004 period and deal solely with nonfarm industries. The industry projections in this report are based on the following assumptions: (1) the institutional framework of the U.S. economy will not change radically; (2) recent technological and scientific trends will continue; (3) the long-term employment patterns will continue in most industries; (4) federal, state, and local government agencies will continue to operate under budgetary constraints; (5) no major events will occur that will significantly alter the industrial structure of the economy, the occupational staffing patterns, or the rate of long-term growth; (6) population growth rates and age distributions will not differ significantly from

Department of Finance projections presently available; and (7) attitudes toward work, education, income, and leisure will not change significantly. The detailed methodology is available on the LMID web page at http://www.calmis.ca.gov.

4. This occupational analysis focuses on new jobs created by industry growth and does not discuss job openings resulting from the need to replace workers. That is, not all job openings depend on new growth. Some job openings result from the need to replace workers who enter other occupations, retire, or leave the labor market for other reasons. The detailed data on job openings by industry and occupation are not presented in this report; however, they are available on the EDD's LMID web page at http://www.calmis.ca.gov.

References

Almaraz, Araceli. 2004. "Economic Bases for Cross-Border Planning at the Imperial-Mexicali Border." In *Imperial-Mexicali Valleys:Development and Environment of the United States-Mexican Border Region*. San Diego: San Diego State University Press.

Arizona Department of Economic Security. 2001. "Census 2000 Population by Sex, by Age by County." (Cited 29 June). http://www.de.state.az.us/links/economic/webpage/page14.html.

Department of Finance. 2001. "Revised Historical City, County and State Population Estimates, 1991–2000, with 1990 and 2000 Census Counts." (Cited 1 June 2002). http://www.dof.ca.gov/HTML/DEMOGRAP/HistE-4.htm.

Employment Development Department (EDD). 2000a. "Size of Firm Data for Imperial County." Sacramento: Employment Development Department. Unpublished.

Employment Development Department (EDD). 2000b. "Employment Projections by Industry, 1997–2004." (Cited 2 December). http://www.calmis.ca.gov/htmlfile/subject/indtable.htm.

Employment Development Department (EDD). 2000c. "Occupational Employment Projections, 1997–2004." (Cited 2 December). http://www.calmis.ca.gov/htmlfile/subject/occproj.htm.

Employment Development Department (EDD). 2000d. "Occupational Employment Statistics (OES) Employment and Wages by Occupation, 1997." (Cited 2 December). http://www.calmis.ca.gov/file/occup$/oes$.htm.

Employment Development Department (EDD). 2001. "Labor Force and Industry Employment." (Cited 2 June 2002). http://www.calmis.ca.gov/htmlfile/subject/indtable.htm.

San Diego Dialogue and Centro de Estudios Económicos del Sector Empresarial de Mexicali, A.C. 1998. "Survey of Border Crossers: Imperial/Mexicali Valleys." Report presented to the Imperial County Board of Supervisors, 23 June.

U.S. Census Bureau. 1990. "1990 Summary File 3, Social Characteristics 1990." (Cited 4 June 2002). http://factfinder.census.gov/servlet/BasicFactsServlet.

U.S. Census Bureau. 2000. "Census 2000 Demographic Profiles." (Cited 4 June 2002). http://factfinder.census.gov/servlet/BasicFactsServlet.

12

Economic Bases for Cross-Border Planning at the Imperial-Mexicali Border

Araceli Almaraz Alvarado*

Abstract

This essay analyzes employment trends in Mexicali, including its population, civilian labor force, local industry, and occupational employment. It also includes central aspects of industrial growth in Mexicali and its effects on the local economy. The main focus of the essay is the maquiladora *(assembly) sector and its electronics subdivision in particular. Differences between incomes earned by* maquiladora *workers in Mexicali and workers in the Imperial Valley are also examined. Finally, some thoughts are provided on the challenges that Mexicali faces in the effort to achieve regional development.*

Introduction[1]

The reorganization of production in Mexicali began in the 1970s when regional economic activity changed radically. Employment in the agricultural sector declined, while activity in the commercial, service, and industrial sectors increased. Accelerated industrial growth in Mexicali is a result of the process of globalization and the implementation of the North American Free Trade Agreement (NAFTA) in 1994.

Changes in population growth and structure of the municipal economy have also taken place. Likewise, the trend toward specialization in electronics can be noted. In addition, changes in job distribution are accentuated with growing diversification in the size of plants in each sector. For example, while the commercial and service sectors tend to be small- and medium-sized enterprises, large companies are predominant in

---

Almaraz Alvarado is Researcher at El Colegio de la Frontera Norte in Mexicali.

industry. Mexicali's economic history over the last decade should be analyzed with the participation of the *maquiladora* industry and its impacts in mind because it represents a dynamic that will surely be maintained over the following decades.

These changes have made Mexicali the second center for investment in Baja California and have reduced unemployment rates. Less obvious indicators, such as levels and types of occupations and their corresponding real salaries, however, must also be analyzed.

A History of Economic Activity in Mexicali and Changes in Population

The primacy of agricultural activity in Mexicali is demonstrated by the growth of its rural population prior to the 1970s that resulted from the rise in cotton production in the Mexicali Valley.[2] During the 1980s and 1990s, however, the municipality's urban population became predominant. Currently, more than 80 percent of the municipal population is concentrated in the urban area.

Toward the end of the 1990s, urban growth continued to increase, while the rural population declined to 13.4 percent of the municipality. Population growth rates were between 2 and 4 percent over this period. Over the last thirty years, several notable characteristics of Mexicali's population are apparent. In 1950, Mexicali exceeded 100,000 inhabitants. Over the following decade, Mexicali almost tripled its

Figure 1. Population Growth in the Municipality of Mexicali, 1930–2000

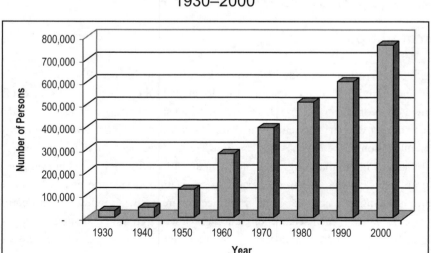

SOURCES: Dirección General de Estadística (1930, 1940, 1950, 1960, 1970); Secretaría de Programación y Presupuesto and INEGI (1980); INEGI (1990, 2000).

population, reaching 281,000 inhabitants in1960. By 2000, this number reached 750,000 (see Figure 1).

Using these growth figures and the expansion of economic activity as a basis, it is projected that by 2005, the population of the City of Mexicali will reach more

Figure 2. Population Growth Projections for the City of Mexicali, 2001–2005

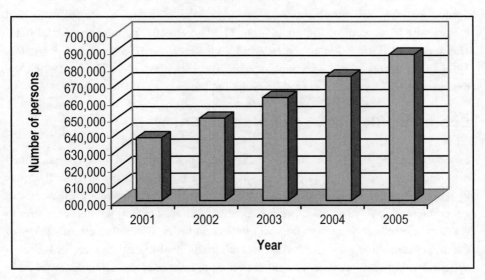

SOURCE: Based on INEGI (2000).

Table 1. Population of Mexicali, 1990–2000

Year	Population
1990	601,938
1991	612,171
1992	622,578
1993	633,162
1994	143,925
1995	654,872
1996	671,899
1997	689,368
1998	707,292
1999	725,681
2000	764,069

SOURCE: Based on INEGI (1990, 2000).

than 700,000 inhabitants and the municipality could surpass 830,000 (see Figure 2 and Table 1).

Regarding age structure, 50 percent of the population was 15 to 64 years old in the 1960s and 1970s. In 1980, this figure rose to 56 percent. Those inhabitants 0 to 14 years old decreased from 45 percent to 41 percent from 1960 to 1980. Those 64 years and older remained stable (2–3%) in the same period.

A substantial increase in the 16- to 64-year range has been observed over the last decade. In 1990, this group was 60.3 percent of the total population and in 1995 it was almost 63 percent of the population. The share of the population 65 and older also increased during this period, reaching 3.8 percent in 1990 and 4.3 percent in 1995. The group of those younger than 14 decreased slightly; in 1990 they represented 33.7 percent of the total population, but only 32.7 percent in 1995.

Economically Active Population (EAP)[3]

Since the second half of the 1970s, localities in northern Mexico have maintained high industrial growth. This dynamic process resulted from the National Border Program (Programa Nacional Fronterizo–PRONAF) implemented by the Mexican government in 1961. The main purpose of PRONAF was to link the border region to the Mexican economy through the *maquiladora* industry. Before the establishment of the *maquiladora* industry, the border region's traditional industries were linked with agriculture, but these experiences did not promote investment and innovation in other industrial areas. The main cities that benefited from the PRONAF program were Nogales, Tijuana, Ciudad Juárez, Matamoros, and Piedras Negras. About 20 percent of the budget was invested in Nogales alone. Although PRONAF's focus was to improve the manufacturing activities, there were other short-term goals to relieve some of the unemployment caused by the end of the Bracero Program in 1964.

The principal advantages of the northern border region for investments derived from tariff rates, geographic location, quantity and quality of the available labor force, and low costs in transportation and communication infrastructure. This provided for easy access to skilled employees, such as technicians, in the United States.

These opportunities were primarily exploited by American investors who also established part of their companies on the U.S. side of the border. New capital also followed quickly from Asia, particularly from Japan, South Korea, and Taiwan. The investments continued to grow throughout the 1980s and 1990s with the approval of the General Agreement on Tariffs and Trade (GATT) in 1986 and the North American Free Trade Agreement (NAFTA) in 1994. Both of these agreements stimulated new capital sources through direct foreign investment.

The most important industry sectors in the border region have been electronics, textiles, and automotive. The border cities with the greatest concentration of *maquiladoras* in the number of employees and plants are Tijuana, Ciudad Juárez, Nogales, and Mexicali (INEGI 2000).

Since the 1980s, Mexicali's productive structure has experienced unprecedented growth in industrial activity, while primary activities, commerce, hotels, and restaurants have also continued to have a notable presence (especially in the services sector). Changes derived from the reorganization of production toward industry are seen not only in labor statistics, but also in the type of establishments that are predominant, especially the electronics industry, and a more intense use of labor.

In 1950, Mexicali's EAP was concentrated in the primary sector, which employed 61.10 percent of the population, while the industrial sector was only 11 percent. In 1980, agricultural, commercial, and industrial activities employed an estimated 13.36 percent, 11.30 percent, and 12.24 percent of the population, respectively. From 1990 to 1995, manufacturing experienced its greatest growth (7.15%) in comparison to previous decades. The primary sector also grew strong by 4.5 percent and commerce grew by 3 percent.

Mexicali's productive framework in the 1980s was not shaped only by industry's considerable role. During this decade, 38 percent of the population was concentrated in the services sector, only 27.1 percent in industry, 18.6 percent in agriculture, and 15.9 percent in commerce.

In the second half of the 1990s, the number of workers employed by primary activities diminished rapidly, dropping to only 10 percent. Meanwhile, the industrial,

Figure 3. Insured Workers in Mexicali, 1990–2000*

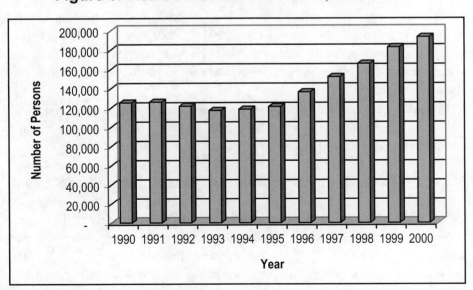

*The year 2000 is only through September.
SOURCE: Based on IMSS.

Figure 4. Projections of Insured Workers in Mexicali, 2001–2005

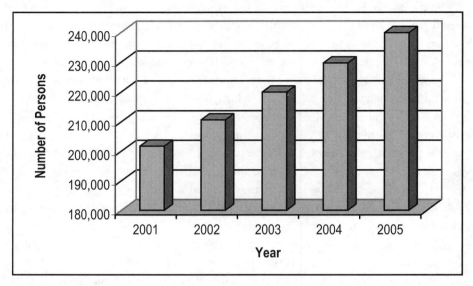

SOURCE: Based on IMSS.

commercial, and services sectors collectively employed 83 percent of the population. If this continues, growth trends forecast a dominant urban tertiary sector with an industrial manufacturing center based heavily on the *maquiladora* industry.

The Mexican Institute for Social Security (Instituto Mexicano del Seguro Social–IMSS) notes that for the first half of 1999, the Mexicali delegation of IMSS registered 43.6 percent of affiliated workers in the industrial sector, followed by 14.4 percent in commerce, and 12.2 percent in services. Although the number of insured workers dropped slightly in the mid-1990s, this number could reach 240,000 in 2005 (see Figures 3 and 4).[4]

Maquiladoras represent the majority of the manufacturing industry, employing more than 80 percent of the sector's 60,000 workers. The average age range of workers in the *maquiladoras* is between 20 and 26 years of age.[5]

Size of Establishments in Relation to Number of Employees

Increased participation by micro-establishments (1–30 employees) in the primary sector began in the mid-1990s. Small establishments (31–100 employees) were more heavily represented in the commercial and primary sectors, while large establishments (more than 300 employees) were concentrated in the transformation industry and, more specifically, in the *maquiladora* industry, where the average number of employees per company was 326 in 1999 (see Figures 5–8).

Figure 5. Agriculture, Livestock, and Forestry Employment by Company Size in Mexicali, 1995

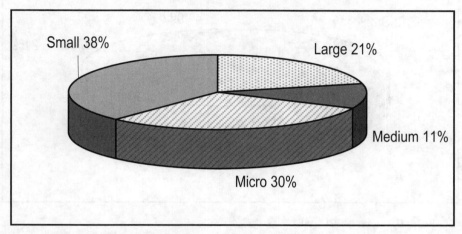

SOURCE: Based on INEGI (1995b).

Figure 6. Transformation Industries Employment by Company Size in Mexicali, 1995

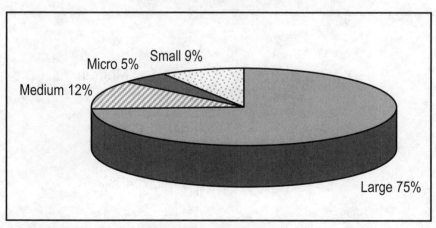

Note: Figures may not add up to 100 percent due to rounding.

SOURCE: Based on INEGI (1995b).

Figure 7. Commerce Employment by
Company Size in Mexicali, 1995

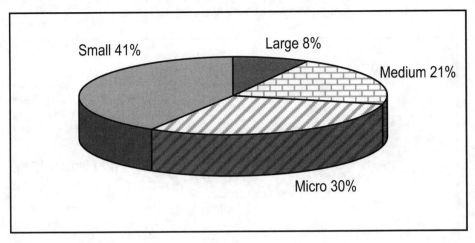

SOURCE: Based on INEGI (1995b).

Figure 8. Communications Employment by
Company Size in Mexicali, 1995

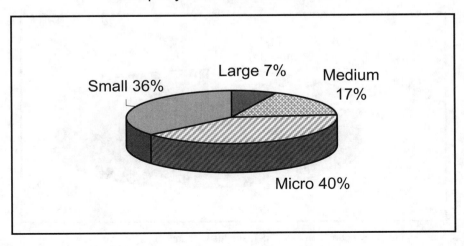

SOURCE: Based on INEGI (1995b).

Figure 9. Employment Growth by Productive Sector in Mexicali, 1995–1999

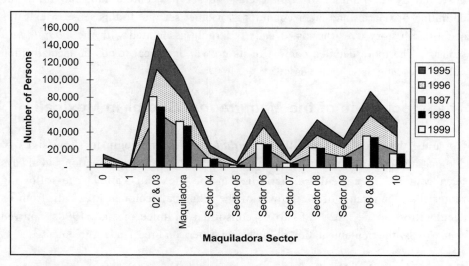

SOURCES: Based on INEGI (1995a); SEDECO (1997–2000).

Figure 10. Employment Projections by Productive Sector in Mexicali, 2000–2004

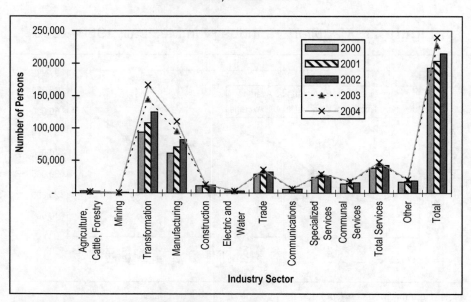

SOURCES: Based on INEGI (1995a); SEDECO (1997–2000).

The data presented demonstrate the feasibility of a considerable increase in industrial establishments over the next few decades (see Figures 9 and 10). This rise will be headed primarily by the *maquiladora* sector, whose local repercussions can be observed by the number of commercial and service centers and, above all, the definition of salaries and labor conditions for other sectors. In this sense, Mexicali's economic history over the last decade is largely associated with the *maquiladora* industry. The more detailed context of its growth and local trends in specialization will be presented later in this essay.

The Importance of the *Maquiladora* Sector in Mexicali

Not until the late 1970s did the *maquiladora* industry begin to show signs of dominating other economic activities in Mexicali.[6] Previously, production had always been centered in agricultural activities in the Mexicali Valley. The following represents a panorama of the growth of the industrial sector in Mexicali, from its acceleration in the late 1980s to its consolidation since the late 1990s, spurred primarily by the implementation of the North American Free Trade Agreement.[7]

The Industrial Boom

In 1980, Mexicali's *maquiladora* sector employed a few more than 7,000 workers in 79 plants. By 1996, the number of employees surpassed 30,000 working in more than 130 plants. In the last trimester of 1998, those numbers had increased to over 50,000

Figure 11. *Maquiladora* Industry in Mexicali, 1980–2000

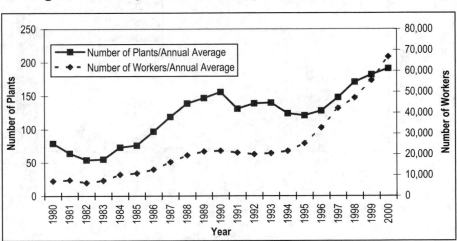

Note: Data for 2000 correspond to the average of the first semester.

SOURCES: Programa Sectorial de Industria (1993); SEDECO (1990–1993).

workers and more than 180 plants. As of 2000, there are more than 185 plants that employ more than 60,000 workers in Mexicali (see Figure 11).[8]

More than 30 percent of capital invested in the *maquiladora* industry originates in the United States,[9] nearly 25 percent comes from Asia (Korea, Japan, and Taiwan), and the remaining 45 percent from either mixed investments or domestic sources. Employment distribution among the different branches of the industry is 46 percent in electronics, 19 percent in metal-mechanics, 11 percent in plastics, 8 percent in textiles, and the remaining 16 percent is distributed among other sectors. More than 30 percent of the companies belong to multinational corporations that specialize in the production of televisions, computers, and their parts (Almaraz 1999a).

Incentives for Growth in the *Maquiladora* Industry

The attraction of *maquiladoras* to the City of Mexicali is primarily associated with its ability to provide certain services locally, the availability of industrial land, the accessibility of labor, and the overall productive environment in the regional and local context.[10] *Maquiladoras* in Mexicali are distributed throughout more than twenty industrial parks. The majority are concentrated in the Colorado Industrial, Las Californias, and PIMSA industrial parks.

In the regional context in terms of investment, Tijuana began to be saturated in the early 1990s. Tijuana also began to run low on space for use by industry and the scarcity of water began to pose a threat. Both of these aspects have favored the location of new *maquiladoras* in Mexicali, making it the second choice for relocation and expansion in Baja California, especially with regard to electronics.[11] In 1999, more than 30 percent of multinational corporate affiliates that specialized in electronics production and that located in the northwest region, chose to locate in Mexicali. The border region as a whole, including Mexicali and Tijuana in Baja California, San Luis Río Colorado in Sonora, and Ciudad Juárez in Chihuahua, houses more than 60 percent of the *maquiladoras* that specialize in electronics in Mexico (see Table 2).

The number of electronics plants that currently operate in Mexicali exceed the 30 establishments that were in operation in 1995. Athough television assembly and parts production remain dominant activities in the electronics sector, much more diversification is evident (Gobierno del Estado de Baja California 1998). The electronics sector employs more than 23,000 workers,[12] or more than 35 percent of employees in the *maquiladora* industry. The average number of workers per plant is 328. A marked concentration in employment is noticeable in seven of the mega-establishments in Mexicali that are dedicated to the production of televisions, computers, and key components.[13]

A comparative advantage for Mexicali is its geographic location in relation to the California market (including San Diego and Los Angeles). However, Mexicali's

Table 2. *Maquiladora* Plants and Percentages by State for
Baja California, Sonora, and Chihuahua, 1989–1998

Year	National	B.C.	%	Mexicali	%	Sonora	%	Chihuahua	%
1989[a]	1,655	730	44.1	ND	ND	144	8.7	343	20.7
1990[a]	1,938	723	37.3	ND	ND	149	7.6	360	18.5
1991[a]	2,031	742	36.8	ND	ND	169	8.3	341	16.9
1992[a]	2,129	802	37.6	ND	ND	173	8.1	357	16.7
1993[a]	2,143	850	39.6	ND	ND	186	8.6	303	14.1
1994[a]	2,064	727	35.2	ND	ND	175	8.4	303	14.6
1995[a]	2,267	781	34.4	ND	ND	186	8.3	347	15.3
1996[a]	2,553	841	32.9	ND	ND	203	7.9	390	15.2
1997[a]	2,867	954	33.2	ND	ND	236	8.2	414	14.4
1998[a]	2,895	974	33.6	68[c]	6	241	8.3	392	13.5
1999[b]	3,166	1101	35.0	70[c]	6	270	8.0	402	13.0

[a]Data from the 1989–1997 period are for the month of December for each year. For 1998, the data are through the month of March.
[b]Data through May 1999 (Delegación de SECOFI-Mexicali).
[c]Data are based on AMMAC directories.

SOURCE: INEGI (1998).

participation in the market does not imply a substantial change in the circulation of commodities from northwestern Mexico to the United States, nor does it imply changes in transportation costs. Another advantage for Mexicali is its urban-industrial environment, which is positioned not only for accepting new capital, but also for expanding existing plants. According to the reports of Mexicali's Industrial Development Commission (Comisión de Desarrollo Industrial–CDI) (2000), the number of plant expansions in 2000 greatly surpassed the number of new investments in Mexicali.[14]

Mexicali differs from other border cities such as Tijuana or Ciudad Juárez in that its population growth has not been as rapid, making its labor market slightly less attractive to investors. The low availability of unskilled labor needed by *maquiladoras* and the considerable increase in the number of people achieving a higher education demonstrate the paradoxes of local economic development in Mexicali. By contrast, concentration and productive specialization in the city have not yet come to include local suppliers and domestic capital.[15] The role of local businesses has been important in the reorganization of production in Mexicali, but major determinants of industrial growth have been guided by measures taken by corporations that operate in the city through their local affiliates. Finally, specialization in the manufacture and assembly of electronics has not affected salary levels for the majority of *maquila* workers.

The impact of foreign capital through the *maquiladoras* on Mexicali has modified Mexicali's concept of economic development. It creates an environment in which industrial growth dominates, but at the same time is framed by the rules of production and global competition. The investment of foreign capital can be attributed to the process of globalization and the strategies of multinational corporations, which still do not reflect local Mexican priorities for the transfer of knowledge or better salaries.

The Industrial Boom in Mexicali and Its Effects on Employment and *Maquiladora* Wages

One of the paradoxes of the accelerated process of industrial growth in Mexicali is that better salaries for workers should come with the reorganization of production. This, in turn, should improve quality of life for the local population. Local development should then be sparked by the multiplier effects that such activities generate. Considering the range of possibilities that "industrial progress" has to offer, urban and social development should become parallel processes, especially since the slowdown of the agricultural sector has already affected the local economic base, as in the case of Mexicali.

The reorganization of production also assumes changes in salaries, the levels and types of jobs available, lifestyle, and consumption levels. The next section of this essay analyzes the impact of this process on the jobs generated by the *maquiladora* industry and also looks at wage levels.

Occupations and Salaries in the *Maquiladora* Industry

An analysis of salary levels and the types of jobs associated with the growth of industry in Mexicali reveals a system of production that has low levels of unemployment (see Figure 12) and most employment in factory positions. A small percentage of the positions is made up of administrators and an even smaller number of managers.

One characteristic that clearly demonstrates the paradox of industrial development based on the *maquiladora* industry is real salary levels earned by the majority of its workers. According to the local State Council of Population (Consejo Estatal de Población–CONEPO) of Baja California, 52.1 percent of the population in Mexicali that worked in a productive sector received two to five national minimum salaries (NMSs) (salarios mínimos nacionales–SMN) in 1999.[16] That totals 2,280–5,700 pesos ($240–$600) per month. Twenty-one percent of the economically active population received more than five NMSs, or more than 5,700 pesos ($600) per month. Another 20.9 percent earned one to two minimum salaries, or 1,140–2,280 pesos ($120–$240) per month, totaling less than 28,500 pesos ($3,000) a year (see Table 3).

This focus on the *maquiladora* industry reveals two important points: (1) workers in this sector earn better wages compared to those in other sectors;[17] and (2) it is difficult to obtain a real value for wages because other aspects of employment must be

Figure 12. Unemployment Rates in Border Cities and Mexicali, 1998–2000

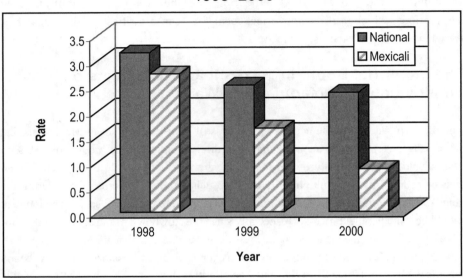

SOURCE: INEGI (1999).

taken into account (such as punctuality, productivity, and so on) and additional benefits are often distributed to *maquiladora* employees, including transportation and food.

An analysis of the relationship between specialization in *maquiladoras* and wage levels reveals that companies that specialize in electronics pay their employees greater wages than other *maquiladoras*. A study of *maquiladora* salaries in June 1999 for 10,452 employees and of more than 70 positions found that 45 percent of the 73 positions received an average of five NMSs. But, these higher paid workers were only 5 percent of all workers in Mexicali. About 32 percent of the 73 positions paid three to five NMSs,[18] representing 13 percent of the workers. The remaining 23 percent of the positions received less than five NMSs, representing 81 percent of the workers.

Table 3. Income Based on National Minimum Salaries (NMSs) in Mexicali, 1999

Percent EAP	Number of NMSs	Yearly Income (in US$)
20.9	1–2	$1,440–2,880
52.1	2–5	$2,880–7,200
21.0	5+	More than $7,200

SOURCE: CONEPO (1999).

To demonstrate the extreme polarity of salaries within the *maquiladoras* according to position, top salaries were given to plant management, which represented less than 1 percent of employees (including managers). These positions include general managers, quality control, materials, production, human resources, transport, customs, superintendents of production, and others. These positions received more than thirty NMSs per day, or 1,140 pesos per day ($3,500 per month/$42,396 per year).[19] On the opposite end of the scale, janitors, assemblers or operators, skilled workers, general assistants, warehouse personnel, industrial electricians, machine and tool operators, and security guards, among others, earned between 1.3 and 2 NMSs, or less than $240 per month, totaling an annual salary of $1,837–$2,826.[20]

Data for those employed by companies that specialize in electronics[21] reveal better wages. Managerial positions, in particular, paid better for this sector. The number of positions with high salaries was also higher.[22] Fifty-three percent of the plants in the study paid more than five and up to 31 NMSs, representing 7 percent of the workers (2% more than the overall average). Twenty-one percent of the plants paid between three and five NMSs, representing 8 percent of the employees. Finally, 26 percent of the plants paid from one to three NMSs, representing 85 percent of the workers.

Wages are generally higher in the *maquiladoras*, especially with large plants that employ more than 250 workers and specialize in electronics. However, this fact is not enough to avoid the paradox of industrial growth in Mexicali where more than 80 percent of workers in each plant make less than $3,500 per year.

This same group of workers barely had an elementary or secondary education; such lack of education contributes to low wages in the *maquiladora* industry. Additionally, it may be argued that low wages also contribute to low levels of knowledge transference; in other words, ability and experience do not reflect a substantial increase in workers' salaries.

For these reasons, the industrialization process in Mexicali, characterized by high levels of specialization and driven by mega-enterprises, has contributed little to the professional development of most of its workers. This is also noted by the very few companies that offer educational opportunities for their employees. The highest level of education attained by workers is vocational training, but their percentage of total employment is minimal. The majority of workers have only a junior high school education.

Impacts of Industrialization on the Imperial Valley

The impacts of Mexicali's industrialization process on Imperial County are not as marked as other sectors, such as commerce, transportation services, or agriculture, and even the cultural atmosphere. Nonetheless, the effects of *maquiladoras* could be greater in the coming years. As such, some of the differences that exist between

Mexicali and the Imperial Valley are presented here, concluding with a comparison of salaries by occupation and using the *maquiladora* plants in Mexicali as a case in point.

Differences in Population and Economic Structure in Mexicali and the Imperial Valley

The relationship between Mexicali and Imperial County is defined by the complementarities of cross-border commerce and the services they are able to offer one another. Specifically, commerce in the City of Calexico is sustained in great part by the consumption patterns of Mexicali's population.

The differences between the populations of Mexicali and the Imperial Valley are significant. Furthermore, current projections for 2004 do not foresee a change in this pattern. The most populated cities in Imperial County are Calexico, Imperial, and El Centro, with 18.6 percent, 15.1 percent, and 26.4 percent of the county's population, respectively. In 2000, the total county population numbered 154,549 inhabitants. By 2004, that number is expected to reach 181,209 (see Figures 13 and 14).

The working population in the Imperial Valley in February 2000 totaled 58,800. Unemployment dropped 3.5 percent compared to the previous year. By sector, agriculture had the greatest economic impact on the county, employing 37.1 percent

Figure 13. Population of Mexicali and the Imperial Valley, 1990–2000

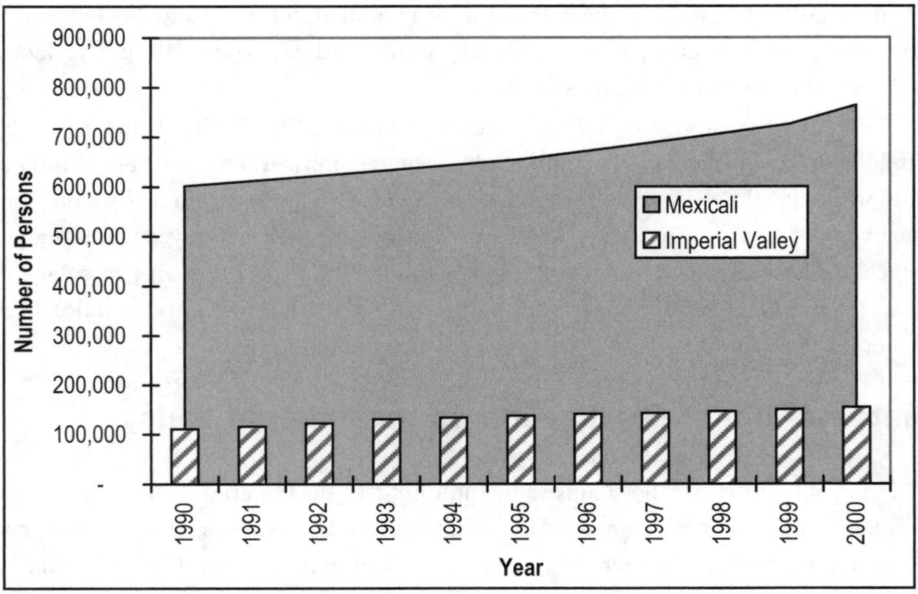

SOURCE: CCBRES (2000b).

of workers. Of the remaining 62.9 percent of workers, 5.8 percent were employed in manufacturing and 57.1 percent were employed in services. Total employees were divided by sector in February 2000 as follows: 21,800 in agriculture; 3,400 in production of goods; and 33,600 in the production of services, of whom more than 50 percent (15,800) provide public services (14,000 in local government and 1,800 in federal government). Thus, there is a great concentration of workers in the agricultural and public service sectors.

It has been observed that industrial growth in Mexicali has not directly affected the Imperial Valley in terms of interfirm relationships. Rather, such relationships have been developed between Mexicali and Tijuana, San Diego, and other cities along the U.S.-Mexican border. These relationships are generated between buyers, between multinational affiliates and their suppliers in northwestern Mexico, or between companies and new subcontractors.

For several years, there has been growing demand in the Imperial Valley for urban services, principally housing, due to pressures from managerial staff in the *maquiladoras*.[23] The relationship that could exist between industry in Mexicali and the Imperial Valley is restrained by the lack of manufacturing activities in Imperial County. Statistics regarding manufacturing in Imperial Valley demonstrate a downturn in the last several years, with a 41.7 percent drop in manufacturing employment from 1990 to 1999 (equivalent to 1,000 employees). Projections for 2004 show minimal growth of only 200 employees. Mexicali, by contrast,

Figure 14. Population Projections for Mexicali and the Imperial Valley, 2001 and 2004

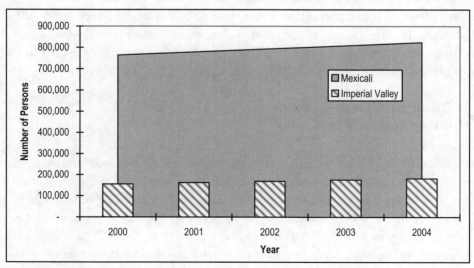

SOURCE: CCBRES (2000b).

Figure 15. Per Capita Yearly Incomes in the Imperial Valley and California, 1995–1998

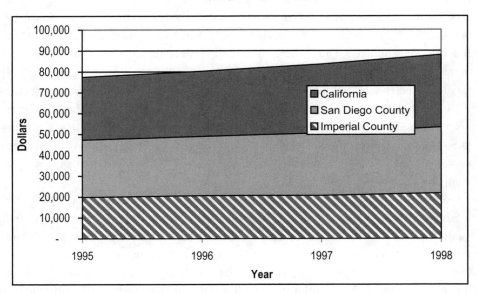

SOURCE: CCBRES (2000b).

demonstrates a sustained increase in manufacturing since the early 1990s, particularly since 1994, and projections forecast continued growth in the coming years.

In summary, Imperial Valley's economic specialization lies in services and agriculture, while that of Mexicali lies in industry, commerce, and specific services. The differences in per capita salaries show notable dissimilarities on either side of the border. In Imperial County, per capita annual income is greater than $20,000, ranking forty-ninth in the United States, even though it is relatively low compared to the average per capita income in California (see Figure 15).

A Comparison of Incomes in Mexicali and the Imperial Valley

One aspect of this analysis that stands out in Mexicali is the evolution of annual income in dollars,[25] which shows an increase in the number of positions that earn between $8,001 and $20,000 per year and a decrease in the number of positions that earn more than $20,000 or less than $8,000 per year. The maximum wage paid per hour in 1997 was $14.10; $10.98 in 1998; $23.10 in 1999; and $26.70 in 2000. The lowest wage paid per hour was $.80 in 1997; $.80 in 1998; $1.00 in 1999; and $1.00 in 2000.

In 1997, in Mexicali, 54 percent of occupations paid less that $8,000 per year. By 2000, this number dropped to 43 percent (see Figure 16). Jobs that are directly related to production and general assistance are found in this category, including operators or assemblers, technicians, assistants, security guards, warehouse personnel, area supervisors, line supervisors, and so on.

Those positions at the $8,000/year salary level that increased by more than 20 percent between 1997 and 2000 were: assistant buyer, assistant engineer, recruitment and training coordinator, area supervisor, quality supervisor, and technical operator of machines and tools. Those positions with annual incomes greater than $20,000 (the average in Imperial County) included all managerial positions such as quality control managers, maintenance, materials, operations, production, human resources, transportation, and customs. However, excluded are buying managers, whose salaries dropped slightly between 1999 and 2000.

Workers who practice a specific trade (such as electricians, welders, or mechanics) earn slightly higher incomes than assemblers or machine operators, but not much more than assistants, including messengers, security guards, or cooks. The salary of an industrial electrician rose from $1.60 per hour in 1997 to $2.10 in 2000, a mechanic's salary rose from $1.80 per hour in 1997 to $2.20 in 2000, and a welder's salary remained at $1.00 per hour over this period. The operator's salary rose 13 percent per hour from 1997 to 2000, but only from $0.80 to $1.10, while that of the skilled worker reached $1.30 per hour in 2000.

Figure 16. Evolution of Annual Income Rankings in Dollars, 1997–2000

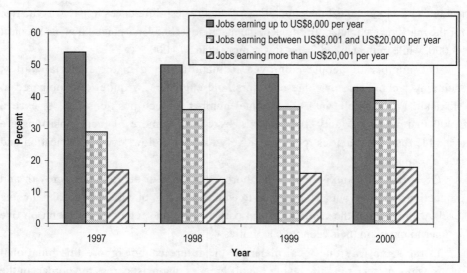

SOURCE: Author's analysis.

The wages received by trade workers and those in assistant positions range from $1.40 to $3.30 per hour, depending on the area of work (the lowest wage corresponds to production assistants and the highest to assistant buyers). Cooks in Mexicali's *maquiladoras* have maintained their hourly wage between $2.10 and $2.20 from 1997 to 2000, while mechanics barely made $2.00 per hour in 2000. Tractor drivers increased their wages from $2.40 per hour in 1997 to $2.70 in 2000, surpassing all trade workers.

In the Imperial Valley, average wage rates ranged from a minimum of $5.50 to a high $53.35 per hour in 1997. Managers of *maquiladora* plants earned an average of $11.14 to $22.30 per hour, with an average annual income of $22,830 to $60,090.

Assistants or apprentices in the Imperial Valley earned wages of about $8.00 per hour, or an annual income totaling $18,860. Compared to those technical positions that paid no more than $3.00 per hour in Mexicali (electricians, mechanics, and welders), similar positions in the Imperial Valley earn an average of $12.73 per hour, or $31,240 per year. A mechanic earns between $11.00 and $13.59 per hour, or $26,540 per year. Assemblers or machine operators earn more than $8.85 per hour, making $18,690 per year.

This comparative analysis of annual incomes in the region also highlights occupations that have small differences in income, including accountants and production managers. In the case of accountants, the difference in income was only $5,210 and in the case of production managers the difference was only $4,949 (see Figure 17).

The number of occupations that were differentiated by more than $20,000 from one side of the border to the other was quite high, including cooks, electricians, systems managers, nurses, buyers, those involved in engineering and operations, information engineers, manufacturers, quality inspectors, mechanics, technical electricians, machine technicians, and technical operators. One of the greatest differences in pay was the rate for the machine technician. In Mexico, the machine technician's annual income was just $3,000, while in the United States it was more than $40,000.

The number of people employed in manufacturing in the Imperial Valley, including technicians, machine operators, and engineers, is quite low compared to Mexicali. For example, in 1997 the total number of such positions did not exceed 3,000 in Imperial County. In Mexicali, by contrast, more of these positions are available, but their salaries remain relatively low due to low levels of education and lack of experience.

Great disparities exist across the border not only in demographic growth and productive structure, but also in access to education, unemployment rates, and income levels. Nonetheless, the two sides form part of the same region and depend on one another to maintain their economic activities.

In the same way that local plans for the future cannot ignore this binational relationship, neither can they ignore the differences that exist across the border. In the

Figure 17. Comparisons of Annual Incomes in Principal Occupations, Mexicali-Imperial Valley

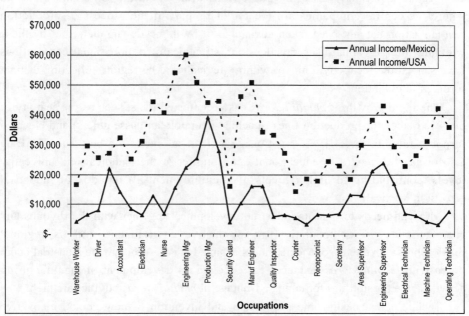

SOURCE: Author's analysis.

last section of this essay, some ideas are presented that could help shape a strategic binational plan for the region.

Conclusions

This essay has pointed to several characteristics of the Mexicali-Imperial Valley region that could be used in a strategic manner to improve quality of life on both sides of the border. The process of industrial development and the impact of the *maquiladora* in Mexicali radically altered the local productive structure beginning in the 1980s. This allowed for the specialization of production in electronics, which is characterized by an intense use of labor. This highlights the process of creating a predominantly urban tertiary sector with an important industrial manufacturing base centered on the *maquiladora* industry.

Sector specialization could be an indicator of vulnerability in the face of such phenomena as unemployment, which could disappear in the future. A decreasing dependency on multinational corporations, however, is not guaranteed. As such, *maquiladoras* in Mexicali should take advantage of their current position.

The *maquiladora* sector has not only influenced the workplace, but also the local organization of production, favoring conglomerate schemes in which new suppliers are located increasingly closer to their buyers, even within the same industrial park where the central companies are located. This part of the process of production reorganization has not been taken advantage of by domestic suppliers, but by those wielding foreign capital. The practices and strategies of multinational corporations have shaped the local environment within Mexicali and he region, reflecting distinct forms of intervention.

The rapid growth of *maquiladoras* has accentuated risks, such as the scarcity of qualified labor for production lines (machine operators and assemblers) and elevated turnover rates in direct labor positions. Mexicali is one of the best cities in Baja California with regard to educational opportunities at the technical and university levels, contributing to higher levels of unemployment—a paradox of industrial growth in Mexicali.

Mexicali needs to plan its industrial development together with the rhythms and characteristics of its population, its productive environment, and its regional relationships with the rest of Mexico and the United States. Although the industrial boom boom with *maquiladoras* distances the endogenous development of manufacturing activities, the possibilities for taking advantage of *maquiladora* activities are high.

Technological design, the production and invention of new goods, innovative products, research and development (urban and industrial), and product development do not necessarily mean competition for those central companies that are already established in Mexicali. Rather, they substitute both simple and complex manufacturing processes, improve specialized services, cooperate to increase the value of goods fabricated locally, and invite *maquiladoras* to participate in the city's social development.

The paradox of industrial development unaccompanied by salaries that improve quality of life will drive an ever-greater importation of inexpensive goods and will increase the consumption of consumer needs with aggregated value. The culture of consumption, waste, or secondhand goods could drop gradually and industrial workers could become the basis of the economic structure.

Certain economic factors demand binational cooperation and the opportunity for new advantages in the location and development of an endogenous industry. The argument that low levels of education correspond to poor salaries would be invalid in the *maquiladora* industry if competition for qualified workers required the recognition of skills and abilities acquired by experience.

Educational opportunity in Mexicali is a resource that has great possibilities for the Imperial Valley. Nonetheless, there should be a strategic plan for industrial development with the goal of improving the participation of manufacturing in the region, improving the regional production environment, and raising competition with the establishment of small supplier companies that could be created with the help of binational enterprises. It is also necessary to have a plan for agroindustrial development that includes the agricultural valley in Mexicali.

Endnotes

1. The author wishes to thank Víctor Ayala C. for the creation of the figures for this essay, and the Association of Maquiladoras of Mexicali (Asociación de Maquiladoras de Mexicali, A.C.–AMMAC) for its help in the completion of this essay.

2. Population growth rates between 1940 and 1970 were greater than 8 percent.

3. The economically active population (EAP), as defined by the National Institute of Statistics, Geography, and Information (Instituto Nacional de Estadística, Geografía e Informática–INEGI), includes those who are 12 and older.

4. These data exclude insured federal or local government workers.

5. It is not surprising that industrial expansion is encouraged by the population between 20 and 24 years old since it totaled more than seventy-six thousand in 1995 and totaled more than eighty thousand by the end of the 1990s.

6. In the early 1970s, the participation of local industry (including *maquiladoras*) in the municipal internal gross product reached 16 percent. Between 1970 and 1975, it dropped to 13.8 percent; at the end of the decade, it rose again to 18 percent (Gobierno del Estado de Baja California, Secretaría de Asentamientos Humanos y Obras Públicas 1993: 10).

7. Of the factors that have influenced the reorganization of production in Mexicali, the implementation of the North American Free Trade Agreement is the most important. Since the negotiation of the agreement, Asian capital began to have a greater presence in the region. Two of the largest companies in electronics production in the world (Sony and LG) made Mexicali their home and remain the largest to this day. Currently, Asian companies (particularly those from Japan, South Korea, and Taiwan) dominate investments in the *maquiladora* industry in Mexicali. With the signing of agreements such as the General Agreement for Tariffs and Trade (GATT) in 1986 and NAFTA in 1994, other ways to attract foreign investment have been sought. The disadvantages of such integration have also been put into question, particularly those among Mexico, the United States, and Canada.

8. Participation in the *maquiladora* industry by gender is 49 percent male and 51 percent female.

9. Most U.S. headquarters are located in California (80%), which can be explained by this state's importance in the electronics industry (Clement and Jenner 1987: 105–36).

10. In many cases, cities have not been able to acquire the urban services necessary for industrial organization (Kopinak 1996: 58–60).

11. Baja California's *maquiladoras* produce the highest percentage of electronic products and parts along the border. The state contains more than 46 percent of the plants and employs more than 32 percent of *maquila* workers nationwide. The electronics industry represents more than 20 percent of the plants and 45 percent of the employees of the total activities performed by *maquiladoras*. In Mexicali, although the production of televisions, monitors, computers, and parts is concentrated in the *maquiladora* industry, some local and national enterprises exist that complement the activities of this sector. Thirty percent of all affiliates of multinational corporations that produce televisions, computers, and parts in Mexico are located in Mexicali (Almaraz 1999a).

12. This number was calculated using information provided by AMMAC.

13. In terms of local production, the largest plants in the group are experiencing local expansion and vertical reintegration. Expansion is derived from diversification in the number and type of products in the following ways: (1) some enterprises that had only one type of television have begun to operate new product lines (different sizes and models); (2) some have incorporated the manufacturing of new product lines (computers and their parts, cellular and conventional telephones), a trend shown in 90 percent of these plants; and (3) new plants in the region produce goods and components needed by the electronics sector in Mexico that were once imported (hard disks, computer parts). Six of the largest companies in the electronics sector expanded their facilities in 1998.

14. For every four new investments there are 10 expansions (CDI 2000).

15. New networks between companies and local suppliers have been formed, but the local dynamic indicates an immature integration of local suppliers and a greater integration between central plants of the electronics sector and satellite plants brought to the region by multinational corporations.

16. In Mexico, geographical zones are defined to determine the minimum salary compared to the cost of living. Baja California corresponds to zone A, the highest level.

17. As of September 2000, the average daily wage paid in Mexicali was about 124 pesos, or 3.1 NMSs, excluding vouchers and other weekly benefits (AMMAC 2000).

18. The salary ranges depend on the minimum and maximum wages paid by each company, seniority, the size of the *maquiladora*, and the sector to which it belongs.

19. In some cases, net wages are greater due to additional benefits provided by the employer (vouchers for productivity, attendance, transportation, and so on). For example, 98 percent of the *maquiladoras* give vouchers for provisions, 63 percent provide transportation to work, and 29 percent provide their workers with meals. Other benefits may be distributed, depending on the company.

20. The salary differences between an operator and a janitor are relatively minimal, ranging from .3 to 4.6 NMSs, even though the average differential is three NMSs per day.

21. One hundred percent of these companies were terminal plants manufacturing key products.

22. A growing number of plants in Mexicali are becoming specialized and operate without the intensive use of labor, in which the more important activities include the manufacturing of packaging, cabinets, and specialized plastic components. These companies show a tendency toward concentration in some of the industrial areas, allowing an incipient, but important, standard for large economies (Almaraz 1999a).

23. Data for the construction sector in Imperial Valley show a notable increase, especially in residential construction compared to commercial (CCBRES 1999).

24. It is important to clarify that the size of the examples fluctuated by year in the number of *maquiladoras* and the number of employees per plant. Nonetheless, a general picture of those positions about which information could be collected was completed for 1997 through 2000.

25. Income calculations were made based on annual averages of the dollar and the peso. For example, it was 7.91 pesos to the dollar in 1997; 9.13 pesos to the dollar in 1998; 9.35 pesos to the dollar in 1999; and 9.65 pesos to the dollar in 2000.

References

Almaraz, A. 1997. "Procesos de aprendizaje dentro de un esquema de especialización global: una propuesta de análisis para la llamada IME en la ciudad de Nogales, Son." Pp. 103–30 in *México y Estados Unidos: el reto de la interdependencia económica*, Lara and Velázquez, eds. México, D.F.: El Colegio de Sonora, Colegio Nacional de Economistas, A.C., Gobierno del Estado de Sonora, Colegio de Economistas de Sonora, A.C.

Almaraz, A. 1999a. "La industria electrónica: ramas y contextos específicos." *Revista Indicadores Económicos* 131: 3–9.

Almaraz, A. 1999b. "Estrategias globales impactos locales: empresas japonesas de la rama electrónica en Baja California." *Revista Indicadores Económicos* 133: 5–9.

Alonso, J., and Jorge Carrillo. 1996. "Gobernación económica y cambio industrial en la frontera norte de México: un análisis de trayectorias locales y aprendizaje." *Revista Latinoamericana de Estudios Urbano Regionales EURE* 30 (67): 45–65.

Alvarez, N. 1989. *El reto de la globalización para la industria mexicana.* México, D.F.: Ed. Diana.

Amin, Samir. 1998. *Capitalism in the age of globalization.* London: IPSR Zed Books.

Asociación de Maquiladoras de Mexicali A.C. (AMMAC). 2000. Internal Reports. Mexicali: AMMAC.

California Center for Border and Regional Economic Studies (CCBRES). 1999. *CCBRES Bulletin* 1 (6).

California Center for Border and Regional Economic Studies (CCBRES). 2000a. *CCBRES Bulletin* 1 (1).

California Center for Border and Regional Economic Studies (CCBRES). 2000b. *CCBRES Bulletin* 1 (5).

California Center for Border and Regional Economic Studies (CCBRES). 2000c. *CCBRES Bulletin* 1 (6).

Carrillo, J., ed. 1993. *Condiciones de empleo y capacitación en las maquiladoras de exportación en México.* México, D.F.: STPS and El Colegio de la Frontera Norte.

Carrillo, J., and Alfredo Hualde. 1998. "Third Generation Maquiladoras? The Delphi-General Motors Case." *Journal of Borderlands Studies* 13 (1): 79–98.

Carrillo, J., and Kathryn Kopinak. 1999. "Empleo y relaciones laborales. Las maquiladoras en México." Paper presented at the Cambios en los Contratos Colectivos en México seminar, March, Mexico City, Mexico.

Carrillo, J., Araceli Almaraz, and Maria Eugenia de la O. 1998. "Estrategias empresariales de reestructuración productiva en Tijuana." Pp. 27–64 in *Estrategias de modernización empresarial.* México, D.F.: Fundación Ebert y Rayuela.

Clement, Norris, and Stephen R. Jenner. 1987. *Location Decisions Regarding Maquiladora/In-Bond Plants Operating in Baja California, Mexico.* San Diego: Institute for Regional Studies of the Californias.

Comisión de Desarrollo Industrial para Mexicali (CDI). 2000. "Informe de actividades del primer semestre de 2000." Mexicali. Mimeograph.

Consejo Estatal de Población (CONEPO). 1999. *Apuntes de población de Baja California, municipio de Mexicali* 2 (6). Mexicali: CONEPO.

Contreras, O., Jorge Alonso, and Martin Kenny. 1997. "Los gerentes de las maquiladoras como agentes del endogeneización de la industria." *Comercio Exterior* 47–48: 670–87.

Covarrubias, Alejandro. 1992. *La flexibilidad laboral en Sonora.* Sonora: El Colegio de Sonora and Fundación F. Ebert.

Dirección General de Estadística. 1930. *Quinto censo de población.* México, D.F.: Dirección General de Estadística.

Dirección General de Estadística. 1940. *Sexto censo de población.* México, D.F.: Dirección General de Estadística.

Dirección General de Estadística. 1950. *Séptimo censo general de población.* México, D.F.: Dirección General de Estadística.

Dirección General de Estadística. 1960. *VIII Censo general de población.* México, D.F.: Dirección General de Estadística.

Dirección General de Estadística. 1970. *IX Censo general de población.* México, D.F.: Dirección General de Estadística.

Garza, E., and A. Arteaga, eds. 1998. "Modelos de industrialización en México." *Cuaderno de Trabajo* 15.

Gobierno del Estado de Baja California. 1998. *Guía del inversionista para Baja California.* México, D.F: Ciudad de Mexicali.

Gobierno del Estado de Baja California and Secretaría de Asentamientos Humanos y Obras Públicas. 1993. *Programa sectorial de industria.* Mexicali: Gobierno del Estado de Baja California and Secretaría de Asentamientos Humanos y Obras Públicas.

Instituto Nacional de Estadística, Geografía e Informática (INEGI). 1990. *XI Censo general de población y vivienda.* Aguascalientes: INEGI.

Instituto Nacional de Estadística, Geografía e Informática (INEGI). 1995a. "Censos económicos." http://www.inegi.gob.mx.

Instituto Nacional de Estadística, Geografía e Informática (INEGI). 1995b. *Conteo de población y vivienda.* Aguascalientes: INEGI.

Instituto Nacional de Estadística, Geografía e Informática (INEGI). 1999. *Encuesta nacional de empleo urbano.* Aguascalientes : INEGI.

Instituto Nacional de Estadística, Geografía e Informática (INEGI). 2000. *XII Censo general de población y vivienda.* Aguascalientes: INEGI.

Kopinak, Kathryn. 1996. *Desert Capitalism: Maquiladoras in North America's Western Industrial Corridor.* Tucson: University of Arizona Press.

Lara, Francisco. 1992. "Patrones de absorción de mano de obra en la industria maquiladora de Nogales: elementos para una revalorización." *Estudios Sociales* 3 (7): 163–86.

Lara, Francisco. 1993. "Industrialización y urbanización en la frontera: el caso de Nogales, Sonora." *Estudios Sociales* 4 (7): 95–116.

Reginald, L.D. 1985. *Industria maquiladora y subsidiarias de co-inversión: régimen jurídico y corporativo.* México, D.F.: Cárdenas, Editor y Dist.

Rodríguez, J.M., and Araceli Almaraz. 1998. "Los procesos de conformación urbana en Nogales, Sonora: comercio, inmigración, servicios e industria (1853–1995)." Paper presented at the second Colloqium on Urban History, 28 February, Ciudad Guzmán, Jalisco, México.

Secretaría de Desarrollo Económico (SEDECO). 1990. *La economía de Baja California en cifras.* México, D.F.: Gobierno de Baja California and SEDECO.

Secretaría de Desarrollo Económico (SEDECO). 1991. *La economía de Baja California en cifras.* México, D.F.: Gobierno de Baja California and SEDECO.

Secretaría de Desarrollo Económico (SEDECO). 1992. *La economía de Baja California en cifras.* México, D.F.: Gobierno de Baja California and SEDECO.

Secretaría de Desarrollo Económico (SEDECO). 1993. *La economía de Baja California en cifras.* México, D.F.: Gobierno de Baja California and SEDECO.

Secretaría de Desarrollo Económico (SEDECO). 1997. *La economía de Baja California en cifras*. México, D.F.: Gobierno de Baja California and SEDECO.

Secretaría de Desarrollo Económico (SEDECO). 1998. *La economía de Baja California en cifras*. México, D.F.: Gobierno de Baja California and SEDECO.

Secretaría de Desarrollo Económico (SEDECO). 1999. *La economía de Baja California en cifras*. México, D.F.: Gobierno de Baja California and SEDECO.

Secretaría de Desarrollo Económico (SEDECO). 2000. *La economía de Baja California en cifras*. México, D.F.: Gobierno de Baja California and SEDECO.

Secretaría de Programación y Presupuesto and Instituto Nacional de Estadística, Geografía e Informática (INEGI). 1980. *X Censo general de población y vivienda*. México, D.F.: Secretaría de Programación y Presupuesto and INEGI.

Storper, M. 1992. "The Limits of Globalization: Technology Districts and International Trade." *Economic Geography Review* 68 (1): 60–93.

Storper, M. 1993. "Regional Words of Production: Learning and Innovation in the Technological Districts of France, Italy and USA." *Regional Studies* 27 (5): 433–55.

Turner, B.E., ed. 1994. *México en los noventa. Globalización y reestructuración productiva*. México, D.F.: UAM Azcapotzalco and Universidad Michoacana.

13

Employee Turnover in Mexicali

Mindy S. West*

Abstract

The results of a multiphase study investigating causes of employee turnover in Mexico are discussed. The research project included interviews with human resource managers, focus group interviews with workers, and a questionnaire administered to 299 workers in Mexicali. The results support several of the hypothesized relationships among factors associated with turnover. The results also confirm the hypothesized relationships for benefit satisfaction, job satisfaction, and continuance commitment on withdrawal cognitions. Recommendations for managerial interventions to reduce turnover are presented.

Employee Turnover in Mexicali

Employee turnover is an individual's voluntary termination of paid employment with a company. Turnover is a topic of interest for both academic researchers and practicing managers. An employee's decision to voluntarily quit an organization has important consequences for the firm. Employers incur several direct costs as result of employee turnover, including the costs involved with advertising job vacancies, conducting the application and recruitment process, and providing orientation and training to the new employees (Griffeth and Hom 2001). Companies spend time and resources selecting and training individuals for employment and only recover these costs through long-term employment relationships with the individuals. When employees leave an organization, the business loses the resources invested in them.

*West is Assistant Professor of Management at the Imperial Valley Campus of San Diego State University.

High levels of turnover can dramatically increase selection and training costs for firms. The more firms invest in employee training, the greater the costs associated with turnover and the greater the priority placed on retaining quality workers.

To help managers deal with turnover concerns, academic researchers have conducted numerous investigations into the causes of turnover. Turnover studies have focused on the pivotal role of job attitudes, including job satisfaction, withdrawal cognitions, and continuance commitment as factors that can contribute to turnover decisions. Previous academic work (see Hom and Griffeth 1995 for a thorough review) shows that job satisfaction lowers withdrawal cognitions—the person's thoughts of quitting that precede actual turnover. Additionally, previous research has demonstrated the importance of continuance commitment in reducing turnover. Continuance commitment represents the perceived costs of leaving an organization and can be characterized as a "need" to stay (Meyer and Allen 1997). Continuance commitment can bind workers to their employers because individuals believe that they would lose too much if they were to quit. For example, employees generally lose all bonuses based on seniority when they quit to work elsewhere, and this decreases the probability that an individual will quit.

Although employee turnover is a universal problem, most turnover studies have been conducted in the United States. It remains to be determined if the factors that contribute to turnover decisions in the United States are applicable elsewhere (Maertz et al. 1996). Comprehensive research is now being conducted on the causes of turnover in Mexico. The content and recommendations presented here are based on an integration of the results of a series of turnover research studies conducted by the author in Mexicali. The research project included in-depth interviews with human resource managers, focus group interviews with workers, and a comprehensive questionnaire completed by 299 individuals employed in Mexicali. The insights gained from each stage of the research project are described below.

Human Resource Manager Interviews

The author conducted six interviews with human resource managers from Mexicali. The managers selected were professional contacts of a Mexican professor who introduced them to the author. The managers were asked to address turnover statistics in their firm, why and at what time workers leave their company, and actions the company takes to try to retain employees.

The stated turnover statistics for the firms ranged from .08 percent per month to 18 percent per month, with seasonal highs in the summer and winter months. The primary reasons that employees quit included conflict with child care responsibilities, conflict with work and school schedules, having to work in extreme temperatures and harsh working conditions, the need to return to the interior of Mexico, the need to care for a sick family member, and poor relationships with the supervisor or co-workers. Competitive wages were viewed by the human resource managers as a necessary but not sufficient factor for retaining workers, as interpersonal treatment was just as important. The way people are treated and the quality of the supervisory relationship were considered important factors by the human resource managers for keeping workers.

In order to retain workers, several human resource managers noted that their firms paid higher than average wages, and all the managers emphasized the variety of benefits offered by their firm to reduce turnover. Common benefits include life insurance and company savings plans. Social activities including organized athletic activities and on-site education opportunities are also provided. Unique benefits include extra Christmas bonus days based on seniority, paid vacation time for an individual's wedding, barbecues at the supervisor's home, birthday acknowledgments, employee of the month programs, and organized soccer games and other sporting events. Certain firms offered attendance and performance incentives. Several firms offered transportation programs and one firm was building employee housing. The criteria used by some of the firms to hire new employees included hiring only people who are originally from Mexicali and hiring only people who live near the facility. All of the managers stated that their firms were concerned about turnover, and each firm wanted to reduce turnover to lower costs and to improve employee morale.

Focus Group Interviews

A series of focus group interviews was conducted with groups of five to seven employees per session. Participants were randomly selected from an employee identification list provided by a company and were asked to participate in the project by the firm's human resource manager. The jobs held by the interview participants ranged from entry-level assembly workers to professional employees. Participants were asked to respond to questions dealing with what they liked about their jobs, why some individuals have quit, and why they have remained with their current employer. Individuals were also asked to share their perceptions about the ease with which they could find new employment if they were to quit and the positive things they would have to give up if they were to quit.

The focus group interviews provided several insights. First, the comments highlighted the importance of salary and benefits on turnover decisions. Respondents had left previous employers to increase wages and confirmed that many of their former co-workers had quit for better wages. Satisfaction with benefits was a primary reason why employees did not leave, as those individuals with several years of seniority thought they would lose too much to quit the company. Second, training and development opportunities were highly valued by the individuals. Several employees acknowledged that they were staying with their current company because of the opportunities for skill acquisition and the possibility of receiving a promotion in the future.

Respondents stated that the work atmosphere was an important consideration for employees. If relationships with the supervisor or co-workers were not positive, this would contribute to turnover decisions, even if the company offered acceptable compensation packages. Furthermore, participants highlighted the importance of working conditions and noted that work area temperature, noise level, safety conditions, and work pace are important components of job satisfaction. Similarly, interview participants noted how the work shift is an important consideration, especially for those individuals working while attending school. Finally, job security was an important concern, as individuals felt that layoffs could occur if the peso was devalued or the Mexican economy took a downturn.

Comprehensive Questionnaire

Based on the human resource manager and focus group interviews and previous academic research, a comprehensive questionnaire was developed to determine those factors most closely associated with turnover in Mexicali workers. The purpose of the survey was to determine the extent to which there were significant statistical relationships among the hypothesized factors related to job satisfaction and withdrawal cognitions (thoughts of quitting). Specifically, pay satisfaction and benefit satisfaction were hypothesized to be related to job satisfaction. Job satisfaction, continuance commitment, supervisor satisfaction, and co-worker satisfaction were hypothesized to be related to withdrawal cognitions. By investigating the degree of statistical relationships among the factors, it is possible to determine those factors that most strongly keep an individual from quitting and those most strongly associated with an individual's decision to quit.

Two statistical analysis approaches were used to evaluate the questionnaire results. Covariance structure analysis using the EQS Structural Equations software program was used to determine if the relationship between two factors was as hypothesized. The results support a hypothesized relationship if the relationship between the two factors is in the predicted direction (positive or negative) and is statistically significant at $p < .05$ (Byrne 1994). The second statistical analysis approach was to compare the survey responses of those individuals who indicated they were likely to quit soon and the responses of those who indicated they were not likely to quit; these classifications of responses were defined as "Leavers" and "Stayers," respectively. Thus, individuals who agreed with the statement that they intended to quit within the next six months were included in the Leaver group, while those who indicated they were not likely to quit within the next six months were included in the Stayer group. The survey responses of the two groups (i.e., Leavers and Stayers) were compared and t-tests were used to determine if statistically significant responses (p < .05) between the groups existed. The results of these analyses are discussed below.

Satisfaction with Pay

Previous academic research demonstrates that satisfaction with pay is an important predictor of an employee's job satisfaction (Hom and Griffeth 1995). Thus, a positive relationship between pay satisfaction and job satisfaction should be expected. This hypothesized relationship received partial support, as the relationship between pay satisfaction and job satisfaction was positive but marginally statistically significant at p < .10.

Satisfaction with pay has also been shown to be related to continuance commitment. Individuals who believe that they are being paid more than at other firms are more likely to feel bound to the employer in order to continue to receive high wages. Therefore, a positive relationship should exist between pay satisfaction and continuance commitment. The study results support this prediction. The relationship between satisfaction with pay and continuance commitment was positive and statistically significant. Therefore, the results confirm that satisfaction with pay can make employees feel that they would lose too much if they were to quit.

In addition, the results of the comparisons between the Leavers and the Stayers indicate that pay satisfaction is associated with turnover decisions. The individuals who indicated they were likely to quit (i.e., the Leavers) reported statistically significant lower levels of satisfaction with their pay. The Leavers also indicated that they believed they would receive higher pay if they were working at another company in Mexicali. Overall, the results confirm the belief that pay levels can contribute to turnover decisions through job satisfaction and continuance commitment.

Satisfaction with Benefits

Satisfaction with benefits was predicted to have the same relationship with job satisfaction and continuance commitment as satisfaction with pay. Specifically, satisfaction with benefits would contribute to higher levels of job satisfaction and greater continuance commitment. Firms in Mexico have been successful at attracting and retaining workers through perquisites and benefits targeted specifically for employee needs (Teagarden and Von Glinow 1990). Previous research has shown that profit-sharing plans and company savings plans lower turnover (Miller, Hom, and Gomez-Mejia 2001). As with pay, firms that provide excellent employee benefits create environments where employees believe that they should not leave their current employer. Benefits are not transferable across jobs; the loss of benefits and the forfeiting of seniority-based benefits can be perceived as potential costs in leaving a company. Employees may be reluctant to quit if their current firm offers a superior level of benefits, thus creating continuance commitment to the firm (Meyer and Allen 1997).

The questionnaire results support the predicted relationships. The relationship between benefit satisfaction and job satisfaction was positive and statistically significant. Moreover, the degree of association was quite strong, indicating that satisfaction with benefits contributes to higher levels of job satisfaction than satisfaction with pay. Furthermore, the relationship between benefit satisfaction and continuance commitment was positive and statistically significant. The strength of the relationship was again stronger than the relationship between pay satisfaction and continuance commitment, further highlighting the importance of offering valued employee benefits.

A comparison of the responses of the Leavers and Stayers also highlights the importance of benefit satisfaction on turnover decisions. Those individuals who indicated they were likely to quit reported lower levels of satisfaction for all 18 of the company benefits included on the questionnaire. In addition, 15 of the 18 differences were statistically significant. Thus, the Leavers clearly had lower levels of satisfaction with the benefits offered by their employers, and this may well have contributed to their turnover decisions.

Job Satisfaction

A consistent finding in turnover studies is that job satisfaction plays a key role in turnover and is negatively related to withdrawal cognitions (Hom and Griffeth 1995). Higher levels of job satisfaction should be associated with less desire to quit. The study results for Mexicali supported this hypothesis. The significant relationship between job satisfaction and withdrawal cognitions was negative. Thus, individuals who have higher levels of job satisfaction are less likely to quit.

Moreover, a comparison of the responses of the Leavers and Stayers indicates the relevance of job satisfaction. Those individuals who indicated they were likely to quit reported lower levels of job satisfaction. Specifically, Leavers reported statistically significant lower levels of satisfaction with work pace and work schedule. Although not statistically different, Leavers also reported lower levels of satisfaction with workplace noise and temperature, task responsibilities, and workplace safety. Thus, Leavers reported lower levels of satisfaction for nearly all the elements of job satisfaction investigated.

Continuance Commitment

Continuance commitment is a function of the perceived opportunity costs of leaving. These costs include having to forgo benefits based on seniority. Many firms in Mexico provide bonuses based on job seniority that are forfeited when workers obtain employment elsewhere, thereby increasing the perceived financial costs of quitting

(Miller et al. 2001). Participants were asked to indicate the extent to which they felt obligated to remain with their employer in relation to what they would have to give up to leave. The statistically significant results indicate a negative relationship between continuance commitment and withdrawal cognitions. Those who felt a greater obligation to stay with their employer were less likely to think of quitting. This finding supports the premise that people can feel bound to their current employers and this will, in turn, reduce turnover. Thus, employers who are interested in reducing turnover propensities should focus on ways to bind their employees to the firm.

The responses of the Leavers also highlight the importance of continuance commitment. The individuals who indicated they were likely to quit had more positive attitudes about their chances of obtaining another job and the job search process. For example, Leavers believed more strongly that other employment opportunities would be better than their current jobs. Leavers reported that it would not be difficult for them to quit and believed that their lives would not be disrupted much if they quit.

Satisfaction with Supervisors

The role of the supervisor reportedly takes on special importance in the Mexican culture, as the supervisor-worker relationship is often extremely paternalistic (Kras 1989). Management's role is to take care of the workers and workers become a manager's "extended family" (Teagarden, Butler, and Von Glinow 1992). Loyalty is fostered when supervisors are perceived as fair and understanding about workers' needs. It has been thought that the quality of the interaction and relationship with the supervisor is related to job tenure in the Mexican culture, as Mexican workers may experience loyalty and attachment to supervisors (Lawrence and Yeh 1994). Satisfaction with one's supervisor may contribute to an employee's decision to stay with an organization.

The current results did not support this hypothesized relationship. There was no relationship between supervisor satisfaction and withdrawal cognitions. In addition, many of the survey items addressing supervisor satisfaction were not significantly different between Leavers and Stayers, even though the Leavers did report lower levels of supervisor satisfaction. Although it is premature to conclude on the basis of one study that the quality of the supervisory relationship has no impact on withdrawal cognitions, it is possible that satisfaction with the supervisor does little to keep individuals employed at a company.

Satisfaction with Co-Workers

Satisfaction with co-workers is thought to be a foundation for continued employment with an employer in Mexico (Maertz et al. 1996). Having cooperative and friendly co-workers was noted in the focus group interviews as important to the workers. Friendships with group members can reduce withdrawal cognitions because people would have concerns about having to find new friends if they changed employers. However, the current results indicate no relationship between co-worker satisfaction and withdrawal cognitions. Thus, higher levels of co-worker satisfaction were not associated with lower thoughts of quitting. In contrast, the Leaver and Stayer comparisons did indicate that Leavers had lower levels of satisfaction with their co-workers. The possible relationship between co-worker satisfaction and turnover should be investigated in future turnover research in Mexico to determine if satisfaction with co-workers is as strong of a deterrent to turnover as has previously been thought.

Implications for Managers

The study results have practical implications for managers in firms in Mexico who wish to reduce turnover rates. Knowledge about the factors most strongly associated with withdrawal cognitions will assist managers in developing interventions to reduce turnover. Specific recommendations are discussed below.

First, it is important for managers to review the competitiveness of their firm's benefits package to ensure it is comparable to those offered by similar firms in the local labor market. Managers need to gather information about the type and level of benefits offered by other firms in their city. As satisfaction with benefits had a strong relationship with factors associated with withdrawal cognitions, employee satisfaction with the company's benefits should reduce turnover. Managers can utilize professional contacts to learn from their colleagues about the benefits packages being offered elsewhere. In addition, it is beneficial to ask job applicants as part of the selection process the specific reasons why they are interested in leaving their current employer and what attracts them to the new employer. This will give managers insights into what applicants consider important. It is also imperative to conduct effective exit interviews with any individual who quits. Human resource managers should try to determine the specific factors that contributed to the turnover decision and the reasons why the individual has selected another employer, if the person already has obtained a new position.

Managers should also periodically survey employees to determine which specific benefits are most important to their employees. Managers should use surveys asking employees to indicate their level of satisfaction with each of the benefits offered by the employer to determine the specific benefits receiving low satisfaction scores. Managers would then be able to focus on improving the benefits that contribute the most to job dissatisfaction. It might also prove insightful to ask employees if there are any specific benefits that they wished the employer would offer but currently does not.

A second approach for reducing turnover is to create more of a sense of continuance commitment in new employees. The sooner employees feel that they would need to give up too much in order to quit, the more likely they are to stay with the employer. For example, by making new employees eligible for all benefits from the first day of employment—rather than making some benefits available only after a few months of employment—employees are immediately committed to the firm. Another option to foster continuance commitment is to provide a one-time bonus at the end of the first year of employment that is based on the number of hours worked. The information provided by the study participants indicates new hires were the most likely to quit because they had few financial ties to the company. By providing workers a significant bonus if they work for the company for a full year, a financial investment in the company is created immediately and workers might be less likely to leave the firm. This type of deferred compensation retention bonus is effective at retaining personnel (Griffeth and Hom 2001).

A final recommendation for dealing with employee turnover is to provide ample opportunities for skill development and enhancement. Many comments from the focus group interviews and the questionnaires demonstrate the importance workers place on skill development training. Employees desire to have access to developmental opportunities that would give the employees the opportunity to apply for better positions. Workers value training opportunities as the means to obtain promotions and better positions within the company. One individual commented: "If a person is not given the opportunity to get a better position within the company, this person is going to go where he can advance." Another person stated: "That's the reason why some people leave. They go to places where they are given the opportunity to advance. They start with a lower salary, but in time they progress." Another person commented: "I wanted to work for a company where I could grow and advance." Training opportunities are regarded as the way to advance within a company. English language training and computer skills training appear to be the most highly valued. The additional benefit of providing more developmental training opportunities for employees is that the company creates a pool of employees from which to recruit when higher-level vacancies open.

It appears that workers are willing to invest in companies if the companies invest in them. The key to turnover reduction thus seems to be to create an environment where workers believe that they will give up too many positive things by quitting. By providing benefits and training opportunities that individuals value, companies should be able to convince employees to remain with the firm.

References

Byrne, Barbara M. 1994. *Structural Equation Modeling with EQS and EQS/Windows: Basic Concepts, Applications, and Programming.* Thousand Oaks: Sage Publications.

Griffeth, Rodger W., and Peter W. Hom. 2001. *Retaining Valued Employees*. Thousand Oaks: Sage Publications.

Hom, Peter W., and Rodger W. Griffeth. 1995. *Employee Turnover*. Cincinnati: Southwestern Publishing Company.

Kras, Eva S. 1989. *Management in Two Cultures: Bridging the Gap between U.S. and Mexican Managers*. Yarmouth, ME: Intercultural Press Inc.

Lawrence, John J., and Rhy-Song Yeh. 1994. "The Influence of Mexican Culture on the Use of Japanese Manufacturing Techniques in Mexico." *Management International Review* 34: 49–66.

Maertz, Carl P., Michael J. Stevens, Michael A. Campion, and Alma Fernandez. 1996. "Worker Turnover in Mexican Factories: A Qualitative Investigation and Model Development." Paper presented at the annual meeting of the Academy of Management, August, Cincinnati, Ohio.

Meyer, John P., and Natalie J. Allen. 1997. *Commitment in the Workplace: Theory, Research, and Application*. Thousand Oaks: Sage Publications.

Miller, Janice S., Peter W. Hom, and Luis R. Gomez-Mejia. 2001. "The High Costs of Low Wages: Does Maquiladora Compensation Reduce Turnover?" *Journal of International Business Studies* 32 (3): 585–95.

Teagarden, Mary B., and Mary Ann Von Glinow. 1990. "Contextual Determinants of HRM Effectiveness in Cooperative Alliances: Mexican Evidence." *Management International Review* 30: 23–36.

Teagarden, Mary B., Mark C. Butler, and Mary Ann Von Glinow. 1992. "Mexico's Maquiladora Industry: Where Strategic Human Resource Management Makes a Difference." *Organizational Dynamics* 20 (3): 34–47.

14

Industrial Growth, Urban Expansion, and Industrial Facilities in Mexicali, Baja California

Arturo Ranfla González and César Peña Salmón*

Abstract

This essay focuses on the structure and dynamism of industry located in the City of Mexicali, Baja California, and their impact on the city's form and current organization. It analyzes the evolution of industrial activities in the city, the changes in the industry's sectoral composition, the urban area distribution patterns, and the factors and events that favor the regional growth of industry. Official statistics are used to analyze the dynamics and evolution of the sector and cartographic information is integrated to identify the territorial patterns of industrial location in the city. Finally, information from a 2000 survey on the quality of local industrial plants allows for further analysis of industrial growth and identification of key aspects of location and other characteristics.

Introduction

Mexicali's location along the international boundary with the United States and its customs free zone status[1] are factors associated with the initial development of industry in the Municipality of Mexicali. Its geographic distance from the rest of the Mexican Republic and the existence of a free zone in the region since the 1930s discouraged the establishment of national companies for many years. Regional and local consumption of imported products was favored, thus, limiting the region's

Ranfla González is Director of the Institute for Social Research at the Universidad Autónoma de Baja California and Peña Salmón is Professor of Architecture at the Universidad Autónoma de Baja California.

integration with the national market. This tendency impacted the development of industry in Mexicali and the entire State of Baja California until 1965, when the Border Industrialization Program (BIP) was created to promote the development of *maquiladoras* (assembly plants) in the region. In its first phase, the program was limited to free zones and national perimeters and the location of *maquiladoras* was concentrated in northern Mexico.[2]

Considering its difficult inception due to the small size of local and regional demand and its very active expansion in recent years due to commercial opening, the city's industry is at a crucial point at the beginning of the twenty-first century. In this context, sectoral growth, the diversification of its economic base, and important changes in the expansion and organization of the city as a product of its development are found. These changes are examined under the analysis of the evolution of industrial activities with respect to employment and sectoral distribution, changes in the organization and territorial configuration of the city due to industrial expansion, and the current state of industrial location and infrastructure in the city.

Dynamics and Specialization

Mexicali is an agglomeration in the middle of the desert. Its source of physical expansion and economic growth, until a few years ago, was the product of a hydraulic engineering project that began in the late nineteenth century in what is today the Imperial and Mexicali valleys. This project opened the region to the development of irrigated agriculture. From that moment, the city was in contact with the other side of the international boundary and a changing environment shaped the local economy through the interactions between the two sides of the border. The City of Mexicali was founded on March 4, 1903, although functional economic relationships were recorded prior to this date.

In the border context of northern Mexico, Mexicali is the third largest urban area along the U.S.-Mexican border, with a population of 764,902 inhabitants in 2000, following Ciudad Juárez with 1,217,888 and Tijuana with 1,212,232 inhabitants (INEGI 2000). Municipal population registries from these three cities show average annual growth rates of 4.7 percent in Tijuana, 4.1 percent in Ciudad Juárez, and 2.3 percent in Mexicali. It is important to note the moderate growth of the Municipality of Mexicali compared to Tijuana and Ciudad Juárez, which has enabled the City of Mexicali to adhere to planning criteria and has facilitated a relatively ordered development compared to the other two cities.

Although agriculture long characterized the municipality's activities, there are indicators of greater dynamism in economic activities in the city that are not related to agriculture. Over many years, the growth of nonagricultural economic activities and the increase of employment in the export industry have complemented Mexicali's moderate urban expansion and manageable economic growth. These types of economic activities are typical of other areas of the border region. During the 1993–1998 period, the annual average growth of employment in nonagricultural activities was 4.4 percent in Ciudad Juárez, 3.9 percent in Tijuana, and 3.9 percent in Mexicali (INEGI 1993, 1998). Significant changes were also recorded in employment in the *maquiladora* industry in these cities during the 1980–1990 and 1990–1998 periods, showing variations from 13.16 to 8.37 percent annual average growth in employment in Tijuana, 9.74 to 7.78 percent in Mexicali, and 10.24 to 5.11 percent in Ciudad Juárez.

These data confirm a tendency toward the accelerated growth of Mexicali's economy over the years and a tendency to maintain moderate population growth compared to other border cities. Additionally, Mexicali has at its disposal inputs such as water, energy, and an important educational infrastructure, all of which favor Mexicali as a location for industry. These advantages were confirmed with the arrival of direct foreign investments after the implementation of the North American Free Trade Agreement (NAFTA) in 1994. Its economic base, however, is still modest compared to that of Ciudad Juárez and Tijuana. In 1998, those employed by nonagricultural economic activities in Mexicali represented 42.9 percent of Ciudad Juárez's total and 54.7 percent of Tijuana's total.

Evolution

The origin of industry in Mexicali is rooted in the agricultural development of the valley, in which the cultivation of cotton and wheat determined the first industries that were established in the region. During the first phase of local industry in the 1940s, agroindustrial activities predominated. These modified the regional economy and marked the differences in spatial organization between the valley and the city. Representing the principal industries of this period, the Pacific Industrial Company (Compañía Industrial del Pacífico)[3] and the Oil Producer of the Valley (Aceitera del Valle) came to employ up to five hundred workers each and produced cotton and related products.

In 1952, two companies that modified the profile of regional industry were established: Productos Kerns and Kenworth Mexicana. Both soon became the city's largest employers and the emblematic industries of a new era. With their arrival, local enterprises began the search for alternatives to overcome the limited regional and local market. This was a response in large measure to the region's distance from Mexico's interior and the presence of the free zone, which isolated products made within the zone from the rest of Mexico by only charging import taxes on primary materials used in their fabrication (Bravo Aguilera 1981: 529).

Industry's presence continued to grow in Mexicali's landscape, achieving important growth in the 1960s with the arrival of new companies based on the Border Industrialization Program. During this period, the export industry demonstrated two clearly defined phases in terms of the strategies used by foreign plants established in the region. The first period includes subcontracting as the dominant form of industrial organization. At this time, the majority of plants were called *golondrinas* (swallows) due to their great mobility and their activities.[4] During the second period, evermore frequent direct investments by U.S. and Asian corporations reflected greater regional stability in investments and a tendency to modify the short-term perspective on their investments to a longer-term view. This dynamic and the temporal horizon of new investments affected the city's organization and the changes it and the region experienced in recent decades.[5]

The changes in the sectoral structure of the city and the region show a change in the pattern of activities. In 1950, the employment of the economically active population (EAP)—including the population from 12 to 65 years of age—for the entire Municipality of Mexicali in primary activities was 61.6 percent, which eventually decreased to 20.1 percent by 1980. Industry employment rose from 11.5 percent in 1950 to 26.5 percent in 1980. In the city, these changes were also demonstrated, although less drastically. The EAP employed in primary activities totaled 17.1 percent in 1950 and 13.7 percent in 1980. Industrial employment during the same period increased from 18.8 percent in 1950 to 30.0 percent in 1980. This tendency was intensified in such a way that by 1990, the estimated employed population in the primary sector in the city was 14.0 percent and in industry, 30.0 percent, due to the growth of services.

With this tendency, by 1998, the city and, on a lesser scale, the Mexicali Valley, reflected the arrival of important investments for industrial plants. The majority were linked to production processes in the United States and oriented predominantly toward its vast market and its expansion in the NAFTA framework. This situation has spurred very rapid growth in employment (see Figure 1) and production that exemplifies the nature and dynamism of transborder relationships in the context of a global economy. In the meantime, a large number of Asian companies have also located in Mexicali, using it as a platform for the export of their products to the U.S. market under competitive conditions.[6]

Employment and Specialization

The changes experienced by industry over recent years have modified the sectoral structure in production and in the number of employees. Industry has achieved growth in generated employment and a more diversified activity structure. Changes in the structure of production that can be identified are related to industrial activities and plant size.

In 1965, the most important presence in Mexicali was held by the textile, chemical products, nonmetallic metals, basic metallic (transformation of raw material), automobile, and, less so, electric and electronic industries. By 1994, there was important economic participation by the food, paper, transformation, basic

Figure 1. Variations in Industrial Employment in
Baja California and Mexicali, 1960–1995

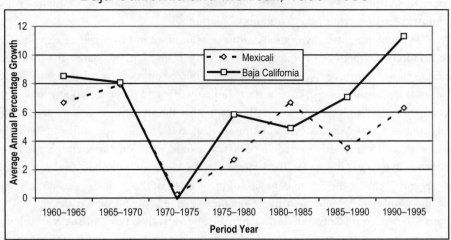

SOURCE: Asociación Mexicana de Parques Industriales (AMPI) (2000).

metallic, machinery, and electric and electronic material industries. In general, the productive structure of this 30-year period is oriented toward the regional, national, and international markets and is less fragile because of its diversity.

Another significant aspect is plant size. Generally, Mexicali has always had an above average plant size compared to other areas in the State of Baja California. This characteristic has been explained in the past by the presence of large plants linked to the transformation of agricultural goods (oil, wheat, and so on), assembly plants that produce for the national market (as in the case of Kenworth[7]), and, more recently, the arrival of large *maquiladoras* that began to appear in the 1970s. Recently, large companies have established themselves in the region in the electric-electronics sector, which has registered positive net balances in the 1991–1998 period. The sector is strategically involved with activities linked to audio and video, computing, electric appliances, and telecommunications. Mexico is one of the principal producer-assembler countries in this sector, producing 20 percent of color televisions worldwide in 1997.[8]

The Maquiladora Export Industry

Prior to the enactment of the Border Industrialization Program in 1965, which changed the industrial profile of the majority of urban concentrations along the border, Mexicali had the greatest number of industrial companies in the State of Baja California. It also generated 80 percent of industrial production and had 75 percent of total investments in the sector.

Acceptance of foreign investment in the 1960s maintained Mexicali's primacy in industrial activities in Baja California, with 53.4 percent of total employment in the *maquiladora* industry in 1973. This surpassed the Municipality of Tijuana, which employed 43.4 percent of the working population.

The development and variations of the *maquiladora* industry can be explained by the relationships between economic opportunity in the United States and structural transformations in recent years in Mexico, reflected in varying fluctuations. These relationships and their repercussions undoubtedly affected the *maquiladora* industry's dynamics in the entire country. The behavior that the *maquiladora* industry in Baja California and in Mexicali demonstrated in the 1975–1996 period, in particular, seems to conform with the idea of a functional relationship between the two countries, which could be identified in the case of Mexicali with industrial activities.

Figure 2 shows the cyclic behavior of the growth of the number of establishments and the employment generated by companies oriented toward export throughout the 1975–1996 period. Between 1975 and 1982, erratic behavior in the variables of employment and the number of establishments seems to respond to this changing instability and to a period of wage appreciation that is reflected in reductions in export activities in Baja California and Mexicali.

After 1982, there was a period of sustained growth for both employment and number of *maquiladoras* in Baja California that can be attributed to the attraction of

Figure 2. Baja California and the Municipality of Mexicali: A Comparative Analysis of the Number of Establishments and Employment in the Maquiladora Industry by Year, 1975–1996

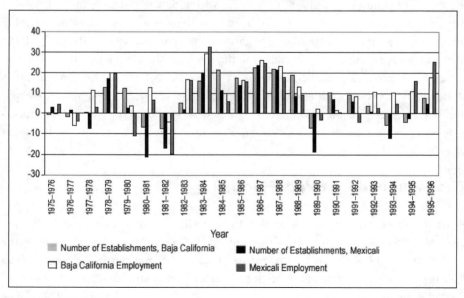

SOURCE: AMPI (2000).

investments to Tijuana. Gradually, the Municipality of Tijuana surpassed Mexicali in the number of companies and the amount of employment generated. This tendency toward growth was maintained until 1989 when the erratic behavior of both variables began. This was associated with a period of wage appreciation that peaked in 1994. The devaluation of the peso in 1994 and the creation of a common North American market one year prior seemed to have contributed to reactivating the growth of employment and new *maquiladoras* in the city after 1994. The signing of NAFTA and the maintenance of the low cost of production as a result of the devaluation of December 1994 formally broadened the market's potential.

Both aspects seem to have stimulated the flow of investments by large U.S. and Asian companies that, after December 1994, established large plants and generated large amounts of employment. Characteristics such as the origin of investments, the increase in plant size, and the sectoral changes experienced by this industry describe its growth in Mexicali and are linked to its capacity to integrate with production and consumption markets. The relocation of export plants to Mexicali is facilitated by the proximity of the California market just across the border, which encompasses about thirty million consumers and is one of the strongest in the United States. The lowering of production costs by the fluctuation and depreciation of the peso in past years and access to U.S. highways and telecommunication systems that have traditionally favored the border have also contributed to plant relocation. These advantages are confirmed by the strategic movement of large corporations now located in Mexicali.

The arrival of large plants quickly modified the profile of local industry to strongly represent the export industry. In 1998, companies established in Mexicali's industrial parks were 48.2 percent of U.S. origin, 32.0 percent Japanese, and 11.5 percent from other Asian nations. These figures represented the development of a platform of industries for the U.S. market that in the coming years will require the regional integration of its products.

Within the framework of this strategy lie two important aspects: (1) the specialization that industry has developed over the years, and (2) the consistency of increased plant size that is characteristic of Mexicali. In 1973, *maquiladoras* located in Mexicali concentrated in the textile and automotive industries, together representing 62.5 percent of employment in the export industry. In 1998, the electronics industry included 46 percent of employment in the *maquiladoras*. Alongside this change is an increase in plant size in the city. Statistics on export activities in 1996 show that while the average plant size in Baja California was 201.3 workers, in Mexicali it was 256.5 workers. These data highlight the impact that the strategies of large international corporations have had on industrial activity in Mexicali.

Industry and Mexicali's Organization

As noted earlier, industry is a relatively recent activity in Mexicali because its current location is shaped by the logic of border cities relative to their distance to Mexico's center and their exterior relationships. The city's major roadways have been a determinant factor since the beginning of the location of industry, with the border crossings that permit communication with the other side of the border playing an important role in the city's activities.

The roadways that provide access to Mexicali and the ports of entry are also determining elements in the territorial organization of the city and industrial production in particular, identifying their close link to the production and distribution processes in the southwestern United States. The arrival of industrial subcontracting processes after 1965 and the gradual establishment of industrial plants with greater size and more permanence later defined new industrial zones to the east of Mexicali. They responded to the strategic articulation between the new border crossing (inaugurated in 1995) and the roadways that unite the city to the extreme west with Tijuana and to the east with San Luis Río Colorado in the neighboring State of Sonora, territorially integrating it with Mexico's interior. The occupation process east of Mexicali's urban area was spurred by the population center's urban development plan in 1984. The plan defined the zone as a more viable alternative for the city's territorial expansion with property located in the González Ortega delegation (Gobierno del Estado de Baja California and Ayuntamiento de Mexicali 1984). The decision was accompanied by the construction of a new wastewater treatment plant in the city in 1987. This plant accelerated new housing developments and the creation of industrial parks that were able to consolidate an industrial corridor sustained by the export industry that can be identified in Figure 3.

The process gave way to the creation of roadway infrastructure that integrated a series of modern industrial parks where companies with medium-term investment horizons were located. This made use of flexible schemes and manufacturing incubation periods in different industrial park categories developed and administered by local companies. These companies brought together a series of multinational plants of different origins that, due to the sum of their investments and the size of their facilities, make them think in terms of long-term horizons and establish more regional roots.

During the second half of the 1980s, growth to the east of the city was developed by a speculative phenomenon that preempted the long process toward the opening of a second border crossing, which finally opened in 1995. The changes that this part of the city experienced prompted Mexicali's urban development plan of December 1991 (Gobierno del Estado de Baja California and XIII Ayuntamiento de Mexicali 1991: 28) to recognize the trends identified by the plan of 1984 and consolidate the industrial areas to the northeast and southeast of the city. Since this document

Figure 3. Location of Industrial Spaces, Mexicali, 1998

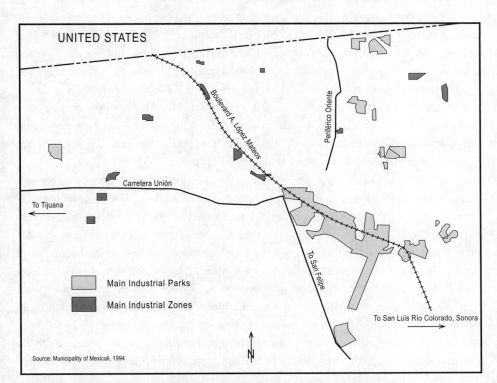

SOURCE: Programa de Desarrollo Urbano de Mexicali, Municipio de Mexicali (1994).

recognized that industrial development in the part of this city quickly exceeded expectations, it introduced a new zone to the southeast to balance future industrial development. In the northeastern zone, the industrial use of "… a reserve established by the 1984 plan that, although it was designated for commercial use and services, is conveniently located next to the land intended for the international crossing, serving as a reserve for the already existing industrial concentration"(Gobierno del Estado de Baja California and XIII Ayuntamiento de Mexicali 1991: 29). As part of the strategy, it indicated that these lands would be for manufacturing and for guaranteeing the supply of infrastructure services within the boundaries of the project (Gobierno del Estado de Baja California and XIII Ayuntamiento de Mexicali 1991: 29).

In the southeastern zone, the land proposed for industrial use includes a series of parcels north of the San Luis Río Colorado highway. Its purpose is to consolidate this roadway as the most important industrial corridor in the city. The lands were designated reserves in 1984 for industrial and residential use and include a reserve section requested in 1989 by Ejido Puebla. This zone's importance lies in its accessibility to the highway, its location within the boundary of the city's integral infrastructure project, and the advantage that the railroad provides for the transport of primary materials and products (see Figure 3).

Again, the plan identifies the southeast as a zone for future industrial activity, distinguishing two periods in the use of a series of parcels: (1) as a zone to be utilized in the short term with the advantages of the Tijuana highway and availability and access to infrastructure services, and (2) as a zone for future growth that, for the moment, lacks projects for the supply of services. With this proposal for future development, indicators of relative saturation are recognized in the city's eastern zone (Gobierno del Estado de Baja California and XIII Ayuntamiento de Mexicali 1991: 29), requiring the identification of alternatives. Currently, these areas house a series of production plants for exportation that can be identified in Figure 3.

Mexicali's urban development plan in 1991 recognized consolidation processes in the city's modern zone of industrial development. The plan began to identify alternative areas for industrial location for the future based on density in the eastern part of the city and a period of rapid growth in the export industry. Currently, this zone encompasses a number of important residential areas with infrastructure and access to a network of primary and secondary roadways, forming a satellite city called Mexicali II. Here, a second border crossing for the management of industrial imports and exports contributes to the creation of a new center that is relatively autonomous from the traditional center of the city. It is a relatively modern border space sustained by modern industrial activity and an efficient border crossing for the export and import of necessary merchandise for international production in Mexicali.

Patterns of Industrial Localization

The distribution of industrial zones and industrial parks throughout the city can be described within the framework of the strategic location of roadways and international crossings. The distinction between traditional industrial zones and industrial parks is that regional industries are distributed largely in the industrial zones as characterized in the first phase of industrialization in Mexicali. The activities of the industrial parks activities are primarily for export. The latter were initiated in the 1970s and are concentrated in the eastern part of the city.

Following this distinction between industrial zones and industrial parks[9] (see Figure 4), a temporal difference in the city's development can be identified. The first phase of industrial development in Mexicali concentrated on the transformation of products linked to agriculture, such as cotton and wheat. Adolfo López Mateos Boulevard linked agricultural activities in the valley in this period with the historic center, where the first international crossing was located. This roadway was a base for the city's development, but it also divided the city in two. It ran almost parallel to the New River channel and integrated the activities of the Mexicali Valley and the City of

Mexicali, whose common reference was the old center. A pattern of expansion to the east of the city currently predominates.

The Pacific Soap Company (Jabonera del Pacífico) and the Valley Flour Company (Harinera del Valle) are found alongside Adolfo López Mateos Boulevard. Both are transformation plants dedicated to agricultural products that profited from access to the highways that linked the city with Mexico's interior and the rest of the state. The Baja California-Pacífico railroad station for cargo and passengers of the old railroad is also located in this central part of the city. The first concentration of industrial, commercial, and service activities was found in this sector of the city, which brought on the construction and development of a modern civic center in the early 1970s.

The logic of the industrial parks is different. The first industrial park in Mexicali (Parque Industrial de Mexicali–PIMSA 1) was constructed to the west of the city, close to the new border crossing. It was planned, developed, and occupied from the beginning by activities that were primarily oriented toward the external market.[10] From this first experience, the development of this type of facility remained relatively stagnant in Mexicali until the mid-1980s, when the expansion of the export industry began to require more space. Mexicali and Baja California are national leaders in the number of industrial parks registered and are third with respect to the area covered by industrial parks (ITESM 1997: 73–77). In Mexicali, the development of industrial parks was integrated with the development of a primary and secondary roadway structure to facilitate communication, the movement of merchandise, and the

Figure 4. Historic Growth of the City of Mexicali, 1900–1990

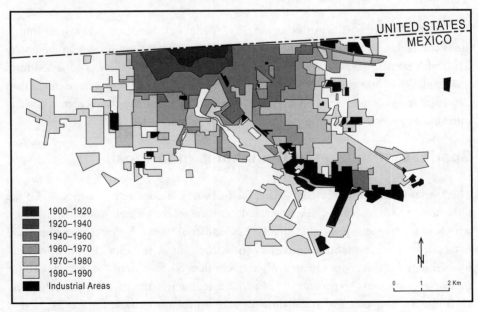

SOURCE: AMPI (2000).

shipment of products. This was made possible by the authorization of a network of roadways in previous years that facilitated the movement of merchandise for export to the new border crossing, its penetration into Mexico, and its transport to Tijuana. In 1996, the prolongation of the Periférico Oriente, which connects this eastern part of Mexicali with the western, was completed. In 1997, the Carretera Unión was widened by four lanes, making it an alternative roadway for communication. The city integrates this with a ring of merchandise flows that strengthens its internal and external markets.

In the span of just over three decades, Mexicali achieved the development of an economic base increasingly sustained by industrial activity and oriented toward the external market, which experienced even greater expansion after 1980. This capacity to integrate a diverse industrial base in such a short period of time is accompanied by a capacity to endow these activities with favorable conditions, thereby promoting them. It seems that while the economic structure was modified in these three decades, the city rapidly adapted to its new functions.[11] Nonetheless, in recent years, labor market shortages steered the location of industrial plants to areas that were not anticipated for industrial use, responding to interests in siting industries in areas that could provide labor pools. This has resulted in the establishment of industrial plants in the middle of large public residential centers to facilitate job opportunities that, as in the majority of border cities, are frequently insufficient compared to demand.

Spatial Logic and Characteristics of Industrial Facilities in Mexicali

The location pattern of industries in the City of Mexicali has been determined from a study of technical norms for the regulation of industrial facilities conducted by Mexicali's sixteenth city council in 2000. The study included 80 surveys collected from 263 small (16 to 100 employees), medium (101 to 250 employees), and large (more than 250 employees) companies. It considered aspects of location, physical construction, and infrastructure services, with its classification by size and industrial branch.

Spatial Distribution of Companies in Mexicali

The spatial distribution of the industrial facilities was divided into five groups. Of the total number of companies, almost half (45 percent) were located in industrial parks, which is an area designed exclusively for industrial use. Another 22 percent were disseminated in residential neighborhoods throughout the city, 13 percent were located in industrial zones (an area where more than 60 percent of the land is used for industrial purposes), 11 percent in industrial areas, where the land is not exclusively for industry use, and 9 percent outside of the urban area (see Figure 5). If it is considered that 58 percent of the industrial facilities are located in industrial parks and zones—as defined by the population center's urban development plan for industrial use—it may be concluded that just more than half of the companies are situated in a planned manner.

Figure 5. Distribution of Industrial Facilities according to Their Location

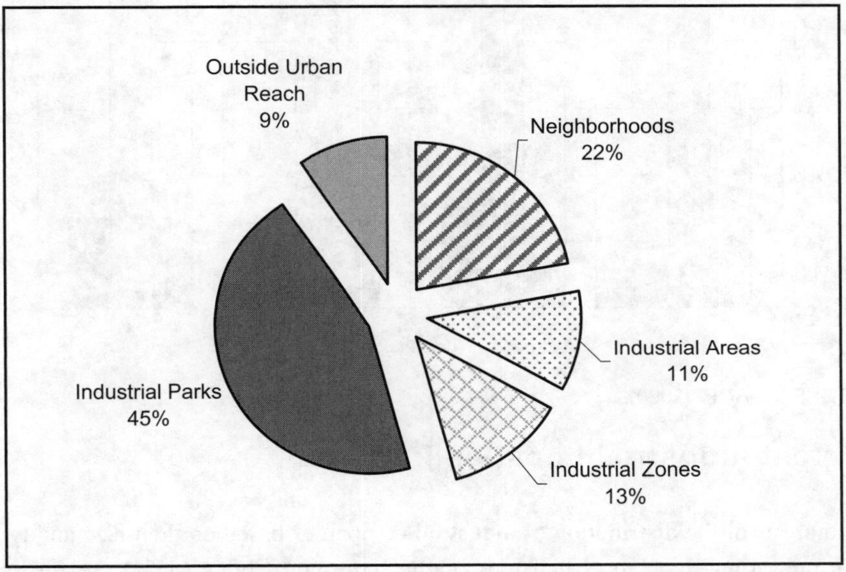

SOURCE: AMPI (2000).

Evolution of Industries Based on Size

An analysis of the age of industrial companies allows for their division into four periods: before 1975, 1976 to 1985, 1986 to 1990, and 1991 to 2000. According to their size, the proportion of small companies has remained practically constant with the exception of the 1986–1990 period, in which it grew. The number of medium-sized companies decreased between 1975 and 1990 from 62 percent to 46 percent and then registered an increase in the 1991–2000 period, reaching 53 percent. The proportion of large companies has varied compared to small and medium companies. It experienced an increase in the last decade to reach 14 percent of all companies (see Figure 6), which can be explained by the installation of large plants following the signing of NAFTA. This increase was principally based on Asian companies positioning themselves to take advantage of the U.S. market.

Figure 6. Age of Industrial Companies by Size

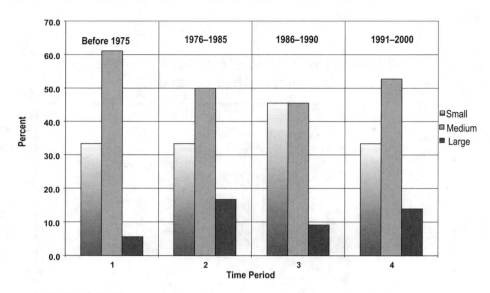

SOURCE: AMPI (2000).

Current Industrial Location Patterns

An analysis of the distribution of industrial companies based on their size and type of location shows that more than half of the large companies (55%) are located in industrial parks and one-fourth are located in industrial areas (27%). Large companies do not locate in residential neighborhoods. The largest percentage of small (44%) and medium (43%) companies are found in industrial parks and the rest are distributed almost equally among neighborhoods, industrial areas and zones, and outside of the urban area (see Figure 3).

Location of Industries by Industrial Branch and Size

An analysis of the distribution of companies by industrial branch and location demonstrates that all basic metallic industries are located outside of the urban area due in large part to the characteristics of their productive processes. Almost any type of industry can be found in the industrial parks and residential neighborhoods, including those dedicated to the production of foods, textiles, paper, chemical products, plastics, oilcloth, and wood manufacturing, as well as companies that produce goods based on nonmetallic minerals, such as glass or thermal and acoustic insulators. Although most small, medium, and large industrial companies are located in industrial parks, the fact that companies from almost all of the industrial branches

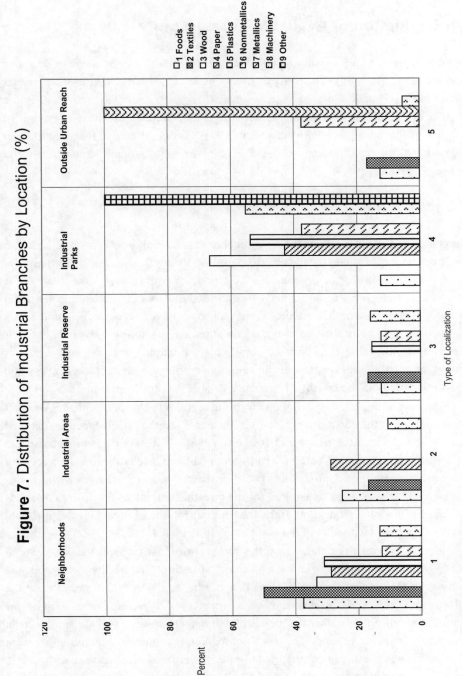

Figure 7. Distribution of Industrial Branches by Location (%)

SOURCE: AMPI (2000).

can locate in residential neighborhoods implies high-risk situations and incompatibility of land uses that should be studied in greater detail (see Figure 7).

An Evaluation of Available Infrastructure

In general terms, the provision of infrastructure for industry in Mexicali is adequate because the location of the majority of small, medium, and large industrial companies is in industrial parks and zones (areas planned for such use). This translates into a high level of urban infrastructure networks, as reflected by the percentage of companies that are supplied with electricity (97%), are connected to the potable water network (90%), are connected to the sewage network (82%), and have storm water drainage systems (70%).

Conclusions

Compared to the other principal border localities, industrial development in Mexicali has been more gradual. It has activities linked to the processing of agricultural products and in other sectors such as the automobile and paper industries. These sectors highlight local business activities and have been determinants in the local economic environment. The *maquiladora* industry and the recent development of a more specialized sector that concentrates on other manufacturing companies, such as electronics, has made for a more diversified local economic base. This aspect is important to highlight because it technically reduces the city's structural fragility and provides stability in the face of an evermore volatile economic environment.

The second aspect that is important to highlight is the response of the Mexicali community with the continued arrival of investments and the establishment of national and foreign plants in the recent past. The evaluation of urban organization and spaces for industry shows that the current urban system has responded to relatively successful planning and regulation processes. These processes have created industrial nodes linked by a network of roads tailored for the direction and intensity of flows of goods articulated for global production. Here, the determinant role of border crossings should be noted for their facilitation of the city's integration in this process.

Finally, the results obtained by the survey of industrial facilities in Mexicali allow for the identification of some key aspects of location and quality to complete the analysis of this sector. The conclusions that can be drawn from these results are the following: (1) there is a tendency for companies to locate in places defined for industrial purposes, indicating the presence of regulatory systems that are applied in an acceptable manner; (2) medium-sized companies predominate, although a recent increase in large plants can be attributed to a positioning by foreign companies to access the U.S. market, according to the NAFTA calendar; (3) recent growth and the impact it has had on more specialized industries—electronics in particular—outline a new direction for local industry; and (4) an evaluation of the availability of infrastructure yields positive data that are interpreted as the direct result of a coordinating process among different local actors (public and private) that have favored active and applied planning in this sector's development in Mexicali.

Endnotes

1. The free zone along the border became a very relevant aspect of border life and activities. It was a determining factor in the development of border localities in northern Mexico and a continuing source of conflict for the two governments in the 50 years following the U.S.-Mexican War (1846–1848). The free zones that make up the Baja California peninsula and part of the State of Sonora were fully formed in 1933. This regime was even more liberal than its predecessors because the importation of merchandise was not subject to the payment of taxes or import licenses, unless the tariff of the general import tax so indicated. The free zones have been extended on various occasions and are maintained through the year 2001.

2. "The *maquiladora* industry arises in Mexico as an alternative industrialization project for the northern border in 1965 and a palliative for the massive unemployment caused by the termination of the Bracero Program, which left thousands of workers unemployed. Despite the projections of the Border Industrialization Program with respect to the temporality of this industry, the *maquiladora* became the center of industrial policy in the northern border region in the decade of the 1970s and national industrial policy in the decade of the 1980s" (González Aréchiga and Barajas 1989).

3. This company was established very early on to gin and bale cotton. It helped to stimulate local agriculture, making it the emblematic industry of the region (UABC 1991).

4. In English-language literature, this quality is termed "footloose."

5. Mexico has rapidly strengthened and specialized in activities related to automobile parts and electric and electronic products for international markets, principally that of the United States. This indicates that the process of regional specialization (within NAFTA) integrates different phases of the global production chain, giving more value to operations in Mexico (Carrillo and Hualde 1998: 79–97).

6. This refers to the certification of origin that will be required in the future for products that circulate in the U.S. market and the competitive advantages that allow for the decentralization of production in Mexico.

7. Kenworth is an assembly plant for heavy-duty trucks. In the first period, it produced vehicles for the protected national market. Currently, its production is basically for export.

8. The most important market for televisions is the United States, which absorbs approximately 95 percent of those produced in Mexico. In the continental environment, excluding the Southern Common Market (Mercado Común del Sur–MERCOSUR), it is estimated that by the year 2003, demand for televisions will reach approximately thirty-five million units.

9. A complete definition for industrial parks, encompassing their objectives and characteristics, does not exist (Aguilar 1993: 41). Nonetheless, the difference established in this study refers to industrial facilities and land use without complete planning, which occurred during the first period of industrialization in Mexicali. Industrial parks are, from their origins, complete infrastructure projects with flexible organization schemes that include rent and the incubation of companies. This difference is clearly established in Figures 3 and 4.

10. The PIMSA industrial park began to sell space in 1968 and established its current structure in 1971.

11. Expansion to the east was planned and anticipated by the City of Mexicali's urban development plan in 1984 (Gobierno del Estado de Baja California and XI Ayuntamiento de Mexicali 1984). The results found here confirm this purpose and highlight the orienting and rationalizing role played by the city's resource infrastructure, which proposed this strategy 16 years ago.

References

Aguilar, B.G. 2000. "Modificación de la organización espacial tradicional originada por el uso del automóvil particular. Casos: Tijuana, Mexicali y Ciudad Juárez." Master's thesis, Instituto de Investigaciones Sociales, Universidad Autónoma de Baja California, Mexicali, Mexico.

Aguilar, I. 1993. *Descentralización industrial y desarrollo regional en México.* México, D.F.: El Colegio de México.

Avilés Muñoz, Ana María, Guillermo Alvarez de la Torre, Arturo Ranfla González, Djamel Toudert Ait El Hocine, Cristina Dorantes González, Annee Collin Delavaud, and Christine Triboulet-Eberhard. 2001. *Atlas de Mexicali, un espacio urbano en la estrategia internacional.* Mexicali: Editorial UABC.

Bravo Aguilera, L. 1981. "La política de desarrollo comercial fronterizo en el norte de México." In *Relaciones México-Estados Unidos, memoria del primer encuentro sobre impactos regionales de la relaciones económicas México-Estados Unidos.* México, D.F.: El Consorcio para la Investigación sobre México and Asociación Nacional de Universidades e Instituciones de Educación Superior.

Carrillo, J., and A. Hualde. 1998. "Third Generation Maquiladoras? The Delphi-General Motors Case." *Journal of Borderlands Studies* 13 (1): 79–97.

Castel, O. 1995. "Les politiques volontaires de l'etat mexicain." In *L'ajustement structurel et apres*, O. Castel, ed. Paris: Editions Maison Neuve-Larose.

Fellman, J., A. Getis, and J. Getis. 1997. *Human Geography, Landscapes of Human Activities.* Madison: Brown & Benchmark.

Gobierno del Estado de Baja California and XI Ayuntamiento de Mexicali. 1984. *Plan de desarrollo urbano.* Mexicali: Gobierno del Estado de Baja California and XI Ayuntamiento de Mexicali.

Gobierno del Estado de Baja California and XIII Ayuntamiento de Mexicali. 1991. *Esquema de desarrollo urbano de la ciudad de Mexicali.* Mexicali: Gobierno del Estado de Baja California and XIII Ayuntamiento de Mexicali.

Gobierno del Estado de Baja California and XIV Ayuntamiento de Mexicali. 1994. *Plan de desarrollo urbano de Mexicali.* Mexicali: Gobierno del Estado de Baja California and XIV Ayuntamiento de Mexicali.

González Aréchiga, B., and E.R. Barajas. 1989. *Las maquiladoras: ajuste estructural y desarrollo regional.* México, D.F.: El Colegio de la Frontera Norte and Fundación Friedrich Ebert.

Instituto Nacional de Estadística, Geografía e Informática (INEGI). 1993. *Censos económicos.* Aguascalientes: INEGI.

Instituto Nacional de Estadística, Geografía e Informática (INEGI). 1998. *Censos económicos.* Aguascalientes: INEGI.

Instituto Nacional de Estadística, Geografía e Informática (INEGI). 2000. *XII Censo general de población y vivienda.* Aguascalientes: INEGI.

Instituto Tecnológico y de Estudios Superiores de Monterrey (ITESM). 1997. *Atracción de la inversión en México. Indicadores de localización de negocios*. Monterrey: ITESM.

Municipio de Mexicali. 1994. *Programa de desarrollo urbano de Mexicali*. Mexicali: Municipio de Mexicali.

Paix, C., and H. Riviere d'Arc. 1997. "Entrepreneurs et espaces de croissance." In *Esprit d'enterprisse et nouveñlles synergies de part et d'autre du pacifique*. Paris: Maison Neuve & Larose.

Universidad Autónoma de Baja California (UABC). 1991. *Mexicali: una historia*. Mexicali: UABC.

15

Agriculture in the Imperial Valley

Refugio A. González*

Abstract

The Imperial Valley was once a harsh and deserted region located in the southeast corner of the State of California. Today, it commands a place as one of the most agriculturally productive regions in the world. According to the value of agriculture receipts, Imperial County was ranked tenth in the state and twelfth in the nation in the 1997 Census of Agriculture. In 1999, agriculture receipts grossed in excess of one billion dollars. Approximately 30 percent of the civilian workforce in Imperial County is employed by the agricultural sector.

Origins of Agriculture

As early as the 1850s, the idea of diverting Colorado River water to the Imperial Valley for irrigation purposes generated the interest of developers—particularly that of Dr. O.M. Wozencraft. At the end of the nineteenth century, the California Development Company was formed to finance C.R. Rockwood's design of Wozencraft's project, which Wozencraft had surveyed extensively for four years. In 1901, the Imperial Canal, also known as the Alamo Canal, was completed. It diverted waters from the Colorado River near Pilot Knob and traversed through Mexico about forty miles before crossing into the United States at what is now Calexico. A couple of years later, a bypass channel was constructed to counter problems associated with high concentrations of salt in the Imperial Canal. In 1904, floodwaters from the Colorado and Gila rivers caused the failure of this temporary structure and nearly two

*González is County Director of the University of California Cooperative Extension in the Imperial Valley.

years of free-flowing Colorado River water. As a result, the Salton Sink was transformed into the Salton Sea and to this day continues to serve as the regional drainage basin (IID 1996: 4).

Recent Agricultural Activities

The Imperial Valley is defined as the land within the boundaries of the Imperial Irrigation District. In 1997, there were 557 farms in the Imperial Valley, spanning a total of 489,726 acres. The median number of acres per farm was 256. Almost 27 percent of the farms consisted of more than one thousand acres. Nearly 21 percent were between 50 and 179 acres. As shown in Table 1, other sizes were pretty evenly

Table 1. Summary of Imperial County Agricultural Highlights, 1997

Description	Number
Number of farms	557
Total farm acres	489,726
Average farm acres	879
Median farm acres	256
Farms 1–9 acres	69
Farms 10–49 acres	68
Farms 50–179 acres	120
Farms 180–499 acres	90
Farms 500–999 acres	61
Farms 1,000+ acres	149
Farms with sales less than $2,500	52
$2,500–4,999	18
$5,000–9,999	25
$10,000–24,999	31
$25,000–49,999	34
$50,000–99,999	51
$100,000+	346

SOURCE: USDA (1997).

distributed. The table also shows that 62 percent of the farms in the Imperial Valley had sales of $100,000 or more.

An examination of Table 2 indicates that six of the top agricultural counties, ranked by total value of products, are situated in the San Joaquin Valley. Three of these counties are in Southern California and one is located in the central coastal region. Imperial County is ranked number 10.

Table 3 identifies cattle as the number one commodity, by total value, in the Imperial Valley. Vegetable crop commodities (9) take the greatest number of

Table 2. Top 10 California Counties Ranked by
Total Value of Production, 1998

Rank	County	Value ($1,000)
1	Fresno	3,286,806
2	Tulare	2,922,057
3	Monterey	2,295,285
4	Kern	2,067,678
5	Merced	1,449,754
6	San Joaquin	1,311,088
7	Stanislaus	1,302,714
8	Riverside	1,199,507
9	San Diego	1,178,391
10	Imperial	1,083,232

SOURCE: CDFA (1999).

Table 3. Top 15 Commodities in Imperial County
Ranked by Value, 1999

Rank	Commodity	Value ($)
1	Cattle	166,910,000
2	Alfalfa	118,613,000
3	Lettuce	101,987,000
4	Carrots	77,222,000
5	Sugar beets	59,231,000
6	Leaf lettuce	48,278,000
7	Misc. livestock	36,998,000
8	Onions	36,661,000
9	Broccoli	35,712,000
10	Certified seed	34,887,000
11	Cantaloupes	33,954,000
12	Misc. vegetables	28,504,000
13	Sudangrass hay	25,871,000
14	Asparagus	19,980,000
15	Cauliflower	19,094,000

SOURCE: Birdsall (1999).

rankings, or "places," on this table, followed by field crops (3). Certified seed and miscellaneous livestock follow with one rank each. Miscellaneous livestock include all livestock other than cattle. Alfalfa and lettuce are the leading field and vegetable crop commodities. These two commodities are described in greater detail later in this essay.

Table 4 presents commodities by major groupings and provides the total value of each commodity group for 1999. While livestock as a single commodity had the highest value, it fell to third place in a group ranking, following vegetables, melons, and field crops, respectively. In 2001, a new beef-processing plant opened in the City of Brawley, which has increased the total value of the cattle sector.

According to Mayberry and others (2000), in their circular 104–F and regarding Imperial County field crops, total preharvest costs for alfalfa were $708 per acre. These costs included the cost of crop establishment, the annual cost of hay production (three- to five-year crop life), land rent, amortization, and cash overhead. Harvest costs were $210.61, bringing the total cost of alfalfa production to $918.61 per acre. The average production was eight tons per acre. Alfalfa plantings normally stay in production three-to-five years. Alfalfa is normally baled from March through October, although limited baling is done year-round. During winter months, both sheep pasturing and green chopping are normally practiced (Mayberry et al. 2000: 4–5). The greatest portion of farmable land in the Imperial Valley is planted with alfalfa.

Mayberry and others (2000) place total preharvest costs for lettuce at $1,932.01 per acre. These costs include crop establishment, the growing period (three-to-four months), land rent, and cash overhead. Harvest costs are $2,526, bringing total cost of lettuce production to $4,557.01 per acre. The average yield is five hundred 50-pound cartons per acre. Lettuce is ranked the number one vegetable crop in the Imperial Valley on the basis of gross receipts. The harvest season is midwinter (December to March). Iceberg lettuce is hand harvested. Crews of approximately twenty-to-thirty people work as units around a mobile field harvest. The solid lettuce heads are cut, trimmed, and each carton is wrapped in plastic film. A film-wrapped carton has a minimum of 38 pounds gross weight (Mayberry et al. 2000: 43–45). Cost of production for other field and vegetable crops is included in the cited circulars and can be obtained at the county offices of the University of California Cooperative Extension.

Table 4. Commodity Groups by Total Value, 1999

Commodity	Value ($)
Vegetables and melon crops	458,114,000
Field crops	257,341,000
Livestock	219,609,000
Seed and nursery crops	72,304,000
Fruit and nut crops	34,743,000
Apiary products	2,981,000

SOURCE: USDA (1997).

Table 5. Economic Impact of Agricultural Production on Local Employment, 1999

Commodities	Gross Receipts ($1,000)	Number of Jobs
Vegetables and melons	458,114	6,891
Cattle and calves	166,910	1,758
Hay and pasture	161,779	4,111

SOURCE: Birdsall (1999).

Table 5 shows three commodity groups and their respective economic impacts on the Imperial Valley workforce. It shows the commodity groups by gross receipts and the number of jobs each commodity group generates. Vegetables and melons generate the greatest number of jobs because of their need for extensive "hand labor." Cattle and calf operations generate the least number of jobs in these selected commodity groups.

The California State Employment Development Department's (EDD) 1999 annual average statistics show that the Imperial County civilian labor force totals 55,800 persons, with an unemployment rate of 23.2 percent—four times higher than that of the State of California (5.2%). In 1999, agriculture accounted for over 30

Table 6. Top 15 U.S. Counties Ranked by Market Value on Agricultural Products Sold, 1997

No.	County	State
1	Fresno	California
2	Kern	California
3	Tulare	California
4	Monterey	California
5	Weld	Colorado
6	Merced	California
7	Stanislaus	California
8	San Joaquin	California
9	Riverside	California
10	Yakima	Washington
11	Palm Beach	Florida
12	Imperial	California
13	Ventura	California
14	Grant	Washington
15	Lancaster	Pennsylvania

SOURCE: USDA (1997).

percent of all employment in Imperial County. According to the EDD, industry employment projections indicate that most of the future nonfarm wage and salary jobs will be in retail trade, services, and government. Retail trade is projected to grow by 12 percent, with most of the growth in the business services sector. Government employment is projected to grow by almost 8 percent (EDD 2000).

Table 6 identifies the top 15 U.S. counties ranked by market value of agricultural products sold. An examination of Table 6 reveals that eight of the 15 counties (53%) are located in California. While Imperial County is ranked as the tenth leading county in California, Table 6 shows that it falls to twelfth place at the national level.

Challenges in the Region

Crops are grown year-round in the Imperial Valley; as a result, agricultural pests can and do devastate crop production. Producers wage a constant war against insects, diseases, and weed pests. New pest invasions can mean major economic losses to Imperial County farmers. Within the last decade, the sweetpotato whitefly—*Bemisia tabaci* (Gennadius)—caused major losses to growers and high unemployment among farmworkers. The Imperial County Agricultural Commissioner's Office estimated whitefly damage of fall and winter 1991–1992 crops at approximately $111 million. From November 1991 through January 1992, whitefly devastation of fall vegetable crops resulted in a 21 percent increase in the number of unemployment insurance weeks claimed, compared to the period between November 1990 and January 1991 (González et al. 1992: 7). During the 1990s, however, the sweetpotato whitefly was "muscled out" by the more competitive silverleaf whitefly *(Bemisia argentifoli)*.

There are no controlled experiments that clearly quantify silverleaf whitefly damage to alfalfa in terms of yield or forage quality reduction. This is partly due to the inability to create an uninfested control. Grower records, Imperial County Agricultural Commissioner annual reports, and University of California forage-yield trial records all strongly suggest, however, that the silverleaf whitefly may directly or indirectly reduce alfalfa forage yield by 10-to-25 percent. Imperial County Agricultural Commissioner's reports since 1990 show a 17 percent reduction in annual alfalfa hay yield (Tueber et al. 1997: 25).

Conclusion

Imperial County agriculture has earned a prominent position among the most productive agricultural regions in the world. New challenges and opportunities will certainly be a part of the region's growth. The long-term effects of changing economic conditions will play a major role in the ability of agricultural producers in the Imperial Valley to sustain their competitive position in the markets. Increased cost of production inputs, such as labor, fuel, fertilizers, and so on, will have a major impact on the viability of the agricultural sector in the Imperial Valley. The valley's ability to attract new industries, such as dairies or vegetable-processing facilities, may ensure the future of Imperial Valley agriculture.

References

Birdsall, Stephen L. 1999. *Imperial County 1999 Agricultural Crop and Livestock Report*. Imperial County: Agricultural Commissioner.

California Department of Food and Agriculture (CDFA). 1999. *California Agricultural Resource Directory*. Sacramento: Office of Public Affairs.

California Employment Development Department (EDD). 2000. "County Snapshots." Labor Market Information. http://www.calmis.cahwmet.gov.

González, Refugio A., George E. Goldman, Eric T. Natwick, Howard R. Rosenberg, James I. Grieshop, Stephan R. Sutter, Tad Funakoshi, and Socorro Dávila-García. 1992. "Whitefly Invasion in Imperial Valley Costs Growers, Workers Millions in Losses." *California Agriculture* 46 (5): 7–8.

Imperial Irrigation District (IID). 1996. *Water Requirements and Availability Study (Draft)*. Imperial California: Imperial Irrigation District Water Resources Unit.

Mayberry, Keith S., Khaled M. Bali, Refugio A. González, Juan N. Guerrero, Tom A. Turini, Eric T. Natwick, and Mark D. Stutes. 2000. *Guidelines to Production Costs and Practices for Field Crops*. Circular 104–F. Imperial County: University of California Cooperative Extension.

Mayberry, Keith S., Refugio A. González, Tom Turini, Khaled M. Bali, Eric T. Natwick, José L. Aguiar, and Mark D. Stutes. 2000. *Guidelines to Production Costs and Practices for Vegetable Crops*. Circular 104–V. Imperial County: University of California Cooperative Extension.

Tueber, Larry R., Michael E. Rupert, Larry K. Gibbs, and Ken L. Taggard. 1997. "Breeding Resistant Alfalfa Holds Promise for Silverleaf Whitefly Management." *California Agriculture* 51 (3): 25.

U.S. Department of Agriculture (USDA). 1997. "Census of Agriculture." National Agricultural Statistics Service. http://www.usda/gov/nass.

16

Agricultural Policy in Mexicali and San Luis Río Colorado

Eduardo Sánchez López*

Abstract

This essay reviews the status of agriculture in the Mexicali Valley in Baja California and San Luis Río Colorado in Sonora with five sections dedicated to the Mexicali-San Luis Río Colorado agricultural region; productive structure; the government sector; agricultural policy; and agricultural production. The first section describes the region in terms of location, soil, and water. Section two reviews land tenure as well as the organization and functions of the rural development and irrigation districts. The third section provides a description of government agencies at the federal and state level that support the development of agriculture in the region. Section four describes the important aspects of agricultural policies used by the government to achieve results at the local level. Finally, the fifth section provides concluding remarks and current trends in regional agricultural production.

The Mexicali and San Luis Río Colorado Agricultural Region

Geographic Location and Description

The Mexicali Valley is located between 114°45' and 115°40' longitude and 31°40' and 32°40' north latitude. It is bordered to the north by the State of California in the United States, to the south and southeast by the Gulf of California and the Sierra de

*Sánchez López is Director of the Veterinary Sciences Research Institute at the Universidad Autónoma de Baja California, Mexicali.

las Pintas, and to the east by the U.S. State of Arizona and the sandy mesa of San Luis Río Colorado in Sonora, Mexico. Part of the valley comprises a large agricultural region that is irrigated with water from the Colorado River. This river brings together Baja California and Sonora, specifically the Municipalities of Mexicali and San Luis Río Colorado.

Soils

The valley's soils contain parental material linked to Colorado River deposits with stratified deposits mainly derived from sedimentary rocks that are mixed and carried by the river waters from the Grand Canyon. There are six soil types in the region—Gila light phase, Gila heavy phase, Imperial, Holtville, melolan, and supertition—and 26 textural components dominate. In more general terms, soils are classified by their textures as light, medium, or heavy. The surface area that they occupy is defined in Table 1.

Hydrology

The Colorado River is the primary water supply for the Mexicali Valley and it allows California's and Baja California's agricultural zones to be irrigated (approximately 200,000 hectares). Quantities of water for distribution are guaranteed by the treaty

Figure 1. The Mexicali Valley

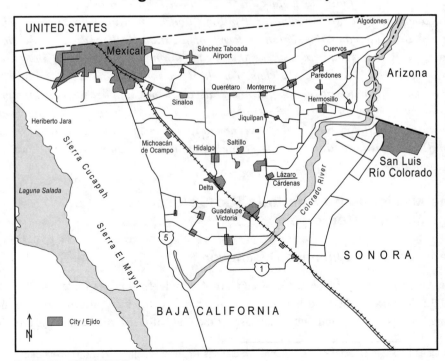

SOURCE: INEGI (1998).

Table 1. Distribution of Soil Types in the Mexicali Valley

Texture	Surface Area in Hectares	Percentage	Surface Area in Acres
Light	98,845	40.0	247,112.50
Medium	110,607	44.0	276,517.50
Heavy	40,548	16.0	101,370.00

SOURCE: SARH (1993).

signed by Mexico and the United States on February 3, 1944. It guarantees an annual volume of 1,502,829 acre-feet (1,850,234,000 cubic meters) of water to Mexico. A second source of water for the region consists of the extraction from subterranean aquifers, totaling 569 acre-feet (700,000 cubic meters), by 725 deep wells located in the valley. From these two sources, a total of 2,071,395 acre-feet (2,550,234,000 cubic meters) of water are utilized each year. Considering into the equation the water used for urban and industrial purposes in the cities of Mexicali, Tecate, and Tijuana, agriculture uses 1,910,830 acre-feet (2,352,551,000 cubic meters) of the total supply (see Table 2).

Table 2. Water Use and Availability for Agricultural Use

Use and Availability	Millions of Cubic Meters	Percentage	Millions of Acre-Feet
Total Resource	2,550,234	100.0	2,068
Urban and Industrial Use	197,638	7.7	160
Available for Agriculture	2,352,551	92.0	1,907

SOURCE: SARH (1993).

Productive Structure

Land Tenure

The regional surface area with productive potential is 207,506 hectares, of which 180,859 correspond to Baja California and 26,647 are in the State of Sonora. Of this land, 126,026 hectares are community-owned property *(ejidos)* and 81,480 are privately owned (see Table 3).

The average size of both *ejido* and private properties is less than 20 hectares and the majority of producers work an area from 10.1 to 20 hectares (25.25 to 50 acres) in size (82.2% of the *ejidos* and 57.37% of private owners are in this range).

Table 3. Distribution of Land Tenure in the Mexicali Valley

Type of Tenancy	Number of Users	Surface Area in Hectares	Percentage	Surface Area in Acres
Ejidal (Community owned)	7,392	126,026	60.73	315,065
Colonos (privately owned)	2,189	14,302	6.89	35,755
Small Proprietors (privately owned)	5,501	67,178	32.38	167,945

Note: *Colonos* and small proprietors differ in the amount of land they are allowed to possess.
SOURCE: SARH (1993).

The Rural Development District

With the goal of optimizing the coordination of government and production activities within one geographic zone, the Secretariat of Agriculture and Hydraulic Resources (Secretaría de Agricultura y Recursos Hidráulicos–SARH) established Rural Development District 002 in 1991. It includes the agricultural regions of Mexicali and San Luis Río Colorado and its purpose is to promote and support the development of the rural zone with the planning and execution of forest and agriculture resource conservation programs. It also provides extension and organization services that allow for regional production and productivity to increase and rural communities to improve.

The district is divided into eight areas, each of which is served by a Rural Development Support Center (Centro de Apoyo al Desarrollo Rural–CADER). The purpose of these centers is to spur agricultural development in the region with the provision of technical extension services tailored to the needs of local producers

Table 4. Basic Information on the Rural Development Support Center (CADER) of Rural Development District 002

CADER	Physical Surface Area		Irrigated Surface Area		Number of Users
	Hectares	Acres	Hectares	Acres	
Benito Juárez	43,000.0	107,500.0	42,425.3	106,063.1	2,861
Hechicera	48,562.0	121,405.0	33,121.2	82,803.1	2,155
San Luis	32,000.0	80,000.0	26,647.7	66,619.2	1,773
Colonias Nuevas	29,000.0	72,500.0	11,896.3	29,740.6	940
Guadalupe Victoria	31,300.0	78,250.0	28,407.0	71,017.4	2,076
Delta	43,566.0	108,915.0	32,524.0	81,310.0	2,166
Cerro Prieto	312,751.0	781,877.5	32,944.1	82,360.1	2,723
Valle Chico	966,734.0	2,416,835.0			483
Total	1,506,913.0	3,767,282.5	207,965.4	519,913.6	15,177

Note: Due to rounding, some numbers may not add up correctly.
SOURCE: SARH (1993).

(see Table 4). The geographic boundaries of the CADER within the district are shown in Figure 2.

The district's operations focus on programs related to the Ministry of Agriculture, Livestock, Rural Development, Fisheries, and Food (Secretaría de Agricultura, Ganadería, Desarrollo Rural, Pesca y Alimentación–SAGARPA).[1] The head of this department is responsible for the district's technical and administrative functions and participates in the planning, programming, and provision of support activities for the sector. He also coordinates and supervises the work of each of the eight CADER leaders. These leaders conduct the program's operational activities through technicians assigned to each of the support centers.

The Irrigation District

Water use, as an agricultural activity input on the 210,970 hectares that are arable is the administrative responsibility of the producers. Since March 23, 1998, producers have received concessions from the federal government through the National Water Commission (Comisión Nacional del Agua–CNA) to distribute water in the Mexicali Valley.

Figure 2. Geographical Boundaries of the Rural Development Support Centers

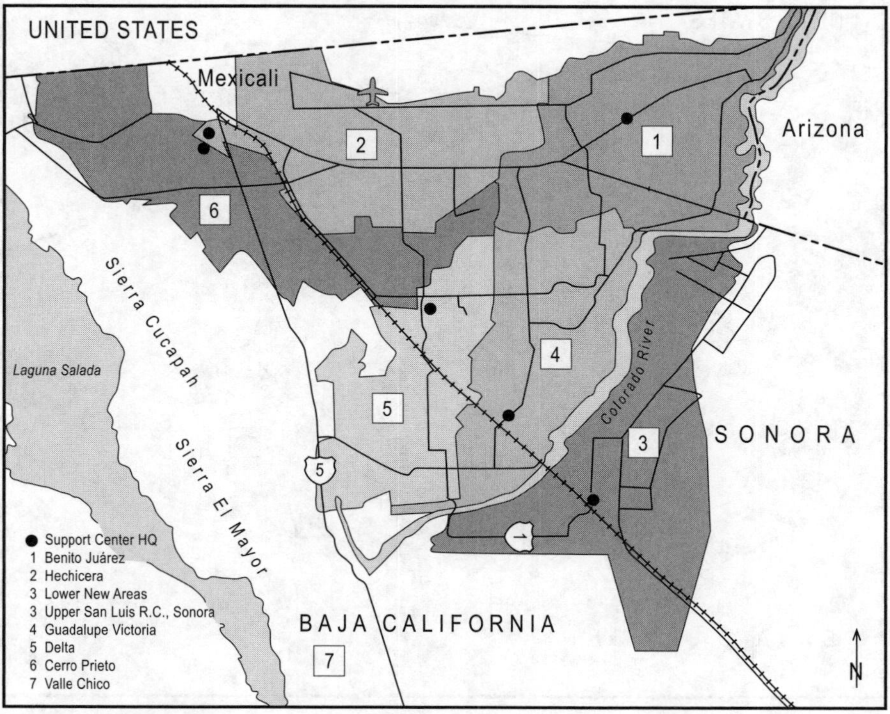

SOURCE: SARH (1993).

Water distribution is based on the use of irrigation permits owned by local farmers and the irrigation district infrastructure is administratively integrated into the Río Colorado Irrigation District (number 14). This district is operated and managed by the same water users endorsed by the CNA.

The users are divided into operational and administrative groups. The first is responsible for the larger infrastructure network that includes the major canals, drains, wells, and pumping plants in the district. These responsibilities are tended to by the office of the Colorado River Society of Limited Responsibility of Public Interest (Sociedad de Responsabilidad Limitada de Interés Público Río Colorado–SRL de IP Río Colorado). The latter is charged with maintaining the smaller irrigation network in geographic zones determined by each of the 23 irrigation modules distributed throughout the district (see Figure 3).

The CNA and the users are responsible for the completion of large projects, surveillance, and maintenance of the Morelos Dam that is the major diversion point of Colorado River water into the irrigation system. They are also in charge of maintenance of the Central and Sánchez Mejorada Canals (16.8 miles/27 kilometers) and the Mesa Arenosa wells.

Figure 3. Irrigation Modules of Colorado River Irrigation Districts

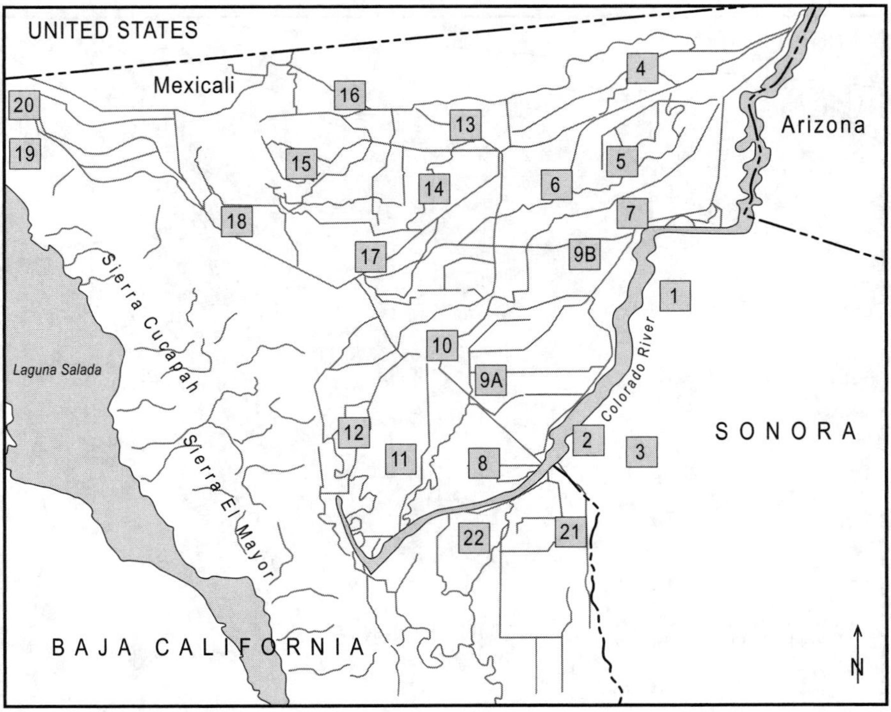

SOURCE: CNA (1998).

The SRL de IP Río Colorado has two operational responsibilities. First, it receives Colorado River water from the CNA and delivers it to the irrigation modules at control points in designated volumes. Second, it maintains the network of larger canals and wells located throughout the district. Figure 4 shows the society's organizational structure.

The irrigation modules are organized as a society of users whose common characteristic is the possession of an irrigation permit within the geographic boundaries of the module. The society is presided over by an administrative board that is elected every three years by its members.

Figure 4. Organizational Structure of the SRL de IP Río Colorado

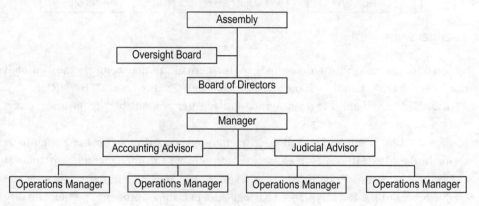

SOURCE: SRL de IP Río Colorado (1997).

The Government Sector

The Municipal Government

Both federal and state government entities are involved in agricultural activities in the Mexicali Valley. Municipal government activities do not have a direct relationship with agricultural production. Instead, municipal government is more focused on supplying public services to the valley's urban population.

The Federal Government

Federal entities directly related to agricultural production include SAGARPA and the CNA. Other departments involved with the sector are the Secretariat of Agrarian Reform (Secretaría de la Reforma Agraria–SRA), which is in charge of the registry of agricultural lands and the definition of properties, and the Secretariat of the Treasury and Public Credit (Secretaría de Hacienda y Crédito Público–SHCP), which is

Figure 5. Organizational Structure of SAGARPA at the State Level

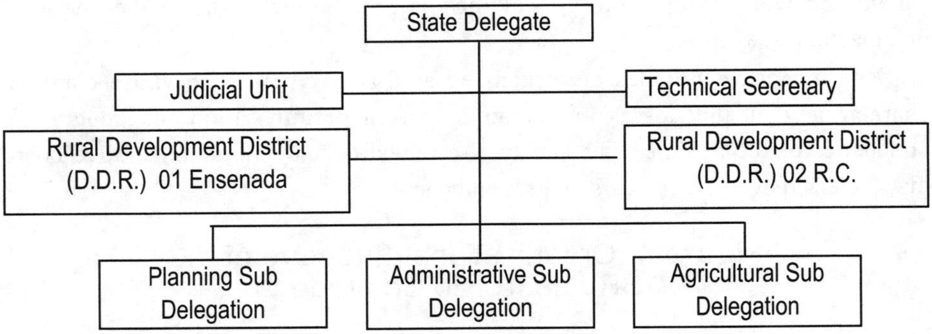

```
                        ┌──────────────────┐
                        │  State Delegate   │
                        └──────────────────┘
┌──────────────────┐                      ┌────────────────────┐
│   Judicial Unit   │                     │ Technical Secretary │
└──────────────────┘                      └────────────────────┘
┌────────────────────────┐              ┌────────────────────────┐
│ Rural Development District │          │ Rural Development District │
│ (D.D.R.) 01 Ensenada     │            │ (D.D.R.) 02 R.C.        │
└────────────────────────┘              └────────────────────────┘

┌──────────────┐    ┌──────────────────┐    ┌──────────────────┐
│ Planning Sub │    │ Administrative Sub │    │ Agricultural Sub │
│  Delegation  │    │    Delegation     │    │    Delegation    │
└──────────────┘    └──────────────────┘    └──────────────────┘
```

SOURCE: SARH (1993).

responsible for assigning federal budgets for agriculture and controls the National Bank of Rural Credit (Banco Nacional de Crédito Rural–BANRURAL). AGROASEMEX is the Mexican agricultural insurer responsible for insuring crops and cattle.

SAGARPA is undoubtedly the most important department for the agricultural sector in the Mexicali Valley because it is responsible for implementing agricultural policy in the region. Nonetheless, it is important to note that since 1991, with the establishment of the Rural Alliance (Alianza para el Campo) program, participation by the state government in the design and application of agricultural policy has increased. SAGARPA's organizational structure at the state level is shown in Figure 5.

The State Government

At the state level, the government office most directly involved with the agricultural sector is the Secretariat of Agricultural Promotion (Secretaría de Fomento Agropecuario–SFA). The SFA's function is to promote rural development in the State of Baja California while fostering and coordinating agricultural and forestry activities. To do so, its activities are based on the state development plan generated by the state government every six years. The SFA's central office is located in the City of Mexicali and also includes the delegations of Ensenada-San Quintín, Tijuana-Tecate, and Playas de Rosarito. The SFA's promotional efforts for agricultural activity present a moderate grade of coordination and integration with SAGARPA, especially concerning programs under the Rural Alliance support system.

Figure 6. Organizational Structure of SFA

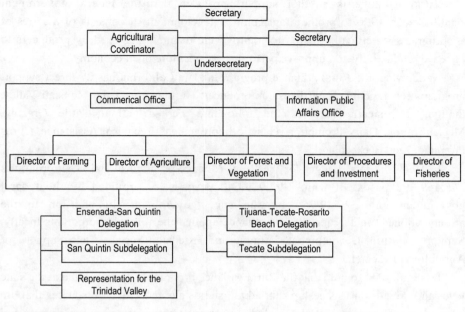

SOURCE: SFA (1999).

Agricultural Policy

Agricultural policy at the national level can be divided into two periods: before and after 1994. Prior to 1994, the government's support strategy for rural areas was fundamentally comprised of indirect support measures, including fertilizers, water, credit, and so on. It also included a production commercialization program through the National Public Subsistence Company (Compañía Nacional de Subsistencias Populares–CONASUPO), as well as a program of fixed agricultural prices or a system of guaranteed prices that began in 1953 and was terminated in 1991.

In 1994, this antiquated strategy was brought to an end and the current strategy of agricultural policy was consolidated. This strategy was based on the application of a rural direct subsidy program known as Programa de Apoyos Directos al Campo–PROCAMPO, and the implementation of the Rural Alliance program that, beginning in 1996, attempted to improve productive technologies in the Mexican agricultural sector in a way that producers could succeed in the face of open competition.

In the case of the Mexicali Valley, the new policy adopted by SAGAR is carried out through its office for Support and Services for Agricultural Commercialization (Apoyos y Servicios a la Comercialización Agropecuaria–ASERCA), which is represented by PROCAMPO. This program has been considered the most important support mechanism for the agricultural sector because of the levels of funding it transfers to producers registered in the program (see Table 5).

Rural Alliance is another support program that the federal government established in 1996 to promote agricultural development. It consists of a series of subprograms specifically geared to improve the technologies used by producers to increase productivity and improve performance in a more open economy.

Nationwide, the Rural Alliance program in Baja California has 27 direct support programs for agriculture and livestock producers. In the case of the Mexicali Valley, though, it basically includes the following: Ferti-irrigation, Cattle Grazing, Mechanization, Dairy Promotion, Genetic Improvement, Technical Assistance, Citrus Promotion, and Beekeeping.

In 1998, the total budget for the Rural Alliance program in Baja California was 145,459,390 pesos, of which, 92,929,640 pesos were provided by the federal government and 52,529,750 by the state government. In addition to the aforementioned eight programs, the alliance applied the following programs locally: Support for Rural Development, Training and Extension Services, and Support for Agricultural Research.

It is important to note that the Rural Alliance program is decentralized at the state level and includes a trusteeship that administers state and federal resources that are allocated to the program. It also includes a series of commissions in which state and federal authorities participate along with producers.

The hedging program also has great potential because it encourages the use of options on future contracts as a protection against risk. ASERCA supports this by covering 50 percent of the expected wheat and cotton crops. In the 1997 spring-summer agricultural cycle, 29 cotton contracts were made. In 1998, this number increased to 315. In 1999, there were 260 contracts made and the number in 2000 was

Table 5. PROCAMPO Aid in Rural Development District 01

Year	Land Surface in Hectares	Aid per Hectare (pesos)	Land Surface in Acres
1994	112,410.35	350	281,025.88
1995	112,274.99	440	280,687.48
1996	109,324.70	484	273,311.75
1997	98,366.26	556	245,915.65
1998	93,138.94	626	232,847.35
1999–2000	95,342.04	708	238,355.09

Note: The annual average peso-dollar exchange rate for 1994 was 3.375; for 1995 it was 6.149; for 1996 it was 7.599; for 1997 it was 7.918; for 1998 it was 9.136; and for 1999 it was 9.561.

SOURCE: SAGAR (1999b); BANAMEX-ACCIVAL "Economic Indicators," selective data (2000).

496. These statistics show the slow progress of the program, despite the benefits that result from this protection strategy.

Due to the consistently low wheat prices since 1998, the federal government, through SAGAR, has given extraordinary support to cereal producers. In the 1998–1999 period, this support reached 300 million pesos that consisted of payments of 300 pesos per ton.

Agricultural Production

The Mexicali Valley is an important agricultural area nationwide, not only in terms of the size of its harvest, but also for the variety and quality of its agricultural products. An example of this can be seen in the 1997–1998 agricultural cycle. The average yield of wheat per hectare was 7.212 tons, the highest in the country. In 1999, the production of 37 different commercial crops was reported, including grains, oilseeds, fodder, vegetables, flowers, and fruit trees. Considering the surface area dedicated to their production, the most important crops in the Mexicali Valley are wheat, alfalfa, sorghum, cotton, and rye grass. The value of these crops is shown in Table 6.

Table 6. Mexicali Valley's Most Important Crops by Value, 1998–1999

Crop	Value in Pesos
Cotton	746,036,980
Wheat	572,664,990
Alfalfa	312,057,900
Onion	297,642,130
Asparagus	230,262,370

Note: The annual average peso-dollar exchange rate for 1999 was 9.561.

SOURCE: SAGAR (1999a); Banamex Citigroup "Economic Indicators," selective data (2003).

Table 7. Comparison of Production in the Mexicali Valley and the Nation, 1995

Crop	Mexico	Mexicali Valley	National Ranking
Cotton	2.8 bales/hectare	3.33 bales/hectare	1st
Wheat	4.68 ton/ha	5.40 ton/ha	2nd
Alfalfa	73.05 ton/ha	55.34 ton/ha	15th
Onion	11.20 ton/ha	11.87 ton/ha	1st
Asparagus	3.62 ton/ha	3.08 ton/ha	3rd

SOURCE: SAGAR (1999b).

It may be concluded that agricultural producers in Mexicali and San Luis Río Colorado apply techniques and their experiences well. The region is among the most productive in Mexico as measured by crop production per hectare as shown in Table 7.

Production Tendencies

Two cultivation periods are defined according to the region's climate: spring-summer (of the same year) and fall-winter (the last three months of a year and the first three of the next) cycles. In the spring-summer production period, the most important crops are cotton, sorghum, alfalfa, corn, and asparagus. Their historical evolution can be seen in Figure 7. In the fall-winter cycle, the three most important crops are wheat, green onions, and rye grass. Hectares planted in these crops since 1994 are presented in Figure 8.

Based on the number of producers that plant wheat each year, the economic importance of this grain in the Mexicali Valley is greater than other crops. In 1999, a total of 61,083 hectares was dedicated to wheat, more than ten times the area devoted to any other crop. As such, recent low wheat prices had a significant impact on the income of the majority of farmers in the region. Figure 7 shows that the second most important crop in the spring-summer cycle is cotton, even though its production has fluctuated due to low prices or insect infestations.

In October of each year, the farmers of these two principal crops decide which to plant according to when they want to use their water permits and the prices of both

Figure 7. Most Important Crops by Area during the Spring-Summer Cycle

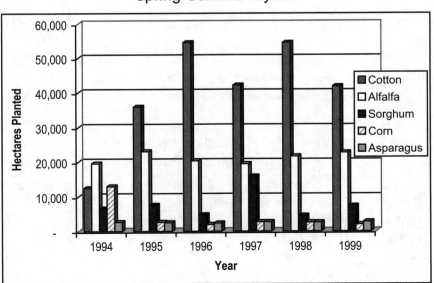

SOURCE: Author's calculations based on SAGAR data (1999a).

Figure 8. Most Important Crops by Area during the Fall-Winter Cycle

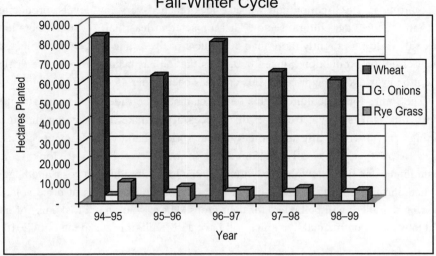

SOURCE: Author's calculations based on SAGAR data (1999b).

crops. The production cycles of the two crops do not allow for their simultaneous production. In 1999, for example, 41,832 hectares in the Mexicali Valley were planted with cotton and 61,083 hectares with wheat, for a total of 102,915 hectares for both crops. This means that almost 50 percent of the producers in the region planted one of these two crops in 1999, demonstrating their economic importance that these products represent for the region.

Conclusions

Almost one hundred years of experience in agricultural production, using modern techniques backed by a strong water irrigation and distribution system, a good regional highway network, excellent technical support services, and agricultural supplies, have resulted in very high crop yields in the Mexicali-San Luis Río Colorado region. These crops include cotton, wheat, alfalfa, rye grass, asparagus, and green onions and are grown on nearly 200,000 irrigated hectares throughout the region. However, farmers in the Mexicali Valley have had a difficult time since the reduced tariff protection that resulted from the North American Free Trade Agreement (NAFTA) in 1994, and changes in agricultural policy made by the Mexican government. These policy changes ended indirect subsidies and minimum prices paid for most crops, as well as direct subsidies paid per hectare. These changes have also resulted in the disappearance of the protectionist environment established to safeguard farmers from the volatility related to agricultural prices. Needless to say, in a very short time, the Mexicali and San Luis Río Colorado farmers were faced with a complicated market situation.

Starting in 1998, cotton and wheat prices reached very low levels, producing a crisis in the local agricultural sector. This impacted at least half of the farmers in the Mexicali Valley, as slightly more than 50 percent of the total acreage was dedicated to wheat or cotton production. Since 2000, the situation has become even more difficult for cotton growers as the price for this crop has been under 45 cents per pound.

The future for agriculture in this region cannot be considered as uncertain; it has what it needs to survive. However, it is necessary to take into account that in the coming years it will be affected more by market prices than by government actions. In order to prosper, Mexicali and San Luis farmers have begun to look to new technologies that will allow them to farm with the lowest production costs and begin to use hedging instruments that will enable them to reduce the effects of price volatility ensuring that there will be buyers for their crops. Those who do not make use of these productive and commercial dynamics will have a difficult time surviving until 2010.

Endnote

1. Beginning December 2000, the Ministry of Agriculture, Livestock, and Rural Development (SAGAR) is also responsible for fishing activities, changing its name to the Ministry of Agriculture, Livestock, Rural Development, Fisheries, and Food (SAGARPA).

References

BANAMEX-ACCIVAL. 2000. "Review of the Economic Situation of Mexico" 76 (889): 36.

Banamex Citigroup. 2003. "Review of the Economic Situation of Mexico" 79 (929) 226.

Comisión Nacional del Agua (CNA). 1998. *Mapa del Distrito de Riego No. 14 con Localización de Módulos de Irrigación.* México, D.F.: CAN.

Compañía Nacional de Subsistencias Populares (CONASUPO). 1987. *Los precios de garantía, boletín informativo.* México, D.F.: CONASUPO.

Instituto Nacional de Estadística, Geografía e Informática (INEGI). 1998. *Mapa Topográfico del Norte de Baja California.* Aguascalientes: INEGI.

Organization for Economic Cooperation and Development (OECD). 1997. *Review of Agricultural Policies in Mexico.* Paris: OECD.

Secretaría de Agricultura, Ganadería y Desarrollo Rural (SAGAR). 1998a. *Evaluación del ciclo otoño-invierno 1997–1998.* Mexicali: SAGAR.

Secretaría de Agricultura, Ganadería y Desarrollo Rural (SAGAR). 1998b. *Evaluación del ciclo primavera-verano 1998.* Mexicali: SAGAR.

Secretaría de Agricultura, Ganadería y Desarrollo Rural (SAGAR). 1999a. *Avance de siembras, siniestros y cosechas en el Distrito de Desarrollo Rural 002 ciclo primavera-verano 1999.* Mexicali: SAGAR.

Secretaría de Agricultura, Ganadería, y Desarrollo Rural (SAGAR). 1999b. *Datos Básicos de PROCAMPO 1994–1999.* Documentos Básicos. Mexicali: SAGAR.

Secretaría de Agricultura y Recursos Hidráulicos (SARH). 1993. *Información básica del sector agropecuario y forestal.* Mexicali: SARH.

Secretaría de Agricultura y Recursos Hidráulicos (SARH). 1994. *PROCAMPO, boletín informativo*. México, D.F.: SARH.

Secretaría de Fomento Agropecuario del Estado de Baja California. 1999. Documentos Básicos.

Sociedad de Responsabilidad Limitada de Interés Público Río Colorado (SRL de IP Río Colorado). 1997. Documentos Básicos.

17

Imperial County Livestock Industry, 1910 to the Present

Juan N. Guerrero and Alecsandro Rufino dos Santos*

Abstract

Fed cattle populations in Imperial County have been decreasing for the last two decades. Although the revenues from fed cattle still represent the largest single revenue-producing commodity in Imperial, the cattle feeding industry does have some problems. The principal problem of the local cattle feeding industry was the lack of cattle processing facilities in Southern California; today, there is one abattoir (slaughterhouse) in Los Angeles and a new one in the City of Brawley, Imperial County. The lack of a competitive market makes cattle profits very valuable.

The alfalfa hay crop occupies between 40 and 50 percent of the total arable surface in Imperial County, making it the single most important crop in the county. About three-quarters of Imperial Valley hay is transported to the Chino dairy basin near Los Angeles. The very existence of the Chino dairy basin has been called into question because of environmental concerns. Nitrates in cattle manure have been implicated in the pollution of the Santa Ana River groundwater basin. Were a large number of dairy cows to leave Chino due to environmental concerns, the impacts to the agricultural economy of Imperial County would be cataclysmic.

Introduction

The livestock sector has always been an integral part of agriculture in Imperial County. Of the $1 billion agricultural economy in Imperial County, the single

---

*Guerrero is Area Livestock Advisor at the University of California Cooperative Extension; Rufino dos Santos is Graduate Research Assistant at the Universidad Autónoma de Baja California, Mexicali.

commodity that generates the most revenues is cattle (Imperial Agricultural Commissioner 1999). Since the very first Agricultural Commissioner's annual crop report in 1910, livestock has played an important role in the Imperial Valley economy.

Of the almost one-half million irrigated acres in Imperial County, about 40 to 50 percent of the total crop acreage is dedicated to one crop: alfalfa. The primary use of alfalfa hay is for cattle feed. Whether raising the animals themselves or producing animal feed, animal agriculture is at the core of the agricultural sector in Imperial County.

Cattle

Figure 1 shows cattle populations and cattle revenues in Imperial County from the inception of irrigated agriculture to the present time. Cattle populations reached their highest numbers in the early 1970s—about 750,000 head of cattle—and have steadily decreased since. In 1999, about 324,000 head of cattle (Imperial Agricultural Commissioner 1999) were fed in Imperial County feedlots. California ranks about sixth nationally in fed cattle population. Imperial County has the largest population of fed cattle of all California counties. It is important to note that the data in Figure 1 represent fed cattle populations, not numbers of beef or dairy cows. The cattle that are present in Imperial County are primarily beef steers that are fed high-grain diets until they are sufficiently fat to be processed. Once local cattle have been fed for a sufficient period and have attained their final finished weights, they are transported to nearby abattoirs and converted into marketable retail beef. Due to the typically warm

Figure 1. Imperial Valley Fed Cattle Population and Gross Cattle Sales

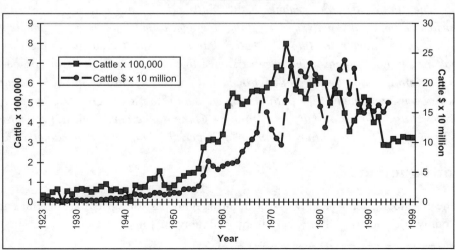

SOURCE: Author's calculations based on Imperial Agricultural Commissioner (1999).

summer climate in Imperial County, cattle that have some Brahman breeding and are heat tolerant have historically been the most desirable type of cattle to be fed locally.

Since the late 1980s, the type of cattle fed in local feedlots has changed. During the 1990s, California became the number one dairy state in the United States. With the increasing number of dairy cows in California, more dairy steers have become an important part of the local fed cattle population. At the current time, Holstein steers represent about three-quarters of the fed cattle population. It should be noted that the dairies in California are located either in Chino, near Los Angeles, or in the southern San Joaquin Valley. The dairy steers, often only two to three months old, are transported to Imperial County for finishing in the feedlots.

The modern feedlot industry evolved in Southern California during the late 1950s and 1960s. A booming post-World War II economy in Southern California made this evolution possible. An abundant supply of water, good cattle feeding weather, a dependable supply of skilled labor, the availability of abundant regional byproduct feeds, and an abundant forage supply made the growth of the modern cattle feeding industry apropos to Imperial County. In the 1960s, there were more than twenty cattle abattoirs in Southern California, making the marketing of locally produced fed cattle very competitive for local cattle feeders. Although Imperial County is considered to be primarily a crop-producing area, since the 1970s (except for only a few years), the single agricultural commodity that produced the most revenues in the local economy is cattle. Cattle revenues represent about 20 percent of total Imperial County agricultural revenues.

Except for three farmer feeders, cattle feedlots in Imperial County are large commercial feedlots. The median size of an Imperial County feedlot is about 20,000 head of cattle, which is considered a large feedlot. A commercial feedlot does not own the cattle, but rather feeds it for cattle entrepreneurs. These cattle entrepreneurs may or may not be Imperial County residents. The feedlot sells feed and cattle services to cattle owners. The only revenues that are obtained from the cattle by local feedlots are from the sale of feed and from fees charged for the care of the cattle. At a commercial feedlot there are about 0.5 to 1 persons employed per 1,000 head of cattle, making the local cattle industry one of the major local employers of agricultural personnel. If the cattle service industry is included in local agricultural employment numbers (including cattle product sales personnel, cattle care personnel [veterinary personnel], cattle feed suppliers, and cattle transport personnel), then the impact on Imperial County by the feedlot industry is even more significant. Every November in Brawley the local community salutes the local feedlot cattle industry with a weeklong celebration named "Cattle Call."

Problems Confronting the Local Cattle Feeding Industry

During the late 1980s and 1990s, the fed cattle populations in Imperial County decreased dramatically (see Figure 1). The reasons for this decline are numerous.

Cholesterol and health concerns have indeed impacted beef consumption in the United States. In the early 1970s, annual per capita consumption of beef in the United States attained a maximum value of about seventy-six pounds; by the mid-1990s, that number had decreased to about sixty-two pounds; and by 1999, it had again increased to about sixty-six pounds. During the 1990s, annual per capita consumption of chicken by U.S. consumers surpassed beef. At the present time, annual per capita consumption of all red meats has actually increased to an all-time high of about two hundred pounds. Although it might be easy to blame the decrease in local cattle numbers on the general decline in beef consumption by U.S. consumers, the reasons are more complicated.

The feeding of cattle in Southern California has always had an economic disadvantage compared to the High Plains (the Texas Panhandle, northeastern New Mexico, eastern Colorado, and southwestern Kansas), the premier cattle feeding region in the United States. The production of feed grains by Imperial Valley farmers has not been economically viable. Therefore, both cattle and feed grains have to be transported into the Imperial Valley, making local feed costs higher in comparison to the High Plains.

The collapse of the Southern California abattoir industry has been particularly detrimental to the Imperial County cattle feeding industry. At the time of writing this essay, only one small abattoir remained operational in Southern California, and another was recently established in Brawley in the Imperial Valley. One medium-sized abattoir also remained operational in southwestern Arizona. The lack of market competition for fed cattle and the lack of abattoir capacity made cattle feeding in Imperial County decreasingly viable. Wage rates of Southern California abattoirs were almost double those in the High Plains. Southern California abattoirs could not compete with the High Plains abattoir industry. At times, Imperial Valley cattle feeders shipped finished cattle to Utah or even to Texas for processing because of the lack of a local cattle market. Local cattle feeders decreased in number because they were unable to generate profits for their cattle feeding clientele, presumably because of a reduced fed cattle market.

Solutions

In 2001, a new abattoir opened in the City of Brawley. This new facility was the first constructed in the United States in about twenty years. As of 2003, this mid-size abattoir is processing about thirteen hundred head per day and has revolutionized the local cattle feeding industry. Were fed cattle numbers to increase to 1980s levels, the benefits to the local cattle feeding industry and to the economy would be substantial.

Sheep

The sheep industry in the United States has almost disappeared. In the 1980s, there were more than 12,000,000 sheep in the United States; today less than 7,000,000 exist. Annual per capita consumption of lamb in the United States has decreased to 0.6 pounds. Most people in the United States have never consumed lamb. Recently, the U.S. Department of Agriculture (USDA) ranked sheep as a minor species of the U.S. livestock sector.

During the winter in the Imperial Valley, the abundant alfalfa supply becomes difficult to bale. Rather than taking risks and losing an entire winter hay crop due to inclement weather conditions, many Imperial Valley hay producers permit their hay fields to be grazed by sheep. Lambs arrive in the Imperial Valley in October and November and graze alfalfa fields throughout the winter. Lambs are shorn for their wool during November and December. They usually attain finished market weights by February and are then transported outside the area for processing. Sheep graziers pay alfalfa growers for the privilege of grazing their fields. Sheep also have been found to control weeds in alfalfa, thereby allowing alfalfa growers to reduce use of herbicides in the fields (Bell, Guerrero, and Granados 1996).

The demise of the sheep industry in the United States has numerous causes. First, the wool market has almost disappeared. Wool sales had always been an important part

Figure 2. Imperial Valley Sheep Population and Gross Sheep Sales

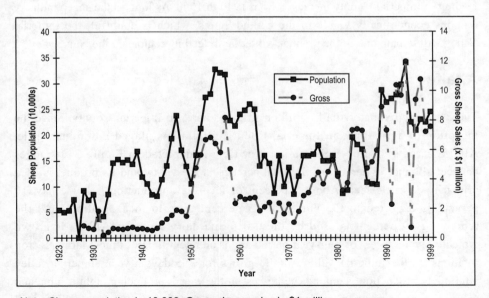

Note: Sheep population in 10,000. Gross sheep sales in $1 million.

SOURCE: Author's calculations based on Imperial Agricultural Commissioner (1999).

of the sheep industry. Synthetic fibers have made wool almost anachronistic and unnecessary. Old federal laws actually required certain military apparel to be made from wool. The U.S. federal government, however, rescinded the wool subsidy paid to sheep ranchers in the late 1990s. U.S. wool now has to compete on the global wool market. Additionally, sheep have always been especially susceptible to wild carnivore predation in the western United States. Federal legislation restricting predator control in the area has increased losses for western ranchers and has increased sheep production costs.

Almost all livestock producers in the United States participate in some commodity checkoff program. Livestock producers tax themselves on their livestock sales to generate funds to promote their own particular commodity. These checkoff funds are also used for research to benefit that particular commodity, producing great benefits for livestock producers. Most U.S. consumers would recognize the immensely successful promotional products of the commodity checkoff programs, including the popular slogans: "Got Milk?," "Pork, the other white meat," "Beef, it's what's for dinner," "California, it's the cheese," and "California fresh eggs." U.S. sheep producers, however, have twice voted against national sheep checkoff programs to the great detriment of their industry. Of all the livestock producers in the United States, only sheep producers do not have a commodity checkoff program to promote their own livelihood.

Despite the bleak nature of the U.S. sheep industry, winter lamb feeding in the desert Southwest still remains economically viable. Figure 2 depicts Imperial County sheep populations over time and the revenues produced by that industry. For the last decade, lamb grazing revenues have fallen along with lamb populations. Winter lamb feeding in Imperial County increased from 1940 to 1960. As long as the sheep industry remains economically viable in the United States, which is doubtful, the Imperial Valley will remain one of the premier winter lamb feeding regions in the country.

Alfalfa

There are approximately half a million irrigated acres in Imperial County. Since the inception of agriculture in Imperial County, alfalfa has played a dominant role. Alfalfa acreage in Imperial County over time is depicted in Figure 3. It ranges between 40 and 50 percent of the total acreage in the valley and its product is used primarily as cattle feed. About 5 percent of local hay production is horse hay, 10 percent is exported to the Far East, 15 percent goes to local feedlots, and the remaining 70 percent is used by the California dairy industry. Alfalfa is grown typically over a three- or four-year period and is an integral part of most farmers' crop rotations. In the Imperial Valley, alfalfa grows for 365 days a year. Imperial Valley alfalfa hay production is among the highest in the world, producing eight to nine and one half tons of hay per acre per year over eight to ten harvests. Thus, alfalfa will remain an integral part of the cropping pattern of Imperial County in the foreseeable future.

Figure 3. Imperial Valley Alfalfa Acreage and Gross Hay Sales

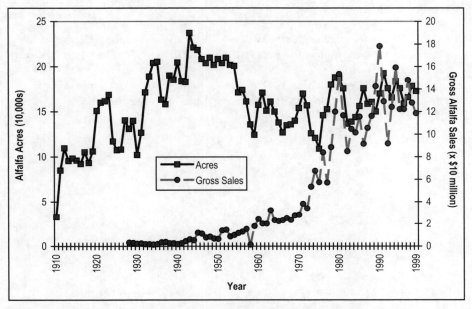

SOURCE: Author's calculations based on Imperial Agricultural Commissioner (1999).

One looming menace in particular puts into question the future of the Imperial County alfalfa hay crop. Most of the hay crop goes to the dairy industry in Chino, where there are about 300,000 dairy cows. The survival of the Chino dairy basin is in jeopardy. The State Water Resources Control Board has determined that nitrates in cattle manure may be increasing groundwater nitrate levels in the Santa Ana River basin. Environmental concerns have placed constraints on the Chino dairy industry, thereby increasing production costs. The agricultural preserve status of the Chino dairy basin has been rescinded by Riverside County. All manure produced by dairy cows in the Chino dairy basin has to be removed from the area at a substantial cost to the dairy producer. Many Chino dairy producers have already opted to leave the Chino dairy basin. Were dairy producers in the basin to precipitously reduce dairy cow populations over a short period of time due to water quality concerns, the consequences for the Imperial Valley alfalfa hay crop would be cataclysmic. The loss of the Chino dairy cattle hay market would place the viability of the Imperial Valley alfalfa hay crop into question.

References

Bell, C.E., J.N. Guerrero, and E.Y. Granados. 1996. "A Comparison of Sheep Grazing with Herbicides for Weed Control in Seeding Alfalfa in the Irrigated Sonoran Desert." *Journal of Production Agriculture* 9: 123–29.

Imperial Agricultural Commissioner. 1999. *Imperial County Agricultural Commissioner's Annual Report, 1910–1999*. El Centro: Imperial Agricultural Commissioner.

PART FOUR

Environmental Concerns and Natural Resources

18

Air Quality Evaluation in the Mexicali and Imperial Valleys as an Element for an Outreach Program

Margarito Quintero-Núñez and Alan Sweedler*

Abstract

The Mexicali and Imperial valleys form a single valley divided by the political line of the U.S.-Mexican border, constituted by a fence in the most populated areas. The valley is characterized by very hot weather during the summer months and an air pollution problem caused primarily by suspended particles arising from the desert environment, a large agricultural sector, the vehicular fleet as a whole, an abundance of unpaved streets in Mexicali, and rural roads in the Imperial Valley. As part of the Border XXI Program—established by the U.S. and Mexican governments in 1996 to improve the environment in the border region—ambient air monitoring stations were established in both valleys. Thus, levels of pollutants and particulate matter (PM) have now been measured for several years. These monitors have recorded exceedances of several gases as well as particulate matter with a diameter that measures 10 microns or less (PM10), resulting in the classification of both the Municipality of Mexicali and Imperial County as nonattainment areas for PM10, carbon monoxide, and ozone by U.S. and Mexican authorities. A study conducted by the Desert Research Institute of Nevada revealed the transboundary transport of PM10 due to wind direction and the amount of particulate matter generated on each side of the border. Several studies have shown that respiratory illnesses, hospital admissions, school absences, and premature deaths occur during periods of

*Quintero-Núñez is Researcher at the Engineering Institute at the Universidad Autónoma de Baja California in Mexicali; Sweedler is Director of the Center for Energy Studies at San Diego State University.

increased PM levels. Such levels can also exacerbate or cause lung diseases including asthma, bronchitis, and emphysema. These increases occur quite often during the seasonal transition. This essay provides some recommendations for improving air quality and awareness of related issues.

A Brief Description of the Geographical Region and Population Distribution

Imperial Valley

The Imperial and Mexicali valleys are located in the Colorado Desert, or the western part of the Sonoran Desert. They share the same valley divided by the international border between the United States and Mexico. The area is partly below sea level and is essentially arid, as it lies north of the Tropic of Cancer and is part of the global area with the greatest amount of solar energy.

Imperial County is located in the southeast corner of California. The county includes over 4,597 square miles, with Mexico to the south, Riverside County to the north, San Diego County to the west, and Arizona to the east. It is the ninth largest county in California.

Approximately one-half of the lands in Imperial County are undeveloped and under federal ownership and jurisdiction. At present, one-fifth of the county's nearly three million acres is irrigated for agricultural purposes; much of this is concentrated in the central area known as the Imperial Valley. The developed area—where the county's incorporated cities, unincorporated communities, and supporting facilities are situated—comprises less than 1 percent of the land. The Salton Sea covers approximately 7 percent of the county.

The Colorado River offers a wide variety of recreational activities. The Salton Sea, which is popular for its fishing and water activities, was created when the Colorado River changed its course and followed an irrigation canal, flooding the lowest part of the valley in the first decade of the twentieth century.

The City of El Centro, the largest of the three major cities in the Imperial Valley, is the county seat and principal trading center for the county. It is accessible via the interstate Highway 8, crossing east to west along the Mexican border, and state highways 86 and 111 from the north, which continue south to the Mexican border.

According to the State Department of Finance, Imperial County had a 2000 population of over 142,361 persons. Table 1 shows the breakdown of Imperial County's population into incorporated and unincorporated areas.

With regard to employment, 35 percent of all jobs are in government services. Employment in the agricultural sector averages 31.7 percent of total employment in the county. It is the dominant industry and follows a seasonal pattern of high

Table 1. Imperial County's Population, 2000

City	Population
Brawley	22,052
Calexico	27,109
Calipatria	7,289
El Centro	37,835
Holtville	5,612
Imperial	7,560
Westmorland	2,131
Unincorporated	32,773
Imperial County	142,361

SOURCE: U.S. Census Bureau (2000).

employment during the winter months, followed by lower employment during the hot summer months. The wholesale and retail trade sectors constitute 29 percent of all employment, while the manufacturing sector accounts for only 5 percent of the employment base in Imperial County. Thus, Imperial County's economy is quite narrowly focused on agriculture and trade.

Mexicali

The State of Baja California is divided into two regions: the Colorado Valley and the Pacific Coast. The city and valley of Mexicali are located in the Colorado Valley. It encompasses 21 percent of the state's territory and 0.7 percent of the country (13,700 km^2/5,288 miles^2) and has a population of 764,602 inhabitants (see Table 2). The shoreline of the municipality is located on the Sea of Cortez and measures approximately 130 miles (210 kilometers). Ten islands that cover approximately eleven thousand hectares (27,170 acres) are also within its jurisdiction. From north to south these are: Gore, Montague, Encantada, San Luis, Ángel de la Guarda, Pond, Partida, Rosa, Salsipuedes, and San Lorenzo.

Three geographical zones are found within the municipality: valley, coastal, and urban. In the coastal zone, the delegation of San Felipe is the most important. In the valley zone, principal delegations include Puebla, Ciudad Morelos, Guadalupe Victoria,

Table 2. Population of Mexicali, 2000

City of Mexicali	549,873
Valley of Mexicali	214,729
Total	764,602

SOURCE: INEGI (2000).

and Estación Coahuila. In the urban zone, the seat of the municipality (Mexicali) and the delegations of González Ortega, Cerro Prieto, and Progreso are found.

The climate is the region's outstanding characteristic. The region is located under the solar band and experiences very long summers and short winters. The weather is dry and the average precipitation is slightly more than 76.2 millimeters per year. Mexicali is located slightly to the north of the ridge of the delta of the Colorado River at an average altitude of 36 feet (11 meters) above sea level. Heading south, the terrain descends to sea level at the Sea of Cortez. Heading north toward the Salton Sea, it also descends to approximately 279 feet (85 meters) below sea level.

Border XXI Program and Border 2012 Program[1]

Border XXI was an innovative binational program that brought together diverse U.S and Mexican federal entities responsible for the shared border environment to work cooperatively toward sustainable development through the protection of human health and the environment and proper management of natural resources in both countries. The main goal of this program was to promote sustainable development in the border region by seeking a balance among social and economic factors and the protection of the environment in border communities and natural areas. In accordance with these concepts, Border XXI promoted sustainable development in the border region, which "meets the needs of the present without compromising the ability of future generations to meet their own needs" (UN 1992). For many years, the United States and Mexico have been involved in both formal and informal cooperative efforts associated with protecting the environment and natural resources of their common border. Numerous bilateral agreements guide both countries' efforts in the border area.

Despite these bilateral efforts, unsustainable practices in the border region have resulted in the degradation of environmental conditions. Industrialization has brought important economic benefits to the border region; however, it has also been accompanied by accelerated population growth and unsustainable production and consumption that surpass the capacity of the natural resource base, as well as that of basic infrastructure (particularly with regard to water resources). These conditions threaten the biodiversity and air and water quality, posing health risks to border residents.

In order to protect, improve, and conserve the environment of the border region, in 1983 both governments signed the Agreement for the Protection and Improvement of the Environment in the Border Area (La Paz Agreement), which provided a formal foundation for cooperative environmental efforts. The La Paz Agreement defined the border region as the area lying 100 kilometers or 62.5 miles to the north and south of the U.S.-Mexican boundary. Work carried out under the La Paz Agreement is coordinated by two national agencies: the International Affairs Coordinator of the Secretariat of the Environment and Natural Resources (Secretaría de Medio Ambiente y Recursos Naturales–SEMARNAT), which was formerly the Secretariat of the

Environment, Natural Resources, and Fisheries (Secretaría de Medio Ambiente, Recursos Naturales y Pesca–SEMARNAP), and the Assistant Administrator for International Activities of the U.S. Environmental Protection Agency (EPA).

In February 1992, the environmental authorities of both governments released the first Integrated Border Environmental Plan (IBEP) for the Mexican-U.S. border area. While the IBEP represented a reasonable point of departure for addressing environmental concerns in the border region and resulted in significant investments in infrastructure, critics held that it was limited in scope, implemented without sufficient public input, and failed to adequately address natural resource and environmental health concerns. The Border XXI Program built on the efforts of the IBEP. As the next phase of binational planning, Border XXI was expanded to include health and natural resources issues. In addition, the Border XXI Framework Document reflected extensive public input and the program was organized to facilitate federal, state, and local involvement. Funding for implementing Border XXI was based on annual appropriations by the U.S. Congress and Mexico's Ministry of Finance.

Border XXI was a five-year program for the period 1996–2000. It was replaced by the 10-year Border 2012 Program that was launched late in 2002. The Border 2012 Program creates regionally focused workgroups to facilitate active participation of local communities, local government agencies, and U.S. tribes. It also sets specific goals and measurable objectives for border environmental improvement.

Air Issues and Problems

Many border residents are currently exposed to health-threatening levels of air pollution. Ozone (O_3), particulate matter (PM), carbon monoxide (CO), and sulfur dioxide (SO_2) are among some of the air pollutants of concern in the border region. The EPA and Mexico's National Institute of Ecology (Instituto Nacional de Ecología–INE) have developed regional strategies to improve air quality. These strategies are based on basic national air quality norms. Both countries have established very similar air quality standards for carbon monoxide, sulfur dioxide, ozone, nitrogen dioxide (NO_2), PM10, and lead (Pb). Table 3 compares Mexican and U.S. health-based ambient air quality standards.

Table 4 lists border cities that exceeded ambient air quality standards in 1996. Currently, there is no guidance by which to determine "nonattainment" with Mexican air quality standards. Additionally, there is insufficient air quality monitoring data to determine if all Mexican cities meet Mexican air quality standards. Taking these limitations into account, Table 4 indicates various Mexican cities that potentially do not meet the Mexican air quality standards based on knowledge of sources, their potential emissions, and pollutant data registered at the monitors.

Table 3. Air Quality Standards of Mexico and USA

Pollutant	Mexico		United States	
	Units	Mean	Units	Mean
Ozone	0.11 ppm	1 hour	0.12 ppm	1 hour
Sulfur Dioxide	0.13 ppm	24 hours	0.14 ppm	24 hours
	0.03 ppm	Annual arithmetic mean	0.03 ppm	Annual arithmetic mean
Nitrogen Dioxide	0.21 ppm	1 hour	0.25 ppm	1 hour
			0.053 ppm	Annual arithmetic mean
Carbon Monoxide	11 ppm	8 hours	9 ppm	8 hours
			35 ppm	1 hour
Total Suspended Particles	260 ug/m^3	24 hours	N/A	N/A
	75 ug/m^3	Annual geometric mean		
PM10	150 ug/m^3	24 hours	150 ug/m^3	24 hours
	50 ug/m^3	Annual arithmetic mean	50 ug/m^3	Annual arithmetic mean
Lead	1.5 ug/m^3	3 months Arithmetic mean	1.5 ug/m^3	3 months Arithmetic mean

SOURCE: U.S. EPA and SEMARNAP (1996).

Table 4. Border Cities that Exceed Ambient Air Quality Standards

Border Nonattainment Areas	PM10	SO$_2$	CO	O$_3$
El Paso, Texas	X		X	X
Doña Ana County, New Mexico	X			X
Imperial County, California	X		X	X
San Diego, California			X	X
Douglas, Arizona	X	X		
Nogales, Arizona	X			
Yuma, Arizona	X			
Tijuana, Baja California	X		X	X
Mexicali, Baja California	X		X	X
San Luis Río Colorado, Sonora	X			
Nogales, Sonora	X			
Agua Prieta, Sonora	X	X		
Ciudad Juárez, Chihuahua	X		X	X

SOURCE: U.S. EPA and SEMARNAP (1996).

Development of Air Monitoring Stations

Pollution does not recognize political borders; therefore, authorities on both sides of the border are just as interested in air quality as those who live and work in the region. There is much interest in measuring air quality in the populated areas of both valleys. Federal, state, and local authorities are eager to know the levels of pollutants in the communities they represent.

Mexicali

Mexicali's air quality monitoring network began operations in January 1997, rooted in the Border XXI agreements with funding from the U.S. Environmental Protection Agency and the California Air Resources Board (CARB). There are a total of six monitoring stations (see Figure 1), of which four are automatic, registering ozone, nitrogen dioxide, sulfur dioxide, carbon monoxide, and various meteorological parameters such as temperature, humidity, and wind speed and direction. Manual samplings of PM10 also occur at these stations. The other two stations only sample PM10. The six stations are located at the Vocational Center for Industrial Technology and Services (Centro de Bachillerato Técnico Industrial y de Servicios–CBTIS), the Engineering Institute of the Autonomous University of Baja California (Instituto de

Figure 1. Location of the
Air Quality Monitoring Stations in Mexicali

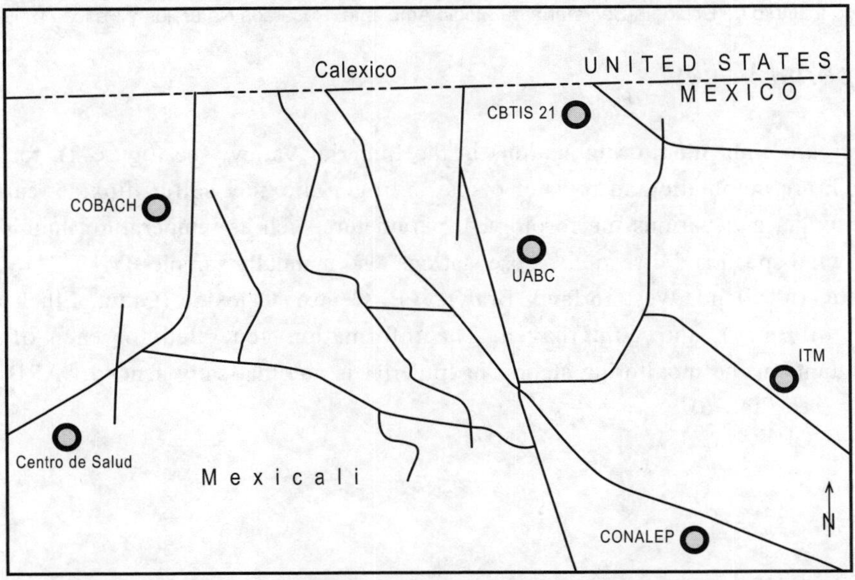

SOURCE: Gobierno del Estado de Baja California, Municipio de Mexicali, Secretaría de Salud, and Instituto de Ecología-Secretaría de Medio Ambiente, Recursos Naturales y Pesca (1999).

Ingeniería de la Universidad Autónoma de Baja California–UABC), the Technological Institute of Mexicali (Instituto Tecnológico de Mexicali–ITM), the Vocational School of Baja California (Colegio de Bachilleres de Baja California–COBACH), the Health Center in Colonia Progreso (Centro de Salud en la Colonia Progreso), and the National College of Professional Technical Education (Colegio Nacional de Educación Profesional Técnica–CONALEP). This monitoring network is operated and financed by the EPA through a contractor.

The information generated for each one of the pollutants at the monitoring stations in the City of Mexicali is sent automatically to CARB via radio and validated in the Data Analysis Office at the National Institute of Ecology (INE). Table 5 shows the monitoring stations and pollutants measured.

Table 5. Mexicali's Monitoring Stations and Parameters Measured

No.	Zone	Station	O_3	CO	SO_2	NO_2	PM10
1	North	CBTIS21	X	X	X	X	X
2	South	UABC	X	X	X	X	X
3	Southwest	ITM	X	X	X	X	X
4	West	COBACH	X	X	X	X	X
5	West	Health Center					X
6	Southeast	CONALEP					X

SOURCE: Gobierno del Estado de Baja California, Municipio de Mexicali, Secretaría de Salud, and Instituto de Ecología-Secretaría de Medio Ambiente, Recursos Naturales y Pesca (1999).

Imperial Valley

There are eight monitoring stations in the Imperial Valley (see Figure 2), four of which are automatic and register ozone, nitrogen dioxide, sulfur dioxide, carbon monoxide, and various meteorological parameters such as temperature, humidity, and wind speed and direction. These stations also manually sample PM10. They are located at Niland, Westmorland, Brawley, El Centro, Calexico (Grant, Ethel, and Port of Entry), and Winterhaven. The information generated for each of the pollutants at the monitoring station in Imperial is automatically sent to CARB via radio (see Table 6).

Figure 2. Location of the Air Quality Monitoring Net in Imperial Valley

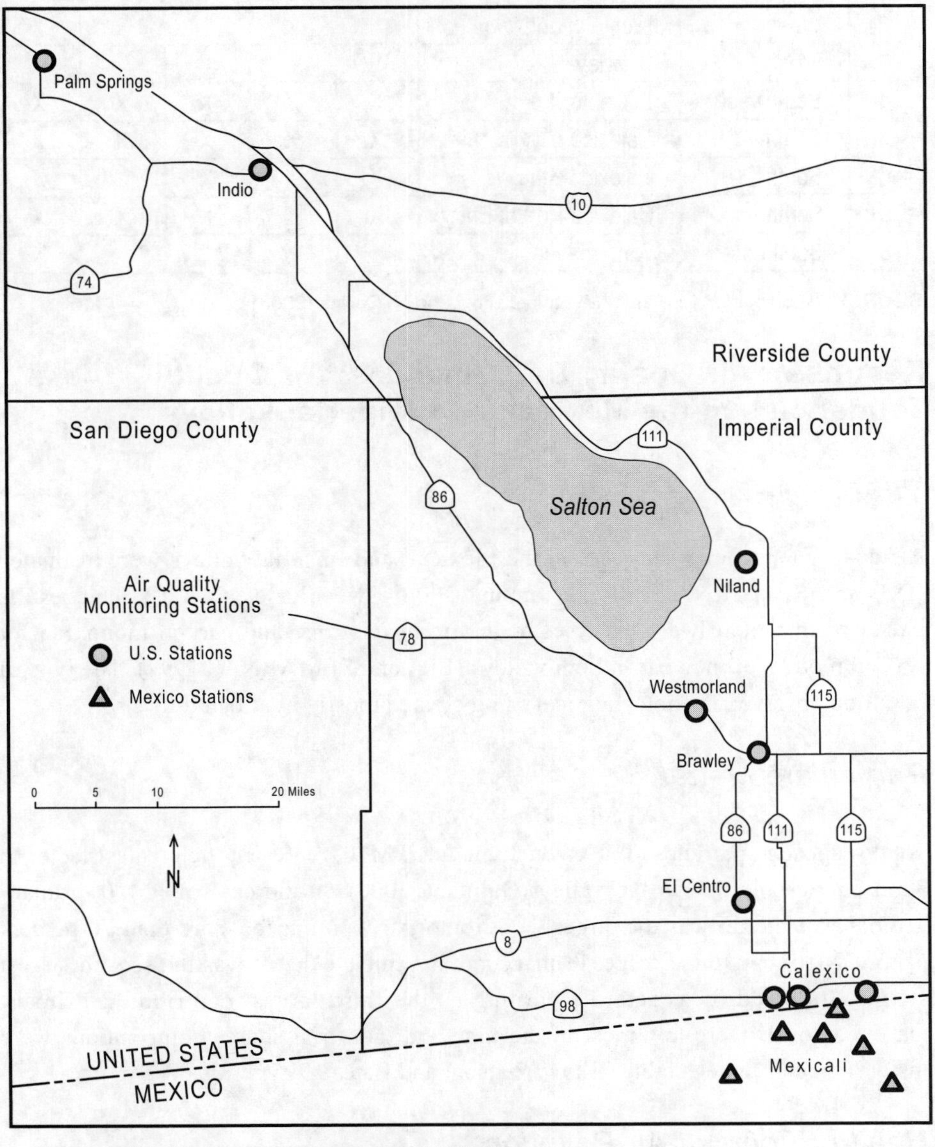

SOURCE: California Air Resources Board (1998).

Table 6. Imperial's Monitoring Stations and Parameters Measured

No.	Zone	Station	O_3	CO	SO_2	NO_2	PM10
1	North	Niland					X
2	West	Westmorland					X
3	West	Brawley					X
4	Southwest	El Centro	X	X	X	X	X
5	South	Calexico-Grant	X	X	X	X	X
6	South	Calexico-Ethel	X	X	X	X	X
7	South	Calexico-Port of Entry	X	X	X	X	X
8	Southeast	Winterhaven					X

SOURCE: A. Sweedler, M. Fertig, M. Quintero N., and K. Collins (2003).

Results of Air Quality Data Analysis: Air Quality Tendencies in the Mexicali and Imperial Valleys

Gases

Air quality tendencies for gases in the Mexicali and Imperial valleys were evaluated (INE and SEMARNAP 2000; Quintana 2000; Sweedler et al. n.d.). The results indicated that there were excesses to the norm in ozone and carbon monoxide for several months of the year in both valleys (EPA and SEMARNAP 1997). The type of pollution observed is photochemical smog created mostly by urban traffic.

Particulate Matter

Total suspended particles (TSP), which include PM10, represent the greatest factor in atmospheric pollution in the valley (Quintana 2000). In the case of PM10, primary geological material was the largest contributor, accounting for more than 70 percent of the PM10 mass on average. Primary motor vehicle exhaust was the second largest source, followed by vegetative burning as the third largest contributor. Primary marine aerosols were low most of the time and industrial source contributions were insignificant or undetectable (Chow, Watson, and Bates 1995).

Health Effects of Air Pollution

In the San Diego and Imperial county region, particulate matter and ozone are the two most serious air pollution problems (ALA 2000). Calexico is especially problematic, where measurements show the highest levels of particulate matter (TSP, PM10, and PM2.5) in the state due to wind, soil composition, agricultural processes, and industry.

A study by Reyna and Álvarez (1999) shows that, in Mexicali, more respiratory illnesses, hospital admissions, school absences, and premature deaths occur during periods of increased PM pollution. These periods can exacerbate or cause lung diseases including asthma, bronchitis, and emphysema.

Air pollution comes in many forms, from both manmade and natural sources. The human body has to deal with pollutants such as noxious gases (O_3, CO, SO_2, NOx) and particulate matter (TSP, PM10, PM2.5). Particulate matter is composed of microscopic particles including dust, soil, mold, pollen, smoke, soot, and ash. PM may be made up of minute droplets of liquid or solids called aerosols. Toxic and cancer-causing agents can attach to PM and be inhaled into the lungs. Particulate matter can range in size from visible pieces of sand to particles so small that thousands of them could fit onto the period at the end of this sentence. Most particulate matter is trapped in the nose or upper lungs where small hairs and mucus remove them from the body. Nonetheless, PM10 can be inhaled and slip past the body's defenses.

Recent studies (Sullivan 1999) indicate that even smaller particles can enter the deepest parts of the lungs and remain trapped there, causing even more serious health effects for people. After a review of more than three thousand research studies (Sheth and Giel 2000) related to PM and ozone, the EPA proposed new air quality standards to regulate these smaller particulates that measure 2.5 microns in diameter (PM2.5).

The lungs are very sensitive to air pollution. Particulate matter can damage the lungs by inflaming or destroying the lung tissue, damaging or destroying the protective hair lining in the airways, or inflaming lung tissue and restricting air passages. Breathing becomes difficult and produces symptoms such as coughing, wheezing, and shortness of breath.

Institutional Entities Dealing with Air Quality Issues

In the Imperial Valley, the most important entities that deal with air quality issues are the Imperial County Air Pollution Control District (APCD), the State of California Air Resources Board (CARB), and the U.S. Environmental Protection Agency (EPA) at the federal level.

Imperial County is located within the Southeast Desert Air Basin (SEDAB), which encompasses the Imperial, Coachella, and Antelope valleys eastward to the California border. The APCD was established in 1971 and has countywide jurisdiction.

In the Mexicali Valley, the entities that deal with air quality issues are the National Institute of Ecology (INE), which is part of the Secretariat of the Environment and Natural Resources (Secretaría de Medio Ambiente y Recursos Naturales–SEMARNAT); the

Department of Ecology of the State of Baja California (Dirección General de Ecología del Estado de Baja California); the Department of Ecology of the Municipality of Mexicali (Dirección de Ecología del Municipio de Mexicali); and the Federal Attorney General for Environmental Protection (Procuraduría Federal de Protección al Ambiente–PROFEPA), Mexico's environmental enforcement office.

Air Quality Policies on Both Sides of the Border

In the United States, air pollution is regulated under the federal Clean Air Act, which was most recently amended in 1990. The Clean Air Act is one of the most complex environmental laws in the United States. There are numerous federal regulations and guidelines that go into even greater detail on many aspects of its implementation. The following summary is intended only to give broad outlines; therefore, it necessarily oversimplifies details that may be important for individual sources.

Universal Attainment of National Ambient Air Quality Standards (NAAQS)

Since 1970, the United States has followed an air pollution control strategy that focuses on the Universal Attainment of National Ambient Air Quality Standards (NAAQS) for six common air pollutants: particulate matter, sulfur dioxide, carbon monoxide, nitrogen oxide, ozone, and lead. The NAAQS are set at the federal level— according to scientific criteria—to protect public health within a margin of safety. They typically include standards for both short-term peak concentrations and long-term concentrations.

Geographical regions that have not yet attained the NAAQS for a pollutant are termed "nonattainment areas." According to these U.S. standards, the Imperial and Mexicali valleys are nonattainment areas for ozone, carbon monoxide, and particulate matter. Although many U.S. cities exceed the ozone standard, Imperial and Mexicali are among only a few areas that are considered nonattainment for three separate pollutants. All statutory deadlines for attainment of standards passed in late 1996, except for cities or areas with severe ozone, carbon monoxide, or particulate matter problems, as in the case of the Imperial and Mexicali region.

Under U.S. law, a nonattainment area is subject to stringent cleanup requirements and may be penalized if it fails to meet the requirements. However, a border county such as Imperial cannot be penalized if it shows that it has taken all necessary measures within its jurisdiction to meet the requirement and failure is only due to emissions from outside the United States, which it argues is the case (Simon 2000).

State Implementation Plans (SIP)

In general, it is up to each state to develop a state implementation plan (SIP) that will achieve attainment of all air quality standards. The SIP sets minimum emissions control requirements for sources in many different industry categories and may set different requirements for geographic areas depending on prevailing air quality and the degree of improvement that is needed.

Three federal Clean Air Act requirements must be met before a new or expanded facility can obtain a permit to operate in a nonattainment area. First, the permit applicant must show that other preexisting sources of the same pollutant in the area will "offset" the new emissions with even greater reductions in current emissions (for example, more than one ton of reductions for each ton of new permitted emissions per year). Second, the permit applicant must adopt the most stringent pollution controls at the new or expanded facility, referred to as the "lowest achievable emissions rate" (U.S. EPA 1990). Third, the applicant must certify that all other facilities under its control in the state are complying with their air pollution control requirements. As a rule, the State of California's air standards are tougher than U.S. federal standards.

Emission Reductions

To promote progress toward attainment by emission reductions from existing sources and facilitate the emissions that may allow new or expanded industrial activity in nonattainment areas, EPA rules allow sources to "bank" their credits for emissions reductions. The source can then draw on its "bank account" to offset its own emission increases or sell those credits to a third party that may need them. Government agencies that generate air emissions or can show emission reductions through government programs can also contribute their emissions reductions to private projects. For example, control of emissions from garbage incineration can reduce particulate matter and changes in the specifications for road-paving materials may reduce emissions of volatile organic compounds.

In the Mexicali-Imperial Valley region, the availability of emission offsets—both as an opportunity for new facilities to locate to the region and as an incentive for further reductions in emissions from existing facilities—has been constrained by the fact that the Clean Air Act jurisdiction ends at the international border. This is despite the well-documented regime characteristics of air passing freely back and forth across the border. An important step toward allowing the benefits of offsets and emissions trading to be available to sources throughout the common air basin would be to create a Mexicali-Imperial Valley airshed management structure that is sanctioned by both U.S. and Mexican authorities.

Preventive Measures to Reduce Air Pollution Effects in the Region: Technical and Institutional

Considering that Mexicali and Imperial Valley share the same air basin, in order to improve the air quality of the region it is important to take preventive measures to address key problems. These problems include the growing number of cars and busses being driven in the area, an increase in cross-border truck traffic, ever greater industrial emission, and urban sprawl that brings with it unpaved roads, loss of ground cover, and garbage incineration, among other issues. The following measures are proposed in response to these problems.

1. Establish a vehicular verification program to check the mechanical status of automobiles on the Mexican side in an effort to reduce the degree of pollution by carbon monoxide, nitrogen dioxide, sulfur dioxide, ozone, and PM10. This program was scheduled to be put into practice in 2001 by the Department of Ecology of Baja California (González C. 1999). As of yet, it has not been implemented.

2. Reduce automobile emissions near the international ports of entry by establishing fast lanes for commuters, carpools, or other practical mechanisms.

3. Promote the paving of streets in Mexicali in order to reduce the production of dust and fine articles.

4. Characterize the mixing layer in order to better define the zone of laminar flow in the atmosphere. This is important for evaluating pollution during a thermal inversion.

5. Organize a bilateral commission or entities to address the shared problem of transboundary pollution in both valleys. This will likely increase concern for air quality problems and induce policies to improve its quality in the region.

6. Acute respiratory infections (ARIs) caused by particulate matter (PM10), pollen, and smog are quite common in Mexicali. Preventive measures should be established.

7. Steps should be taken to characterize the emission factors of various sources of pollutants and the thermal inversions that take place in Mexicali.

8. Efforts should be made to carry out studies on air dispersion models to characterize the transport of pollutants in both valleys.

9. The Municipality of Mexicali should plan to take responsibility for the monitoring stations and manage them both technically and financially.

Short-Term and Long-Term Recommendations

As well as general preventive measures previously discussed, there are a number of specific actions or recommendations that should be carried out in order to improve air quality in the binational basin. These include short-term and long-term recommendations.

Short-Term Recommendations

1. Develop programs for the study and improvement of air quality (monitoring, emissions inventory and modeling, and so on).

2. Review and recommend strategies for the abatement of air pollution, focusing on transportation, industry, and natural sources.

3. Substitute diesel and gasoline fuels in official and public transport vehicles to natural gas or liquefied petroleum gas (LPG), setting an example in the community.

4. Characterize the environmental vectors that contribute to air pollution in order to develop and implement more successful prevention campaigns against allergies and respiratory diseases caused by the state of the environment.

5. Promote changes in the conventional refrigerant derived from the chlorofluorocarbons used in home and automobile air conditioning systems to a more environmentally friendly alternative. Each year, hundreds of kilograms of these gases are released into the environment. A substitution program for chlorofluorocarbons is in place in the Imperial Valley, but needs to be developed and implemented for Mexicali.

6. Regulate the timing of the burning of residual agricultural crops in the Mexicali and Imperial valleys according to meteorological reports in order to minimize effects on the nearby population.

7. Increase the number of paved streets in Mexicali and recommend driving at low speeds on unpaved roads.

8. Strictly monitor the burning of used tires, wood, and fireworks in Mexicali at the year's end—a critical period when pollution increases to undesirable levels and a mixture of smoke and dust can be observed in the air.

9. Introduce a more efficient urban transportation system in Mexicali, eliminating older buses and introducing new ones with well-planned timetables to reduce the use of automobiles in the city. The introduction of "express routes," based on studies of transit engineering in Mexicali (Galindo 1994), would also improve the situation.

Long-Term Recommendations

1. Stimulate community participation in the resolution of air quality problems.

2. Study the potential of economic incentives to reduce air pollution.

3. Think in terms of integrating environmental/ecological taxes within reforms that could be passed at the local level; such revenues would increase income that could be used for programs to address air pollution problems. This type of measure should be based on a general community consensus.

4. Establish strict monitoring and enforcement so that norms may be maintained.

5. Establish sanitary waste confinement sites to avoid the accumulation of used tires and plastic material, which produce excessive amounts of smoke when burned. It would be ideal to have a waste classification system developed and in place before material is confined.

6. Establish a vehicular verification program to check the mechanical status of the transportation sector on the Mexican side and train people in emissions diagnostic technologies. This should be accompanied by a campaign to educate the community about the advantages of these measures. Automobile emissions are a very significant source of air pollution in both valleys. It is estimated that more than half of the automobiles from Mexicali would not pass such a test.

7. Use of Geographical Information Systems (GIS). It is important to develop a GIS that includes emissions and other relevant data for the international airshed of the Mexicali and Imperial region. Once completed, this tool would give scientists, politicians, and other interested parties a fundamental tool to determine some of the causes and consequences of pollution in the area.

8. Convince local brickmakers to use a different type of fuel, such as natural gas or LPG or to use a less-polluting brick kiln design.

Endnote

1. The following section is paraphrased from the U.S.-Mexico Border XXI Framework Document (EPA and SEMARNAP 1996).

References

American Lung Association (ALA). 2000. "Particulate Matter: A New Kind of Air Pollution." *Calexico Chronicle* (18 May): 12.

California Air Resources Board. 1998. http://www.arb.ca.gov/aqd/namslams/map_ss.doc.

Chow, J.C., J.C. Watson, and B. Bates. 1995. "Imperial Valley/Mexicali Cross Border PM10 Transport Study." Draft Final Report. Reno: Desert Research Institute, University and College System of Nevada.

Consejo Estatal de Población (CONEPO) and Gobierno del Estado de Baja California. 2000. *Baja California: proyección de población por localidad, Mexicali.* Mexicali: CONEPO and Gobierno del Estado de Baja California.

Galindo, D.M. 1994. *Estudio integral de la vialidad y el transporte de la ciudad de Mexicali.* Mexicali: Instituto de Ingeniería, Universidad Autónoma de Baja California.

Gobierno del Estado de Baja California, Municipio de Mexicali, Secretaría de Salud, and Instituto Nacional de Ecología–Secretaría de Medio Ambiente, Recursos Naturales, y Pesca. 1999. *Programa para Mejorar la Calidad del Aire de Mexicali 2000–2005.* Mexico, D.F.: Litografía Helio, S.A. de C.V.

González C., A. (Director of Dirección de Ecología del Estado de Baja California). 1999. Interview by author. Tijuana, Baja California, Mexico (November).

Quintana, A.T.R. 2000. "Análisis de la calidad del aire en Mexicali de 1997 a 1998." Bachelor's thesis, Instituto Tecnológico de Mexicali, Mexicali, Baja California, Mexico.

Reyna, C.M.A., and C.E. Álvarez. 1999. "El PM10 y las enfermedades respiratorias agudas en la población de Mexicali, B.C., México." Paper presented at the Sixth Interamerican Congress on the Environment/VI Congreso Interamericano de Medio Ambiente, September, Monterrey, Nuevo León, Mexico.

Sheth, A., and T. Giel. 2000. "Understanding the PM2.5 Problem." *Pollution Engineering* 32: 32–35.

Simon, D. 2000. "Lawsuit May Force County to Take Steps More Quickly." *Imperial Valley Press* (1 December): 1.

Sullivan, R.A. 1999. "Reigning in Fugitive Dust." *Environmental Protection* 10: 36–40.

Sweedler, A., M. Fertig, M. Quintero N., and K. Collins. 2003. "Air Quality in the California-Baja California Border Region." Pp. 15–58 in *The U.S.-Mexican Border Environment: Air Quality Issues along the U.S.-Mexican Border*, Alan Sweedler, ed. San Diego: San Diego State University Press.

United Nations. 1992. UN conference on Environment and Development, Rio de Janeiro, Brasil, 13–14 June.

U.S. Census Bureau. 2000. *Population Estimates Program.* Washington, D.C.: U.S. Census Bureau.

U.S. Environmental Protection Agency (EPA). 1990. *Clean Air Act, Air Quality Prevention and Control.* U.S. EPA. http://www.epa.gov/air/caa/caa111.txt.

U.S. Environmental Protection Agency (EPA) and Secretaría de Medio Ambiente, Recursos Naturales y Pesca (SEMARNAP). 1996. *U.S.-Mexico Border XXI Framework Document.* Washington, D.C., and México, D.F.: EPA and SEMARNAP.

U.S. Environmental Protection Agency (EPA) and Secretaría de Medio Ambiente, Recursos Naturales y Pesca (SEMARNAP). 1997. *United States-Mexico Border Environmental Indicators.* Washington, D.C.: EPA and SEMARNAP.

19

Energy Profile of the Baja California-California Border Region with Emphasis on the Mexicali-Imperial Valley

Margarito Quintero-Núñez and Alan Sweedler*

Abstract

The California-Baja California portion of the U.S.-Mexican border region is an excellent area in which to develop an energy profile. This region is home to almost 50 percent of the total border population and presents many of the opportunities and problems associated with the development of cleaner fuels and energy-efficient processes for the greater border region.

The California-Baja California border region constitutes an energy island, meaning that almost all energy resources (with the exception of geothermal heat) are imported into the region. Additionally, the Baja California electric power grid is not connected to Mexico's main power system, but rather to the California electric network at two interconnections: La Rosita in Mexicali and Mesa de Otay in Tijuana. Such is also the case for natural gas, which has two interconnections: one at the port of entry in eastern Mexicali and another at Mesa de Otay in Tijuana. Construction is in progress in Mexicali to build the North Baja cross-border pipeline starting at Colonia Morelos that would provide fuel to new power plants that are under construction at Colonia Progreso.

In Baja California, the industrial and residential sectors are the major users of electricity, followed by the commercial, irrigation, and public lighting sectors. This differs from electricity use patterns in the Imperial Valley, where the

---

*Quintero-Núñez is Researcher at the Engineering Institute at the Universidad Autónoma de Baja California. Sweedler is the Director of the Center for Energy Studies at San Diego State University.

commercial and residential sectors consume more electricity than the industrial sector. This tendency helps establish the development profiles of each valley.

In Mexicali, a very well-established energy demand-side management program exists for residential users. It is known as the Integral Systematic Savings Program (Programa de Ahorro Sistemático Integral–PASI), which has been successful so far in reducing energy consumption and the burning of conventional fuels. Imperial County has a similar program, but to a lesser degree as there are established construction codes for good quality housing. Its impact on energy consumers is not as significant as that of Mexicali.

Brief Description of the Geographic Area and Population Distribution

The Imperial and Mexicali Valleys

The Imperial and Mexicali valleys are located in the Colorado Desert, the western part of the Sonoran Desert. Part of the region is below sea level and is arid. California and Baja California share the same valley divided by a political line. One outstanding physical characteristic in the region is its weather, as it is located under the solar band and experiences very long summers and short winters. The climate is hot, dry, very arid with average precipitation of less than 7.62 centimeters (3 inches) per year. Humidity increases slightly during the peak of the summer season.

Imperial County

Imperial County is located in the southeast corner of California and has a population of over 144,051 inhabitants. The county extends over 4,597 square miles (11,909 square kilometers), with Mexico to the south, Riverside County to the north, San Diego County to the west, and the State of Arizona to the east. It is the ninth largest county by area in California.

Mexicali

The State of Baja California consists of two regions: the Colorado Valley and the Pacific Coast. The City and Municipality of Mexicali are located in the Colorado Valley region. Its territorial extension represents 21 percent of the state and 0.7 percent of the country (5,288 square miles/13,700 square kilometers). It has an approximate population of 850,000 inhabitants. Three geographical zones are found within the municipality: valley, coastal, and urban. The delegation of San Felipe, its most important, is found in the coastal zone.

Mexicali is located slightly to the north of the ridge of the Colorado River Delta at an average altitude of 36 feet (11 meters) above sea level. To the south, the terrain descends to sea level at the Sea of Cortez. To the north, its altitude descends toward the Salton Sea at approximately 279 feet (85 meters) below sea level.

The Baja California-California Border Region: An Energy Island

Almost all energy resources, with the exception of geothermal, come from outside the region. This, along with the fact that the power grid and natural gas pipelines are not connected to the Mexican national system, qualify the region as an energy island. The electric power grid in Baja California is connected to the California electricity network at two interconnections: Mesa de Otay in Tijuana and La Rosita in Mexicali, where the import and export of electricity takes place.

Baja California also must import its natural gas from the United States via two cross-border pipelines. One is located at the eastern port of entry in Mexicali to supply natural gas to industry and residential consumers. The other is located at Mesa de Otay in Tijuana to supply fuel to one of the Rosarito power plants.

Construction of a natural gas pipeline (Olivieri, Quiñónez, and Uribe 2001) has been completed and is supplying gas to the La Rosita power plant complex near Mexicali. The La Rosita complex consists of a combined cycle 1060 MW facility owned by InterGen and a 600 MW combined plant owned by Sempra (Abreu and Simoes 2001). The pipeline extends to Tijuana and Rosarito transporting natural gas to the Rosarito power plant and, potentially, to the San Diego area. Total power production by Termoeléctrica de Mexicali and 75 percent of La Rosita output will be exported to California. The remaining power will be for local consumption.

Power Generation Infrastructure

Mexicali

Baja California derives its energy from two primary sources: petroleum products and geothermal generation. All petroleum products are imported to the region from other parts of Mexico and southern Mexico in particular. The transportation sector uses unleaded gasoline and diesel. Liquefied petroleum gas (LPG) is used mainly by residential consumers. However, the use of natural gas has increased during the last few years in Mexicali's industrial, residential, and commercial sectors as the gas distribution system network has expanded.

Baja California's electric infrastructure consists of two large power-generating facilities (about 1,326 MW thermal and 720 MW geothermal), several smaller generating plants, and appropriate transmission lines. The power grid is connected to San Diego via two 230-kilovolt lines—one now upgraded near Tijuana and the other near Mexicali. Generating facilities and the electricity grid system are shown in

Figure 1 and Table 1 (note the isolation of the Baja California power system from the main Mexican network).

There are no oil refineries in Baja California and most petroleum products enter the region via tankers at the products terminal in Rosarito. There is a 10-inch pipeline that transports petroleum and refined products between Rosarito and Mexicali and a similar eight-inch pipeline between Rosarito and Ensenada (Quintero 1990). LPG is brought into the region by truck or rail and is distributed by truck. Petroleum-based products (fuel oil, unleaded gasoline, diesel, LPG, and natural gas) account for 69 percent of the state's total energy supply. Geothermally generated electricity accounts for the rest.

The Imperial Valley

The Imperial Irrigation District (IID) provides electrical services within its service area that covers 6,471 square miles (16,790 square kilometers), including all of

Figure 1. Western Section of the Electric Power System

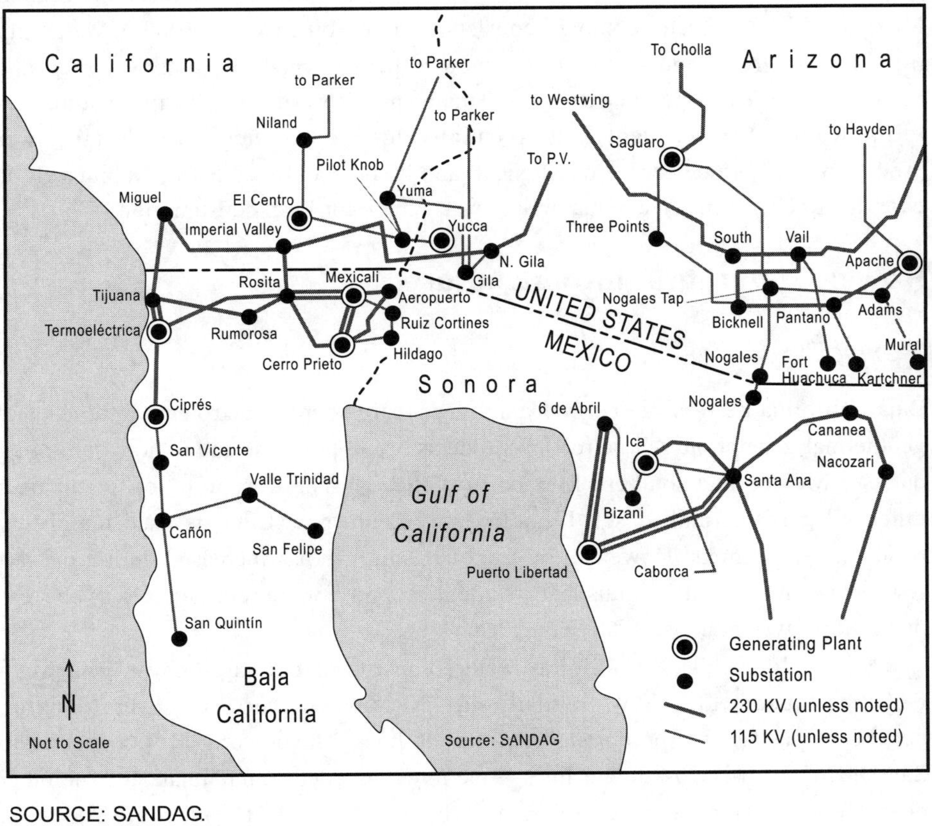

SOURCE: SANDAG.

Table 1. Baja California Generating Facilities

Municipality	Site	Fuel	Capacity in KW
Rosarito	Rosarito	Diesel	60,000
	Rosarito	Fuel oil & natural gas	620,000
Mexicali	Mexicali:		
	Cerro Prieto I	Geothermal	180,000
	Cerro Prieto II	Geothermal	220,000
	Cerro Prieto III	Geothermal	220,000
	Cerro Prieto IV	Geothermal	100,000
Ensenada	Ciprés	Diesel	54,860
Total			1,454,860

SOURCE: SDE and Gobierno del Estado de Baja California (2000).

Imperial County and parts of Riverside and San Diego counties. The IID is the sixth largest electric utility by demand in California (630.1 MW in 1996). There are several power plants in the Imperial Valley that range from geothermal to microhydroelectric to thermal. Table 2 shows the total installed capacity of 1,102 MW. The primary fuel used to generate power is natural gas, which provides 51 percent of the fuel for IID electric generation in the Imperial Valley (Cox 1998).

The IID's electricity supply by fuel type is 51 percent steam and gas turbines (natural gas), 18 percent power purchase, 12 percent steam (coal), 9 percent small hydro, 8 percent gas turbines (diesel only), and 2 percent nuclear. The IID's electric transmission system consists of 43 percent IID-generated power, 26 percent imported power, and 31 percent geothermal power for export. Most of the energy produced by geothermal power plants is sold to Southern California Edison (SCE) through long-term contracts established prior to the deregulation of the electric utility industry in 1998. This is the case of the CalEnergy power plant that sells only 35 MW. The energy produced by the Salton Sea Number 5 generating plant is sold in the spot market. It is important to note that, among the independent producers of energy within the IID area, there are two plants that burn agricultural waste or biomass. The first is known as Imperial Valley Resource & Recovery Co. (IVRRC); it has a capacity of 14 MW and is located in Imperial Valley. The second is Colmac, with a capacity of 50 MW and it is sited in Mecca in the Coachella Valley. IID electricity end use by sectors is 83 percent residential, 14 percent commercial, 1 percent agricultural, and 2 percent other.

The Southern California Gas Company (SCGC), part of SEMPRA Energy, supplies natural gas to the Imperial Valley. SCGC is privately owned and is one of the largest natural gas distribution companies in the United States. The natural gas that is delivered to the Imperial Valley is odorized and compressed at a major natural gas transmission processing center in Desert Center, California. The bulk of natural gas

Table 2. Power-Generating Facilities in Imperial Valley

1. Imperial Irrigation District Generation System	
Hydrogeneration	**KW**
Drop 1	5,850
Drop 2	10,000
Drop 3	9,800
Drop 4	19,600
Drop 5	4,000
Pilot Knob	33,000
East Highline Turnout	2,415
Total	84,665
Thermal Generation	**KW**
El Centro Steam Station	260,000
Brawley G.T. Station	18,000
Coachella G.T. Station	80,000
Rockwood G.T. Station	50,000
Axis-Yucca Plant	75,000
Axis G.T. 21	22,000
Total	505,000
2. Independent Power Producers Connected to IID Transmission System	
Thermal Generation	**KW**
Colmac	49,000
Western Power No. 1	15,000
Western Power No. 2	15,000
Total	79,000
Geothermal Generation	**KW**
Gem No. 1	0
Gem No. 2	27,000
Gem No. 3	27,000
Ormesa No. 1	38,000
Ormesa No. 2	19,000
Earth Energy No. 1	10,000
Earth Energy No. 2	20,000
Heber Geo Inc.	47,000
Vulcan Power	38,000
Second Imperial	33,000
Del Ranch	42,000
Elmore	42,000
Leathers	42,000
Desert Power	50,000
Total	435,000

SOURCE: Cox (1998).

delivered locally originates in Texas and is shipped via the Southwest Transmission pipeline. As mentioned previously, the IID uses natural gas to generate 51 percent of its locally produced electricity and the electric utility uses a significant portion of the natural gas in the Imperial Valley.

One natural gas pipeline is connected to Mexicali by the existing Imperial transmission pipeline. The Vecinos (Neighbors) Project is a 20-mile extension costing an estimated US$100 million (EIA 1996). The Vecinos Project has the capacity to supply 500,000 cubic feet of natural gas per day to industrial and commercial end users in the Mexicali Valley. Tenneco Baja Mexicali Export plans to build a new one-mile-long pipe to add 40 million cubic feet of natural gas per day (MMcf/d) to Mexicali. The availability of natural gas for industrial processes provides a new energy source that is friendlier to the environment than the diesel and fuel oil now being used in Mexicali. Natural gas burns cleaner than diesel or fuel oil and contributes less pollution to the atmosphere.

Environmental Impacts of Energy Use in the Border Region

There are several ways to measure the environmental impact of energy on the region: *(a)* through the generation of electric energy based on the use of several resources, such as fuel oil, diesel, geothermal steam, natural gas, and recycled tires among others; *(b)* through the use of different fuels in the transportation system, such as various types of gasoline and diesel that have become the main polluters in the area; *(c)* through the use of various fuels in the industrial, commercial, domestic, and government sectors, such as fuel oil, diesel, natural gas, LPG, and recycled tires, among others.

Mexicali

The origins of Cerro Prieto's geothermal resources date back some four to six millions years, to when the peninsula of Baja California began to separate from the mainland of Mexico and formed a protogulf. This allowed hot material from the mantle to flow to the surface along a system of faults now known as the San Andreas Fault.

This geothermal area at Cerro Prieto first became known when an expedition led by Hernán Cortés discovered the Baja California peninsula in 1535 (Ives 1973). In later expeditions other explorers, such as Melchor Díaz in 1540, came upon the Cerro Prieto zone as they marched toward the northwest from the lower Colorado River Delta. They were astonished by the many emissions of steam and sulfurous gases in the area.

Cerro Prieto is geothermal potential was demonstrated in 1852, when a strong earthquake struck the Mexicali Valley and Yuma areas. At Cerro Prieto, the event was manifested by columns of steam that rose to great heights for several minutes and then subsided only to appear again every so often.

The Cerro Prieto geothermoelectric power plant is the most important geothermal development in Mexico (Quintero 1989). It is located 19 miles (30 km) to the south of the City of Mexicali. Some of the wells of the field were drilled at the end of the 1960s. However, power production began only in April 1973 when the two 37.5 MW units started operating. Currently, 720 MW of capacity have been installed. It is divided among four power stations: Cerro Prieto I (180 MW), II (220 MW), III (220 MW), and IV (100 MW).

As a byproduct of power production, the geothermal process also generates carbon dioxide, hydrogen sulphide, and ammonia, collectively known as noncondensible gases (NCGs), as well as residual brine. Release of NCGs into the atmosphere and solid residue resulting from evaporation of the brine are the principal sources of environmental impacts from Cerro Prieto (Gallegos, Quintero, and García 2000). Table 3 shows emissions of hydrogen sulphide into the atmosphere from chimneys and the cooling towers at the Cerro Prieto power plants, totaling 1,379 kilograms per hour.

Once the two-phase geothermal fluid reaches the surface, it separates into its two main components: geothermal steam and residual brine. The latter is a significant pollutant (GPG 1994). Geothermal field operations produce about 6,400 tons per hour of residual brine, which is handled and disposed in an evaporation pond that covers an area of 7.2 square miles (18.6 square kilometers). An annual average of 88 percent of all wastewaters are disposed here, thus polluting the soil and potentially the region's aquifer. Reinjection of gravity brine is still practiced at some old wells, with 60 percent of the total brine reinjected.

Table 3. Hydrogen Sulphide Emissions at the
Cerro Prieto Geothermoelectric Power Plant (kg/hr)

Power Plant	From Chimneys	From Cooling Towers
Cerro Prieto I	101.61	132.84
Cerro Prieto II	276.34	295.91
Cerro Prieto III	276.34	295.91
Total	654.29	724.66

SOURCE: Magaña (1987).

Imperial Valley

The environmental impacts of geothermal power production in the Imperial Valley are considerably less than those of Cerro Prieto. This is due to a lower level of power production and the reinjection of geothermal fluids that prevents the effects of gases and residual brine on the atmosphere and soil. The solids that are separated at some plants when the concentration of the geothermal fluid is too high are used to fill out the embankment of the Salton Sea as a reinforcement for earthquakes, which are quite common in this area. There is strict control of geothermal byproducts in the Imperial Valley, which allows geothermal exploitation to be considered environmentally friendly. The opposite is evident with regard to the Cerro Prieto geothermal field in the Mexicali Valley.

Pollution from natural gas fired thermal plants at combined cycle plants consists mostly of nitrogen oxide and is regulated by state and federal entities. The IID was fined by the Imperial County Air Quality Control District for not meeting these air quality standards (Simon 2000). The microhydroelectric power plants (83 MW capacity) located along the All American Canal do not produce negative environmental impacts.

IID shares Unit Number 3 of a power plant called San Juan, located in New Mexico. It utilizes coal as a fuel for a total capacity of 544 MW, but with a net generation of 497 MW. IID owns 104 MW of this capacity. This plant meets appropriate federal and state air emission regulations. The IID is working to diversify its sources of power and to reduce its dependence on natural gas for the production of electricity.

Energy Demand by Sector

Industrial and residential sectors are the major users of electricity in Baja California, followed by the commercial, irrigation, and public-lighting sectors. This differs from electricity use patterns in the Imperial Valley, where the commercial and residential sectors consume more electricity than the industrial sector. The differences in electric energy use between Mexicali and Imperial reflect the fact that manufacturing and assembly activities form a larger part of the economy in Mexicali than they do in Imperial. This is primarily due to *maquiladora* (assembly plant) operations located in Mexicali and Tijuana and some energy-intensive industries in Mexicali, such as glass and steel production.

Import and Export of Energy

Import

One outstanding characteristic of the energy sector in the California-Baja California border region is its almost total dependence on energy resources from outside the region. With the notable exception of the geothermal fields in Mexicali at Cerro Prieto and in Imperial Valley at Heber, East Mesa, and Calipatria, virtually all of the energy consumed in the region originates in distant places. These imported energy resources are in the form of petroleum products (gasoline, diesel, jet fuel, liquefied petroleum, fuel oil, natural gas) and imported electricity. All of Baja California's transport, industrial, and residential fuels must be transported long distances from refineries located far to the south in Mexico.

The Imperial Valley also imports most of its natural gas from several sources, both domestic and foreign, including northern California, Texas, and Canada. In the Imperial Valley, aside from generating electric energy from geothermal resources (435 MW), which is transmitted by the IID to Southern California Edison (SCE), there are also several gas fired plants (584 MW) that use natural gas as a primary fuel. Microhydropower plants located along the All American Canal (83 MW) also provide electric energy for the local market.

Export

The only indigenous energy source used on a large scale in Baja California is geothermally generated electricity, produced south of Mexicali at Cerro Prieto. The current installed capacity at Cerro Prieto is 720 MW.

Before 1997, about 35 percent of the power from Cerro Prieto was exported to Southern California under a contract with SCE and San Diego Gas and Electric (SDG&E). San Diego's share of Mexico's geothermal power was 150 MW, which accounted for 6 percent of SDG&E's installed capacity in 1991 (DOE 1991). In 1990, SDG&E imported over one billion kilowatt/hours and SCE imported 0.6 billion kilowatt/hours from Mexico. SDG&E also exported over 400 million kilowatt/hours to Mexico, accounting for most of Mexico's electricity imports. In 1992, electricity exports from Cerro Prieto to California totaled 1,406 gigawatt/hours to SDG&E and 614 gigawatt/hours to SCE (CFE 1993). This represented almost 10 percent of SDG&E's supply. The situation has dramatically changed in recent years. From the mid- to late 1990s, Baja California imported power from California. During 2000 and 2001; however, Baja California supplied power to California during its energy shortages. As of November 2003, both the Sempra and InterGen facilities have been exporting power to California.

In addition to the two large plants at Cerro Prieto and Rosarito, the Federal Electricity Commission (Comisión Federal de Electricidad–CFE) operates several smaller gas turbine plants in Ensenada, Tijuana, and Mexicali that use diesel as a fuel (see Table 1).

Economic and Energy Indicators

Electricity Rates

In Mexico, the Secretariat of the Treasury (Secretaría de Hacienda) has issued 22 specific electrical rates and five general electric rates for the various sectors of society. These tariffs become more complicated during the summer when consumers are generally subject to seasonal rates. Since Mexicali is classified as one of the cities with the highest average summer temperatures in Mexico, it has a subsidized residential electric tariff termed "1E" to diminish the impact of energy consumption on the family budget. Still, residential users in Mexicali consume as much electricity during the summer months as the five Mexican States of Colima, Nayarit, Tlaxcala, Chiapas, and Veracruz combined (Delgado 2001). Mexicali residents pay a significant portion of their salaries (depending on their economic status) just to cover the monthly electric bill.

Such problems are not the case in the Imperial Valley, generally due to higher salaries and the area's small manufacturing sector (workers in Mexicali earn one-thirteenth of the income of those in the Imperial Valley). The 12 electricity tariffs established in Imperial are very similar to those in Mexicali, but they do not subsidize residential tariffs during the summer as they do in Mexicali.

During the summer season, industry in Mexicali must pay more for power during peak hours from noon to six in the evening. This has caused complaints from the private sector, which claims that such pricing reduces its ability to compete with other regions of the country (SDE and Gobierno del Estado de Baja California 1999). Electric energy peak demand at Imperial Valley was 696 MW in 2001, whereas in Baja California it was 1200 MW during the same year (Treat 2001).

The Energy Management Program

To reduce the economic impacts of high energy consumption by residential users in Mexicali, an energy management program has been established called the Integral Systematic Savings Program (ISSP). It offers high energy efficiency equipment, such as air-conditioning systems, fluorescent light bulbs, and roof insulation through a soft credit system. It also includes a long distance automatic interruption system to control the demands of air-conditioning equipment and provides a discount for those enrolled in the program (25 pesos/ton installed). The Imperial Valley has no similar policies, but during the summer months it does provide some economic assistance to those residential users below certain income levels.

New Sources of Energy in the Area

Indigenous Renewable and Nonrenewable Energy Sources

One of the central themes developed in this analysis is the region's almost complete dependence on fossil fuels that originate outside of the region, often at great distances. They not only represent an outflow of capital from the region, but the burning of fossil fuels also represents the major source of air pollution in the transboundary region. The Cerro Prieto geothermal power plant, as noted, is also a source of atmospheric contamination. An examination of the potential for developing less-polluting indigenous and renewable sources of energy in the border area is therefore of interest.

Hydrocarbons

Northwestern Mexico, including Baja California, does not produce hydrocarbons and no refineries are located in the region. Although the Mexican Petroleum Company (Petróleos Mexicanos–PEMEX) has conducted various field explorations in Baja California, it has not found significant deposits of hydrocarbons. No coal deposits have been found in Baja California either and any coal used in the state is imported from other regions of Mexico.

Liquefied petroleum gas (LPG) is also imported to the region. Most of the LPG produced in Mexico is exported to the United States at the northeastern border and then reimported for use in Mexico. In the case of Baja California, LPG is purchased from a company in Texas and transported to each of the five municipalities in Baja California, including Mexicali, by tanker trucks or railway.

Since 1997, Baja California has imported natural gas from the United States through two pipelines. One is located at Mesa de Otay, Tijuana, transporting fuel to the reconverted Rosarito power plant, and the other is located at the eastern port of entry in Mexicali, which is meant to be used by commercial and private vehicles.

A new pipeline will be constructed in Imperial County due to increased demand for natural gas in the Mexicali Valley and the fact that the existing pipeline is no longer able to supply gas to both valleys.

In Mexicali, industries that converted to natural gas decided to retrofit the systems to support diesel or fuel oil burning while natural gas prices stabilize at a lower price than what existed in 2000 and part of 2001. The California energy crisis has not significantly affected the Imperial Valley since it has a sufficient supply of natural gas and alternative sources of energy.

Renewable Energy Sources

Renewable energy resources in Mexicali and Imperial consist of geothermal (already exploited in both valleys), microhydroelectric (exploited since 1951 at the All American Canal in Imperial), biomass, wind, solar, solar pond, and tidal sources. Other than hydro and geothermal, none of the renewable resources have been significantly exploited to date.

Geothermal

The current installed capacity at Cerro Prieto is 720 MW. According to studies carried out in the past (Alonso 1988), Cerro Prieto geothermal has an estimated reserve of 1,200 MW, with proven reserves of 840 MW. At the Salton Sea area, the current producing capacity is 335 MW, with proven reserves of 1,105 MW and a potential of 2,330 MW (Sandoval 2002). IID has contracted for 170 MW with Cal Energy Company for a new geothermoelectric power plant, "Salton Sea IV," that will be in operation in 2005 (Sandoval 2002).

Geothermal Binary Cycle

Part of the residual brine of Cerro Prieto is now disposed of at the evaporation lagoon and 60 percent is reinjected by gravity. This resource may be used to generate electricity through the binary cycle process, which is currently being implemented in Imperial Valley.

Solar, Solar Pond, Wind, Biomass, Tidal, and Microhydroelectric Energy

There is the possibility of using the Salton Sea in the Imperial Valley to generate energy utilizing solar pond technology that is currently being exploited in Israel.

IID is in the process of installing five new microhydroelectric plants that will add 2 MW of capacity. The energy resource will primarily be used for irrigation purposes and to satisfy urban demands.

There are a large number of irrigation canals in the Mexicali Valley. Quintero and Riva's study (1995) regarding the possibility of exploiting this resource to produce electricity showed that the potential installation of a series of microhydroelectric plants would produce 5 MW of electric energy.

A macro project known as Proyecto Maremotriz Montagne has been proposed to generate 800 MW of electricity based on tidal energy in the Gulf of California (Shields 1998). This project would generate large amounts of electricity to support the regional development of the northwest of Mexico. It also would help to attenuate the massive erosion that is produced on the Colorado River Delta.

There is interest from Spanish investors to exploit wind energy in the area of Cañón de San Martín, Valle de la Trinidad, located 260 km southwest of Mexicali. The plan is to construct a 250 MW wind field to supply energy to Mexicali, although the potential wind energy for this area is estimated to be as high as 4,000 MW (Rivero 2002).

Table 4 lists the potential for renewable energy development in Baja California (Huacuz 1995). As already noted, geothermal power is well developed. Although Baja California has a high level of incident solar energy that is estimated to be in the range of 3.3 to 6.9 kilowatt hours per square meter, there are no solar installations of any appreciable size in the state; the same can be said for wind facilities. The Imperial Valley also does not have significant solar installations or wind facilities.

Conclusions

Undoubtedly, there are both similarities and differences between the Mexicali and Imperial valleys in terms of energy. The present situation in the energy sector has been discussed. A few comments are now presented regarding the likely future evolution of the energy situation.

The structure of the energy sector will likely experience very important transformations over the next ten to twenty years, especially on the Mexican side of the border. This conclusion is based on trends in the region's economic development, high energy rates, population growth, and the rapid changes taking place in the regulatory structures of both countries.

Table 4. Baja California's Potential Energy Resources

Energy Source	Potential
Geothermal	1,000 MW proven reserves (Mexicali)
Solar	3.3–6.9 kWh/m^2
Wind	100–250 W/m^2
Biomass: Agricultural waste	3,600 m^3 NGE/day (Mexicali)
Solid urban waste	25–30 MWe + heat
Seaweed	~75,000 BOE/year
Fuel wood	Negligible
Microhydroelectric	~80 MWe (Mexicali)
	~20 MWe (Tecate)
Tidal Power	~1,200 MWe (Sea of Cortés)

SOURCE: Huacuz (1995).

As a result of continued population growth and industrial expansion, especially in Mexicali, demand for energy services will continue to increase during the first decade of this century. A growth rate of 7.5 percent per year for electricity in Baja California and more than 100 percent increase in generating capacity for the year 2003 has been estimated (Sweedler, Quintero, and Collins 2003). The 2.5 percent growth rate per year for electricity in the Imperial Valley has been stable in recent years (Sandoval 2002).

Mexicali and Baja California as a whole represent significant demand for natural gas. The ability to supply these quantities is one of the major energy issues to be dealt with by the private sector and government authorities on either side of the border.

Inevitably, there will be greater levels of cross-border trade in energy services due to the restructuring of electricity in California and the growing economic interdependence of California and Baja California. This is also evident in the case of Mexicali and Imperial, as exemplified by current sales of electricity by the CFE to SCE and supplies from U.S.-based companies. The advantage that both valleys have is that each has its own independent power-generating system, making the two valleys relatively autonomous from outside suppliers unless there is a large increase in peak demand.

It is expected that with time the international border will become less of a barrier to energy flows, once more power exchange points are established along the common border and power generation increases as a consequence of the demand on both sides of the border.

References

Abreu, A., and Octavio Simoes, 2001. "Termoeléctrica de Mexicali." Paper presented at Segundo Foro: Ciudad y Medio Ambiente, 4 October, Mexicali, Baja California, Mexico.

Alonso, E.H. 1982. *Estado de la geotérmica en México, reservas y estrategias de desarrollo.* Morelia: Dirección de Proyectos Geotermoeléctricos, Comisión Federal de Electricidad.

Alonso, E.H., 1988. "Cerro Prieto: una alternativa en el desarrollo energético." In *Memoria de la Reunión Nacional Sobre la Energía y el Confort*, Carlos R. García Flores, ed. Mexicali: Instituto de Ingeniería, Universidad Autónoma de Baja California.

Comisión Federal de Electricidad (CFE). 1993. Private communication (27 September).

Cox, R. 1998. *1998 Power Report.* Imperial: Imperial Irrigation District.

Delgado, J. 2001. "Equivale a cinco el consumo de energía." *La Crónica* (14 November): 20A.

Energy Information Administration (EIA). 1996. *Natural Gas 1996: Issues and Trends.* Washington, D.C.: U.S. Department of Energy.

Gallegos, O.R., M. Quintero N., and O.R. García C. 2000. "H_2S Dispersion Model at Cerro Prieto Geothermoelectric Power Plant." Pp. 579–84. In *Proceedings of the World Geothermal Congress 2000, Kyushu-Tohoku, Japan, May 28–June 10.* Internet search.

Gerencia de Proyectos Geotermoeléctricos (GPG). 1994. *Panfleto publicitario sobre el campo geotermoeléctrico Cerro Prieto.* Mexicali: Residencia General de Cerro Prieto Mexicali, Comisión Federal de Electricidad.

Huacuz, J. 1995. "Non-Fossil Fuel Based Energy Sources." Pp. 133–40 in *Energy and Environment in the California-Baja California Border Region*, A. Sweedler, P. Ganster, and P. Bennett, eds. San Diego: Institute for Regional Studies of the Californias and San Diego State University Press.

Ives, I.R. 1973. "La última jornada de Melchor Ocampo Díaz." *Calafia-UABC* 2: 18–19.

Lund, J.W., and D.H. Freeston. 2000. Worldwide direct uses of geothermal energy 2000. Proceedings. WGC 2000: 1–21.

Magaña, L.M. 1987. "Remoción de ácido sulfhídrico en la planta geotermoeléctrica de Cerro Prieto." Bachelor's thesis, Instituto de Ingeniería, Universidad Autónoma de Baja California, Mexicali.

Olivieri, F., L.P. Quiñónez, and J. Uribe. 2001. "Proyecto gasoducto Baja Norte." Paper presented at Segundo Foro: Ciudad y Medio Ambiente, 4 October, Mexicali, Baja California, Mexico.

Quintero N., M. 1990. "Fuentes actuales y potenciales de energía en Baja California." Paper presented at Segunda Reunión Nacional Sobre la Energía y el Confort, 3–25 May, Mexicali, Baja California, Mexico.

Quintero N., M., and R.J.M. Peña. 1989. "Geothermal Development in Mexico." *GRC Bulletin* 18 (1): 5–12.

Quintero N., M., and L.M. Rivas. 1995. "Microhydroelectric Plants in the Valley of Mexicali." Pp. 129–32 in *Energy and Environment in the California-Baja California Border Region*, A. Sweedler, P. Ganster, and P. Bennet, eds. San Diego: Institute for Regional Studies of the Californias and San Diego State University Press.

Rivero, M. 2002. "Promueven planta eólica." *La Crónica* (16 June): 2F.

Sandoval, J.C. 2002, Imperial Irrigation District. Conversation with authors. El Centro, California (February).

Secretaría de Desarrollo Económico (SDE) and Gobierno del Estado de Baja California. 1999. *Estudio sobre el análisis de las tarifas industriales eléctricas de Baja California.* Mexicali: SDE and Gobierno del Estado de Baja California.

Secretaría de Desarrollo Económico (SDE) and Gobierno del Estado de Baja California. 2000. *Estadísticas básicas del estado.* Mexicali: SDE and Gobierno del Estado de Baja California.

Shields, D. 1998. "Buscan apoyo para proyecto de generación de energía en Mexicali." *El Financiero* (8 June): 38.

Simon, D. 2000. "$800,000 Air Pollution Settlement on IID Agenda." *Imperial Valley News* (11 September): 3.

Sweedler, A., M. Quintero N., and K. Collins. 2003. "Energy Issues in the U.S.-Mexican Binational Region: Focus on California-Baja California." Pp. 57–103 in *The U.S.-Mexican Border Environment: Trade, Energy, and the Environment: Challenges and Opportunities for the Border Region, Now and in 2020*, David A. Rohy, ed. San Diego: San Diego State University Press.

Treat, J. 2001. "La propia crisis energética en ciernes de México." *Borderlines 77* 9 (4).

U.S. Department of Energy (DOE) and Secretaría de Energía, Minas e Industria Paraestatal (SEMIP). 1991. *United States/Mexico Electric Trade Study.* Washington, D.C.: DOE and SEMP.

Young, J. 2001. "Planta termoeléctrica central La Rosita." Paper presented at Segundo Foro: Ciudad y Medio Ambiente, 4 October, Mexicali, Baja California, Mexico.

20

Energy Savings Plans and Domestic Consumers: An Analysis

Silvia Ahumada Valdez and Ramona Fuentes Valdez*

Abstract

The Mexicali and Imperial valleys have very similar climatic characteristics that intensify during the summer months (May through October). Systematic electricity savings plans and programs offered by the Federal Electricity Commission (Comisión Federal de Electricidad–CFE), on the Mexican side of the border, and those by the Imperial Irrigation District (IID) on the other, emerge from both the need to save energy and as a consequence of high electricity consumption on both sides of the border. Programs that focus on savings, assistance, and reimbursement for the residential consumer, when correctly applied, can bring substantial benefits. This essay provides a comparative analysis of energy savings plans and programs that are offered by both the CFE and IID.

Introduction

Due to their geographic location, the Mexicali and Imperial valleys (see Figure 1) experience extreme climatic conditions. During the summer these conditions intensify, bringing extremely high temperatures to the region. As such, residents on both sides of the border must condition their homes with artificial climate controls.

*Ahumada Valdez and Fuentes Valdez are Researchers at the Institute of Engineering at the Universidad Autónoma de Baja California in Mexicali. The authors acknowledge the Imperial Irrigation District—Steve Vasquez and Mike Jaramillo, in particular—for facilitating this work and supporting its development.

Such conditioning implies high use of electricity, which causes financial repercussions at home.

Different measures to save energy have been taken in both valleys. These include the modification of construction patterns so that electrical energy is used more efficiently as well as the implementation of home energy diagnoses that promote the adoption of electricity savings plans. These programs are applicable at all levels and some are specific to residential or commercial use.

The savings plans that were developed on each side of the border offer different options to consumers that, if adopted, would be beneficial. However, this is not the case because such options are impractical or unattractive. Consumers of electricity, by their own resolve, must acquire practices that are not only beneficial in terms of saving energy, but also in terms of reducing family expenses.

Figure 1. Geographic Location of the Mexicali and Imperial Valleys

This essay provides a comparative analysis of the savings measures or plans offered by the Mexicali and Imperial Valley institutions (IID 2000; CFE 2001) with the purpose of exchanging ideas and recommending those that are feasible and beneficial to the consumer. With this in mind, it is necessary to evaluate the consumer's knowledge of, and interest in, existing savings plans. Knowing and analyzing these levels of understanding might foster the emergence of new programs that offer other options.

A Geographic-Climatic Overview of the Valleys

Given the geographical conditions of both valleys and their temperature ranges, residential electricity consumers face similar problems on both sides of the border (IID 2001; CFE 2001). Table 1 and Figure 2 show annual average temperatures for both valleys.

Consumer Habits and the Inefficiency of Electric Appliances

Cultural habits and behaviors exhibited through consumer purchases reveal economic levels and the way resources are used. High energy use is directly related to the type of electric appliances purchased, their level of efficiency, and their proper use (INEGI 1999; COPLADEM 1999). Mexicali residents can easily purchase used electric appliances at a very low cost, especially household appliances, and these appliances

Table 1. Average Temperatures for Mexicali and Imperial Valleys

Months	Maximum		Minimum		Imperial		Mexicali	
	°C	°F	°C	°F	°C	°F	°C	°F
January	20.10	67.90	4.08	39.30	13.22	55.60	12.49	54.30
February	23.24	73.50	6.22	43.10	15.74	60.10	15.00	58.80
March	25.31	77.20	8.34	46.90	17.92	64.00	17.36	63.00
April	29.06	83.90	11.31	52.20	21.39	70.20	21.28	70.00
May	34.00	92.70	15.68	60.00	25.42	77.40	25.08	76.80
June	39.48	102.50	20.44	68.50	30.24	86.00	29.74	85.10
July	42.17	107.30	25.37	77.30	33.48	91.80	33.38	91.60
August	41.33	105.80	25.20	77.00	33.04	91.00	32.87	90.70
September	38.19	100.20	21.50	70.40	29.85	85.30	30.13	85.80
October	32.42	89.90	14.90	58.60	24.08	75.00	24.06	75.00
November	25.48	77.50	8.57	47.30	17.75	63.70	17.25	62.80
December	20.50	68.60	4.20	39.50	13.22	55.60	13.00	55.20
For the Year					22.90	72.90	22.64	72.50

SOURCE: World Climate (2001a, 2001b).

Figure 2. Average Temperatures for Mexicali and Imperial Valleys with Climate Oscillations/Variations

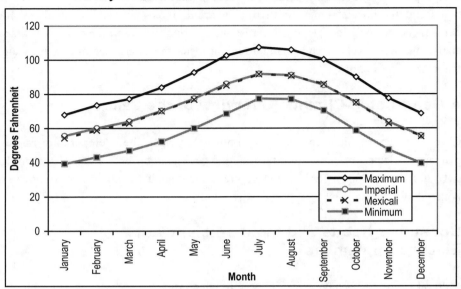

SOURCE: World Climate (2001a, 2001b).

mainly come from the United States. Many consumers purchase such items without taking into consideration recommendations based on efficiency from energy sector authorities and without considering the long-term operating costs of the appliances.

Savings Plans and Policies

The need to save energy is worldwide. Several countries and organizations have undertaken the task of designing a path toward energy savings. Various parameters have been considered, especially in the commercial and industrial sectors, and multiple consumers have benefited. However, many new technologies have been inappropriate for the majority of the population and are not seen by the individual consumer as beneficial.

In Mexico, agencies such as the National Commission for Energy Savings (Comisión Nacional para el Ahorro de Energía–CONAE) have volunteer programs that provide technical assistance to help consumers identify potential energy savings and modify their behavior (CONAE 2000). Such programs (building lights, energy demand control, street lighting, generation and distribution of steam, cooling towers, and so on), however, are directed toward specific technologies and not to the average consumer.

Support plans, programs, and policies for residential consumers (see Table 2) are offered by the IID (energy/marketing services) in the Imperial Valley and the CFE in

Table 2. Residential Energy Savings Plans and Programs in the Imperial and Mexicali Valleys

Mexicali Valley	Imperial Valley
Energy Diagnosis	Energy Diagnosis
"Integral Systematic Savings" (ASI) program for residential consumers	Advisory services plan for the conservation of energy
Thermal insulation subprogram	Discount program for low-income consumers
IDEAA subprogram	Support program for electricity payments
Door sealing subprogram	Incentive program for the acquisition of heating pumps and air conditioners in the residential sector
Fixed payment plan subprogram	Incentive program for the installation of coolers
Substitution of air conditioning subprogram	Air conditioning program
Substitution of fluorescent lights subprogram	High-efficiency refrigerators

SOURCE: IID (2000); CFE (2001).

the Mexicali Valley (Baja California sector). Both valleys have savings programs for the residential sector that focus on electricity consumption. The following section reviews these programs (IID 2000; CFE 2001).

Mexicali Valley

The CFE has special rates based on kilowatt-hour (kWh) consumption for residential consumers during the warm months (May through October) and in specific areas with a minimum summer temperature of 89.6°F (32°C) (CFE 2001). In addition, the CFE promotes general savings plans for the average consumer. These plans are based on the results of energy savings studies. The plans and programs that are currently offered by CFE include the "Integral Systematic Savings" program (Programa de Ahorro Sistemático Integral–PASI) for residential consumers.

PASI offers residential consumers a series of support subprograms that include consultants, services, and even financing. Some of the financing services are interest-free and are described below.

Thermal Insulation Subprogram

The first energy savings plan to be developed was designed to insulate roofs. It is offered to consumers that meet certain criteria, such as a 1,000 kWh minimum monthly electricity use within the special rate period. This plan grants the consumer a credit of up to approximately $926 (8,800 pesos [1 dollar = 9.50 pesos]) for their roof's insulation, to be repaid in 36 monthly installments with no interest.

IDEAA Subprogram

This plan was created alongside the Thermal Insulation Subprogram. It consists of a central control for the intermittent shutdown of compressors in residential air conditioning units. This shutdown takes place every 15 minutes during peak consumption hours (2:00–6:00 p.m.). This subprogram does not provide for adequate cooling or comfort in homes. Compensation for participating only comes through the financial incentive of approximately $3.16 (30 pesos) for each ton capacity of the air conditioning unit.

Door Sealing Subprogram

This subprogram offers the sealing of doors as a practical savings method. It provides a way to prevent cold airflows from leaking out and hot airflows from entering. Both flows contribute to an increase in electricity consumption. This service is offered on credit and without interest.

Fixed Payment Plan Subprogram

An estimate of the current year's consumption is made based on energy consumption from the previous year and divided into 12 monthly payments. This estimate allows consumers to pay the same amount each month, allowing them to organize their recurrent expenses. If by the end of the year consumption is greater than the amount paid, then the user covers the difference; otherwise, the user is granted a credit balance.

Air Conditioning Substitution Subprogram

This program supports consumers in their purchase of high-efficiency air conditioning units. The payment plan is arranged for 36, 48, or 60 monthly installments according to the consumer's request. There are no additional fees, but there is a 15 percent annual interest rate on unpaid balances.

Fluorescent Lights Substitution Subprogram

Another option for better use of electricity is the substitution of incandescent lights for fluorescent ones. This program offers the residential consumer up to 10 lights of 23, 20, or 16 watts with a one-time payment or credit for up to 24 months with no interest.

Imperial County

The IID offers programs that address public benefits, energy savings advisory services, and refunds on exchanges of used appliances for those of higher efficiency. The following are among the programs offered by the IID (2000, 2001).

Discount Programs for Low-Income Consumers

The IID offers monthly discounts of 20 to 25 percent to residential consumers who qualify for this service. The discount amount depends on annual income. Consumers with an annual income that is equal to or less than $17,000 (161,500 pesos) may qualify for a discount of up to 25 percent. In addition, consumers with an annual income greater than $17,000 may receive a discount of up to 20 percent. This program is offered by authorized centers in the Imperial Valley and Coachella.

Support Program for Energy Payments

This program provides funding to IID residential consumers who are in financial trouble. They may apply for these funds to avoid suspension of electricity services due to their inability to pay on the basis of financial hardship.

Residential Sector Incentive Program for the Acquisition of Heat Pumps and Air Conditioners

This program was established for residential consumers who install or substitute their dual air conditioning/heating units for ones ranked with a 12.0 British thermal unit (Btu) minimum efficiency. Reimbursements per unit may be up to $400 (3,800 pesos) or $30 to $80 per ton (285 to 760 pesos). The equipment must be new; reimbursement amounts are determined according to unit tonnage. For a new building, the amount would be $30/ton and $60 (570 pesos) for the installation of a high-efficiency air conditioning unit. If programmable high-efficiency thermostats are also installed, reimbursements of up to $15 (142.50 pesos) may be obtained.

Incentive Program for the Installation of Evaporative Coolers

This program offers $100 (950 pesos) as an incentive to residential consumers who install an evaporative cooler that meets the minimum requirements established by the IID.

Air Conditioning Program

Air conditioning services that minimize electricity consumption are offered to low-income households. At present, only about two hundred consumers have benefited from this plan.

High-Efficiency Refrigerators

Consumers with very low incomes who qualify are provided with a new high-efficiency refrigerator in exchange for their old one. This program also offers consumers who do not qualify as low income a 20 percent discount on the purchase price of a new high-efficiency refrigerator in exchange for a used one.

Lighting Program

The IID has developed a residential lighting program through an alliance with manufacturers and local vendors to promote energy-saving products such as exterior fluorescent lights with photocells. Consumers may shop locally and get discounts directly from the manufacturer through the promotion of market incentives or reduced pricing of these products.

A Comparative Analysis of Residential Savings: Plan Utilization and Implementation

The plans and programs offered in the two valleys are similar in the following ways:

- Energy diagnoses indicate deficiencies related to excessive electricity consumption and suggest necessary household modifications by the consumer to correct and normalize high electricity use

- Economic incentives for substituting air conditioning units are offered

Both programs provide monetary support to the consumer. Table 3 shows the electricity services that each organization offers to residential consumers.

Conclusions

Different energy savings alternatives are available on each side of the border. These include free energy audits as a starting point, flexible credit plans for the purchase of refrigeration equipment, and a number of insulation activities. In addition, economic incentives, reimbursements, and public assistance are offered, including emergency plans for those who are unable to pay their high electricity bills during the summer.

In Mexicali, special summer programs are offered but there is no substantial financial assistance. These programs include attractive credit plans—some interest-free—that provide assistance with the purchase of items such as fluorescent bulbs, air conditioners, and refrigerators. Consumers who are unable to pay their monthly electric bill will, at most, receive a deferment to avoid having their electricity cut off. In the Imperial Valley, no credit is provided to purchase items, but energy savings advice is offered, discounts are provided, and certain reimbursements are granted as

Table 3. Options for the Residential Consumer

Options	Mexicali Valley CFE	Imperial Valley IID
Rates	Offers special rates from May through October. The cost of kilowatts varies in ranges of consumption	Uniform cost per kilowatt-hour throughout the year
Energy audits	Points out deficiencies and gives savings advice on electricity	Points out deficiencies and gives savings advice on electricity
Insulation	Credit with no interest for roof insulation and door sealing	Free consultations on home insulation. Special assistance for field workers who qualify
Substitution of air conditioning and heating units	Credit on the purchase of high-efficiency air conditioning units, no down payment, and 15 percent annual interest, as well as a bonus of $50 (475 pesos) per ton	With the installation or substitution of a high efficiency air conditioning and heating unit in a new building, reimbursements from $30 to $80 (285 to 760 pesos) are provided per ton of capacity. Also, a bonus of $15 (142.50 pesos) is given for each programmable digital thermostat with the air conditioning unit
Installation of coolers	Advice and recommendations for energy savings	Economic incentive of $100 (950 pesos) with installation
Lighting	Provides up to 10 fluorescent bulbs and up to 24 months to pay for them, with no interest	—
Intermittent shutdown	IDEAA—a $3.30/ton (30 pesos/ton) bonus for the intermittent shutdown of air conditioning units' compressors during peak hours	—
Fixed Payment Plan	According to the previous year's energy use, 12 equal payments are made during the year; at its end, the payment for the difference is made or credit is granted. Consumers must be signed up for the substitution of equipment	12 equal payments are made throughout the year
Financial fund and support programs	—	Discounts of up to 25 percent off energy bills for homes that qualify. There is an emergency fund to avoid suspension of energy for those who are unable to make their payments and a special fund to assist field workers who qualify
Refrigerators	—	Exchange of a high-efficiency refrigerator for an older one for low-income persons who qualify

SOURCE: Authors' analysis.

incentives to consumers who apply savings measures. In addition, funds are available for substantial economic assistance to those who need it, thus, avoiding the suspension of electricity services.

A combination of the best savings plans and programs from both sides of the border could provide the most benefits to local consumers in the region. Hopefully, this type of program sharing will happen in the near future.

References

Comisión Federal de Electricidad (CFE). 2001. http://www.cfe.gob.com.

Comisión Federal de Electricidad (CFE). 2002. http://www.cfe.gob.com.

Comisión Nacional para el Ahorro de Energía (CONAE). 2000. http://www.conae.gob.mx.

Comité de Planeación para el Desarrollo Municipal (COPLADEM). 1999. *Anuario estadístico municipal de Mexicali*. Mexicali, Baja California: Ayuntamiento de Mexicali, COPLADEM.

Imperial Irrigation District (IID). 2000. "Economic Development." http://www.iid.com/economic/.

Imperial Irrigation District (IID). 2001. "Electric Rates." http://www.iid.com/economic/electric-rates.html.

Instituto Nacional de Estadística, Geografía e Informática (INEGI). 1999. *Anuario estadístico del estado de Baja California*. Mexicali: Gobierno del Estado de Baja California and INEGI.

World Climate. 2001a. "Climate Data for Imperial County, California." http://www.worldclimate.com/climate/cgi-bin/data.pl?ref=N32W115+1302+044223C.

World Climate. 2001b. "Climate Data for Mexicali, Baja California." http://www.worldclimate.com/climate/cgi-bin/data.pl?ref=N32W115+1202+0011488G2.

21

Environmental Management of Hazardous Waste along the Imperial-Mexicali Valley Border

M. Socorro Romero, Fabio de la Cruz, Roger Vintze, and Magdalena Carrasco*

Abstract

One of the principal worries of contemporary society is environmental contamination due to its effects on human health. Undoubtedly, hazardous wastes are significant causes of environmental pollution. Industry plays a controversial role in the debate surrounding the problem because, on the one hand, it produces the goods demanded by society and generates significant sources of employment. On the other hand, however, it is the generator of great quantities of hazardous waste that pose a serious health risk to surrounding populations. Today, industry confronts new challenges, including compliance with strict norms, an open market, and the demands made by society for a clean environment.

The City of Mexicali, in particular, has witnessed a significant level of industrial development, in the maquiladora (assembly plant) sector. As a result, it has also seen a considerable increase in the production of hazardous waste. This situation calls for an evaluation of how the waste is being managed in order to have a clear picture of the real vulnerabilities facing the inhabitants of the region as well as its impact on the environment of the Imperial-Mexicali Valley. This essay presents a general panorama of the environmental management of

*Romero is Researcher at the Engineering Institute at the Universidad Autónoma de Baja California; de la Cruz is Engineer at the Subdelegation for Industrial Verification at the Federal Environmental Protection Enforcement Agency in Mexicali; Vintze is Hazardous Substance Scientist with the Department of Toxic Substances Control of the Imperial Valley Environmental Protection Agency; and Carrasco is master's candidate in Business Administration at the Iberoamerican University in Tijuana.

hazardous waste generated in the region, focusing on pesticides, infectious biological wastes, and hazardous waste generated by the maquiladoras located in the binational border region.

Introduction

The Imperial-Mexicali border region has witnessed an accelerated industrial growth that, in turn, has induced rapid population growth, principally in Mexicali. As a result, significant environmental problems have been identified in the region, including the scarcity and contamination of water, air pollution, and the generation of hazardous waste. The latter is of particular concern due to the risk it represents with regard to the local population's health.

Industrialization of the Imperial-Mexicali Valley Border

The first signs of industrial activity in the Mexicali economy appeared in the 1920s. At that time, its economic base was centered on agricultural activities. Investments in technology and the modernization of the agroindustrial sector were also carried out. By this time, the cotton industry was important on a global scale (Mena 1994).

Mexicali has been characterized by intense agricultural activity, which boomed in 1940 with an increase in the production of cotton. In the 1960s, the regional economy was severely affected by a drop in the price of cotton caused by the increased production of synthetic fibers. The demographic increase in northern Mexican border cities contributed to a crisis with thousands of unemployed workers. By mid-decade, the federal government created the Border Industrialization Program as an alternative, hoping to alleviate unemployment problems and improve the commercial balance through the promotion of industrial development along the border. This took place through the attraction of foreign capital to the region to establish assembly plants called *maquiladoras* (Herzog 1990).

The number of *maquiladora* plants in the border region further increased with the implementation of the North American Free Trade Agreement (NAFTA), beginning in 1994. In the northern Mexican border region, 41 percent of all *maquiladoras* were located in the State of Baja California between 1980 and 1995. Chihuahua followed with 25 percent in 1985. The fact that Baja California is located so close to California explains this concentration (Carrillo Huerta 1990).

Industrialization of the region has allowed for the creation of many jobs, but it has also produced hazardous wastes that, along with waste generated by the agricultural industry, have a great impact on the regional environment and the health of its population. The greatest risks include those posed by pesticides, solvents, heavy metals, acids, alkalis, resins, plastics, and paints, which in many cases are disposed of improperly or transported illegally (Liverman et al. 1999).

Due to the region's vulnerability, the National Institute of Ecology (Instituto Nacional de Ecología–INE) considers the border a priority with regard to management of hazardous waste. In Mexicali, some companies have disposed of their waste in the municipal solid waste system (INE 1999). Thus, it is necessary that actions be taken to provide for greater monitoring of the management and disposal of hazardous waste generated in the region. This essay focuses on industry primarily in Mexicali since such activity in the Imperial Valley is minimal.

Hazardous Waste Legislation

Environmental legislation establishes that companies that utilize dangerous substances or generate hazardous waste are obligated to comply with the regulation of hazardous waste material. The legislation consists of rules, official norms, and procedures and suggests different levels of sanctions that vary from fines to the closure of companies that do not comply (Zataráin 1998).

Article 5 of the General Law of Ecological Equilibrium and Environmental Protection (Ley General del Equilibrio Ecológico y la Protección al Ambiente–LGEEPA) establishes that the federal government is charged with the regulation and control of high-risk activities and the regulation, administration, and final disposal of dangerous materials and wastes (*Diario Oficial de la Federación* 1988). Article 8 of the regulation for hazardous waste material mandates that those who generate hazardous waste be registered with the Secretariat of Environment and Natural Resources (Secretaría de Medio Ambiente y Recursos Naturales–SEMARNAT). Generators of hazardous waste are also required to adequately manage them to avoid risks to the environment and to the population's health (LGEEPA 1996).

Chapter 6, Article 153, paragraph 6 of the LGEEPA states that hazardous materials and waste generated in the processes of production, transformation, manufacture, or repair of products that use raw materials brought to Mexico as temporary imports must return to the country of origin within the time period determined by SEMARNAT. Thus, the *maquiladora* industry must return its waste to its country of origin by contracting authorized companies that transport hazardous waste (LGEEPA 1996).

The Pollutant Release and Transfer Register (Registro de Emisiones y Transferencia de Contaminantes–RETC) project—equivalent to the Toxics Release Inventory (TRI) program of the U.S. Environmental Protection Agency—is receiving much attention in Mexico. One of its goals is to develop common processes for the distribution of compatible information between the two countries (INE 2000).

SEMARNAT has also established the Mexican Network of Environmental Waste Management (Red Mexicana de Manejo Ambiental de Residuos–REMEXMAR) to strengthen environmental waste management in Mexico. In addition, state waste management networks are being established. One such network already exists in Baja

California and is managed by the Autonomous University of Baja California in Tijuana. The information generated there intersects with that of REMEXMAR.

With respect to the control of pesticides, the Intersecretarial Commission for the Control of the Process and Use of Pesticides, Fertilizers, and Toxic Substances (Comisión Intersecretarial para el Control del Proceso y Uso de Plaguicidas, Fertilizantes y Sustancias Tóxicas–CICOPLAFEST) published an official catalog of pesticides from 1991 to 1994 that listed registered products and their authorized uses, their principal characteristics, and indications for their use. This catalog only included those pesticides that are registered and whose commercialization and use are authorized in Mexico. If Mexican authorities hope to regulate and control pesticides, they need to utilize the information in this catalog alongside consultations with the CICOPLAFEST registries. The registry of new products and the modification or renovation of those already authorized are continuous and permanent (CICOPLAFEST 1996).

Hazardous Waste Binational Agreements

The La Paz Agreement was signed by Mexico and the United States in 1983. It established agreements on binational cooperation to deal with the environmental problems faced by the border region. The third annex of the agreement was signed in 1986 to establish procedures for the transborder movement of dangerous substances. Within the principal criteria of hazardous waste material established by the La Paz Agreement, the exporting country must be notified of the exportation and the importing country must consent to receive those materials. It also establishes that hazardous waste generated by materials acquired by either of the countries for processing will be returned to its country of origin. Such is the case of waste generated by the *maquiladora* industry. The third annex also indicates that an ecosystem should be restored when it suffers any loss due to the inappropriate handling of wastes. Additionally, any damage caused to people, property, or the environment should be compensated (INE 1996).

Border XXI and Border 2012

This binational program between Mexico and the United States was created to address the priorities of environmental protection. It became truly effective in 1996 with Border XXI and represented another period of bilateral cooperation between the two countries. The 1992 Integrated Border Environment Plan (IBEP) for the Mexican-U.S. border region was an important precedent for Border XXI (INE 1999).

One of the five major priorities considered by the Border XXI Program includes the issue of environmental and health risks caused by hazardous waste. The program's framework established actions for the appropriate management and disposal of waste and the strengthening of the system that generates these flows and their transborder movement, especially those of the *maquiladora* industry (INE 1999).

When Border XXI ended, a new program titled Border 2012 was initiated. This program will continue the collaborative effort of Mexico's SEMARNAT and the United States' EPA to work to improve environment and health of the U.S.-Mexican border. Border 2012 has four regionally focused workgroups among whose goals are to incorporate input from local decision makers and community members to address issues of the region.

The *Maquiladora* Industry Management of Hazardous Waste

In 2000, there were 204 *maquiladoras* in operation in Mexicali. Table 1 shows how the industry has grown in the City of Mexicali. Of that number, 111 are registered with SEMARNAT as generators of hazardous waste that return their wastes to the United States, thus complying with the rules established by the LGEEPA. There are 31 textile companies in Mexicali that do not generate hazardous waste and, therefore, are not required to register with SEMARNAT. Nonetheless, there are 62 companies that do not report their hazardous waste management activities.

Table 2 shows that the main activities of *maquiladoras* located in Mexicali correspond to electronics, metal mechanics, plastics, and textiles. These types of industry are the most common and are of interest for this study due to the high volumes of hazardous waste that they generate, with the exception of the textile industry, which does not generate any. The electronics sector is the largest generator of hazardous waste.

As part of this study, a classification of hazardous waste was developed and is presented in Table 3. A great variety of waste was found that requires special handling in conformity with the legislative framework. These were mainly solvents, ash scoria,

Table 1. Number of *Maquiladoras* Established in Mexicali

Year	Number
1993	130
1994	130
1995	127
1996	135
1997	148
1998	182
1999	189
2000	204

SOURCE: AMAQ (2000).

Table 2. Mexicali *Maquiladoras* and Industrial Activities, 2000

Number	Sector	Products
51	Electronics	Computers, dashboards, assembly, tools, lamps, audio cassettes, production, automobiles, aviation, televisions, and cables
32	Textiles	Clothing, sporting goods, and plastic coverings
40	Metal Mechanics	Screws, rail tracks, aviation, automobiles, ducts, prints, assembly, valves, manufacturing, transformation, elevators, and cabinets
22	Plastics	Syringes, suitcases, domestic goods, lenses, packaging, furniture, televisions, music, medical supplies, fans, assembly, and video
59	Others	Paper, food services, polished metal, film, sporting goods, cleaning supplies, propaganda, chairs, asphalt tiles, racket assembly, wood, printing, automobiles, packaging, polish, pallets, televisions, protection and security, polystyrene, boxes, medical supplies, sandblasted cardboard, and others

SOURCE: AMAQ (2000).

chrome, zinc, tin, materials covered with grease and oil, acids, and alkalis. These can cause serious contamination problems and damage public health.

As mentioned previously, the *maquiladora* industry must return its waste to the United States. As such, compliance with this legislation in the last few years has risen as the volume of this repatriated waste grows, as can be seen in Tables 4 and 5. There are also 44 companies registered to handle hazardous waste, of which 26 offer collection and transport services for waste generated by the *maquiladoras*.

Handling of Pesticides

In 1999, the Engineering Institute of the Autonomous University of Baja California conducted a study of pesticides in order to understand the impact they have on the health of Mexicali Valley inhabitants. The results corresponded to similar results in the Imperial Valley, just across the border. The study found that the Mexicali Valley is the most affected area in the region with regard to pesticides. This is the result of both legal and illegal pesticides that negatively impact the health of its inhabitants, including some cases of death from overexposure to these agrochemicals (Valdez et al. 2000).

Currently, temporary storage sites exist for empty pesticide containers. These sites, however, have been managed inappropriately. Receptacles have accumulated alongside many of the landing strips for crop-dusting planes, demonstrating that they are not disposed of properly (Angulo 2000). There are more than twenty landing strips used by crop-dusting companies in the Mexicali Valley that use a variety of pesticides, including carbamates, organophosphates, pyrethroids, and azocyclotin (Valdez et al. 2000).

Table 3. Principal Wastes Generated by the *Maquiladora* Industry in Mexciali

Industrial Activity	Companies Registered with SEMARNAT	Wastes Generated
Electronics	38	Zinc slag, gloves and rags soaked in grease, paint sludge, empty containers, magnetic wire wastes, metal scraps, stripper residual, solids containing solvents, ink and silicon, solvent mixtures, broken kinetoscopes, residual lubricating grease, residual water containing adhesive, plastic wastes, sandpaper, tin-lead slag, lead circuits, residual pain dust
Metal Mechanics	33	Rags, cardboard, paper and protective equipment soaked in solvents, solid sludge, adhesive tape, dry paint, residual grease, solvent mixtures, empty barrels, aluminum oxide dust, sandpaper, sludge containing alkaline salts, evaporators, sludge from the dam's filter, personal equipment containing chrome, waste from welding, empty metal containers
Plastics	14	Paint sludge, Isopropanol residue, oil-soaked rags, water-based paints containing solvents, residual oils
Others	24	Wastes soaked with ink and thinner, solids contaminated with solvents, residual liquid varnish, residual flux, residual soluble oils, rags and filters containing metal, sedimentary sludge, glass dust with refrigerant, empty barrels, empty cans that contained dangerous materials, papers solids, towels soaked with freon
Textiles	1	Empty containers

SOURCES: SEMARNAT and AMAQ (2000).

Various cases of pesticide poisoning have been documented in the Mexicali Valley. From 1968 to 1969, a total of 71 cases were registered (López and Marroquín 1970). In 1970, the City of Mexicali registered 59 cases of poisoning and four deaths among agricultural workers from contact with organochlorine and organophosphate insecticides. In both valleys, local inhabitants experience nausea and some allergic reactions that intensify during the spraying season (Valdez et al. 2000).

In 1997, the Federal Attorney General of Environmental Protection (Procuraduría Federal de Protección al Ambiente–PROFEPA) conducted a program to clean up clandestine dumps where pesticide receptacles were thrown. A total of 240 tons of hazardous waste was recovered and then properly disposed of in a facility in Hermosillo, Sonora (Angulo 2000).

The Secretariat of Agriculture, Livestock, and Rural Development (Secretaría de Agricultura, Ganadería y Desarrollo Rural–SAGAR) estimates that of the 90,500 hectares planted in 2000, more than 87,000 were treated with some type of pesticide, principally dimethoate.

Table 4. CRETI[1] Hazardous Waste Returned to Country of Origin, January to December 1999[2]

Month	Number of Returns[3]	Volume of Waste Returned (tons)[3, 4]	Number of Returns	Volume of Waste Returned (tons)[5]	Number of Returns	Volume of Waste Returned (tons)
January	972	1,357	385	396	1,357	1,753
February	1,162	940	393	518	1,555	1,458
March	1,528	2,208	494	926	2,022	3,134
April	1,287	1,086	372	710	1,659	1,796
May	1,375	1,234	343	690	1,718	1,924
June	1,441	1,486	444	1,038	1,885	2,524
July	1,410	1,360	411	1,967	1,821	3,328
August	1,591	1,495	507	2,822	1,860	4,218
September	1,353	1,396	507	2,822	1,860	4,218
October	1,420	1,808	452	788	1,872	2,596
November	1,453	1,690	483	621	1,936	2,311
December	1,317	1,560	446	1,733	1,763	3,293
TOTAL	16,309	17,620	5,237	15,031	21,308	32,553

[1]CRETI–corrosive, reactive, explosive, toxic, and inflammable.
[2]Includes generation by both Tijuana and Mexicali.
[3]Authors' calculations.
[4]Volume of waste stated in the application to return.
[5]Volume of waste with proof of its return.

SOURCE: CICOPLAFEST (2000).

Table 5. Generation of Hazardous Waste by the Maquildora Industry in Mexicali, January to December 2000

Industrial Activity	Average Monthly Generation (tons)	Annual Generation (tons)	Annual Generation (%)
Electronics	551.062	6,612.747	46.770
Metal Mechanics	396.252	4,755.032	33.630
Plastics	46.582	558.984	3.960
Textiles	0.039	0.473	0.010
Others	184.360	2,212.326	15.650
TOTAL	1,178.295	14,139.562	100.020

SOURCE: CICOPLAFEST (2000).

The use of organochlorine insecticides, such as DDT, endrin, lindane, and chlordane, are now prohibited due to the heavy impact they have on the environment and, especially, the harm they bring to public health. Contact with these chemicals brings a high risk of cancer. In the case of DDT, only authorities from the health sector are allowed to use it for sanitary campaigns (Romero Hernández 1999).

The dangers that pesticides imply are presented in several different phases: in their fabrication and formulation, during their application, and in the consumption of foods contaminated by these substances. Human beings can ingest pesticide residues not only while eating treated vegetables, but also while eating foods of animal origin in which such residues have accumulated. Persistent pesticides such as organochlorine insecticides accumulate in the fatty tissues of animals. Since the food chain begins with vegetables and ends with larger animals, higher quantities of pesticides can be found in the latter. Thus, it is not unusual to find an increased residue concentration throughout the food chain and, finally, in human beings (Coscolla 1993).

Handling of Infectious Biological Wastes

All generators of infectious biological wastes should handle them according to the established LGEEPA law on hazardous waste and the Mexican Official Norm NOM-807-ECOL-1995. This norm established the requirements for the separation, containment, storage, collection, transport, treatment, and final disposal of infectious biological hazardous wastes. This norm affects facilities that provide medical services, including clinics, hospitals, clinical laboratories, laboratories that produce biological agents, sites for teaching and research on both humans and animals, veterinarians that deal with small species, and rabies centers. In such facilities, when more than 55 pounds (25 kilograms) per month or 35 ounces (one kilogram) per day of hazardous waste are generated, they must comply with the stated norm.

Currently, hospitals, clinics, and clinical laboratories are in compliance with the established norm and contract services from authorized companies to transport and dispose of their wastes. As shown in Table 6, two companies are currently authorized by the INE to provide such services, and compliance has been satisfactory. Nevertheless, in the case of individual medical offices, especially in dentistry, very few companies properly handle their wastes according to the established norms.

In 1999, a total of 495 tons of infectious biological hazardous waste was reported by 424 INE-registered facilities. Table 7 shows that, from January to September 2000, there were 535 tons generated. It should be noted, though, that these quantities include both Mexicali and Tijuana.

Table 6. Companies Authorized to Handle Hazardous Waste in Mexicali

Characteristics of Authorized Companies	Number of Companies
Recycles used solvents	2
Manages used lubricating oils	1
Temporarily stores dangerous wastes	9
Collects and transports hazardous wastes	26
Makes alternate fuels with used residual oil	1
Manages alternate fuels	1
Treats infectious biological hazardous wastes	2
Recycles metals	2
TOTAL	44

SOURCE: INE (2000).

Table 7. Generation by Waste

Type of Waste	Number of Companies	1999 Generation (tons)	Jan–Sept 2000 Generation (tons)
Industrial Hazardous	1,864	33,099	34,832
Infectious Biological	495	424	535
TOTAL	2,359	33,523	35,367

SOURCE: INE (2000).

Conclusions and Recommendations

This essay concludes that the inhabitants of the Mexicali and Imperial valleys are in a vulnerable position due to the large quantities of hazardous wastes that are generated in the region. As a result, both human health and the environment are at risk. The substances that most greatly affect the environment are industrial waste and agricultural pesticides. Pesticides, however, require greater attention because they lack an enforcement mechanism for proper application, handling, and disposal, as established by environmental legislation.

By 2000, 204 *maquiladoras* had been established in Mexicali and 111 were registered as returning their hazardous waste to its place of origin. There are 31 companies in the local textile industry that do not generate hazardous waste. One company in the textile industry is found to produce hazardous waste in minimal quantities and is included in the SEMARNAT registries. This study also found that the 62 remaining companies were not registered with SEMARNAT as generating hazardous waste. Although it could be determined that their activities are in the electronics and metal mechanics sectors, the types and amounts of wastes they generate could not be determined. Nonetheless, it is very probable that they are generating hazardous waste due to their industrial activities. For this reason, it is important that authorities verify the type of waste that these companies are generating and confirm that they are complying with the established environmental norms.

The present study estimates that most hazardous waste generated by the *maquiladoras* in Mexicali is being managed in accordance with established environmental legislation. It is also important to highlight that the current environmental legislation is very complete in reference to hazardous waste management. However, it is recommended that programs are implemented for the proper use and handling of pesticides, as well as the disposal of waste generated by agricultural activities. It is also necessary that a program be designed to facilitate the handling and proper disposal of these wastes. Such a program would require not only the participation of PROFEPA, as in the 1997 program, but also that of agricultural workers, those who use pesticides, and the companies that provide the services. Currently, no one assumes responsibility for the disposal of empty pesticide and fertilizer containers.

It is also important to promote pollution prevention programs and cleaner methods of production to minimize the generation of industrial hazardous waste. Greater attention should also be placed on the compliance of legislation on hazardous waste matters and the disposal of wastewaters in sewers and drains, since bodies of water are also being contaminated by significant quantities of dangerous substances.

References

Angulo, César. 2000. "Contaminación por plaguicidas, inadecuado almacenamiento." La Crónica (23 August).

Asociación de Maquiladoras (AMAQ). 2000. Listado de empresas maquiladoras instaladas en Mexicali. Mexicali: AMAQ.

Carrillo Huerta, Mario M. 1990. "Una interpretación del impacto de las maquiladoras en el bienestar familiar y en el desarrollo regional." Estudios Fronterizos 21: 32.

Comisión Intersecretarial para el Control del Proceso y Uso de Plaguicidas, Fertilizantes y Sustancias Tóxicas (CICOPLAFEST). 1996. Catálogo oficial de plaguicidas. México, D.F.: Secretaría de Medio Ambiente y Recursos Naturales.

Coscolla, Ramón. 1993. Residuos de plaguicidas en alimentos vegetales. Madrid: Editorial Mundi-Prensa.

Diario Oficial de la Federación. 28 January 1988.

Herzog, Lawrence A. 1990. Where North Meets South: Cities, Space, and Politics on the U.S.-Mexico Border. Austin: Center for Mexican American Studies, University of Texas.

Instituto Nacional de Ecología (INE). 1996. Programa para la minimización y el manejo integral de residuos industriales peligrosos en México, 1996–2000. Mexico, D.F.: INE.

Instituto Nacional de Ecología (INE). 1999. "Programa frontera XXI."
    http://www.ine.gob.mx/dggia/frontera/p_frontera.html.

Instituto Nacional de Ecología (INE). 2000. "Indicadores ambientales. Residuos peligrosos."
    http://www.ine.gob.mx/dggia/indicadores.

"Ley General del Equilibrio Ecológico y la Protección al Ambiente (LGEEPA)." Congreso de
    la Unión de los Estados Unidos Mexicanos. In Décimo tercera edición actualizada, edited
    by Editorial Porrúa. México D.F.: Editorial Porrúa.

Liverman, Diana M., Robert G. Varady, Octavio Chávez, and Roberto Sánchez. 1999.
    Environmental Issues along the United States-Mexico Border: Drivers of Change and
    Responses of Citizens and Institutions. Tucson: University of Arizona.

López, R.F., and M. Marroquín. 1970. "Intoxicaciones por plaguicidas en Mexicali." Salud
    Pública de México 89 (2).

Mena Moreno, José A. 1994. "La conformación histórica de mercados de trabajo agrícola en el
    valle de Mexicali." Estudios Fronterizos 33: 174.

Romero Hernández, M. Socorro. 1999. "Algunas consideraciones acerca del uso de
    plaguicidas." Revista divulgare de la Universidad Autónoma de Baja California 6 (26):
    40–52.

Valdez Salas, Benjamín, Eva J. García D., Juan M. Cobo R., and Gustavo López B. 2000.
    "Impacto de los plaguicidas en la salud de los habitantes del valle de Mexicali." Revista
    Ecológica Latino Americana 3 (6): 15–21.

Varady, Robert G., Dean E. Carter, Robert G. Arnold, Roberto Guzmán, Carlos Peña, and
    William Suk. 2000. Hazardous Waste and the U.S.-Mexico Border Region. Tucson: Udall
    Center Publications, University of Arizona.

Zataráin, Cándido. 1998. Memorias del curso "materiales químicos peligrosos." Mexicali:
    Cámara Nacional de la Industria de la Transformación.

22

Handling of Waste Tires at the Border

Elizabeth Ramírez Barreto and Sara Ojeda Benítez*

Abstract

The problems associated with handling waste tires at the border are very complex due to the volumes that are generated and discarded annually, as well as the characteristics of this type of waste. Discarded tires pose a problem with regard to their inadequate handling and final disposal due to the existence of few sites that have a large accumulation of tires as well as many clandestine dumps scattered throughout the Mexicali Valley.

This paper will develop an analytical framework of the activities associated with the integral management of waste tires. This implies the selection of an adequate combination of alternatives and technologies that meet the changing needs and participation of stakeholders. It also implies evolving regulations, institutions, and practices to achieve better order and control of the problem of waste tires.

Introduction

Clusters of wastes are generated as a result of human activities that increase with population and economic growth until they become a public health and environmental problem. Municipal solid wastes generated in Mexico in 1994 have been estimated at 27.4 million tons and the volume of hazardous wastes at 7.7 million tons (INE 1999).

*Ramírez Barreto and Ojeda Benítez are Researchers at the Institute of Engineering at the Universidad Autónoma de Baja California in Mexicali.

According to regulations, waste tires are classified as products that require "special handling" because they represent a complex problem in terms of their final disposal. In addition, the large number of tires used and later discarded constitutes a problem in itself.

Waste tires are subject to environmental regulations due to their chemical and physical characteristics and because of the large amounts that are generated. In Mexico, there is inadequate infrastructure to treat this type of waste (INE 1999). As a consequence, the great majority of waste tires end up in canals, streams, vacant lots, and clandestine dumps, thus creating environmental and health problems.

For the most part, waste tires that have been discarded are then utilized inappropriately. For example, they are used as fuel in kilns that do not have emissions controls. Tires that are improperly disposed of are a potential source of air, soil, and landscape pollution. Also, because tires often retain rainwater, they can become a breeding ground for mosquitoes and other disease vectors. The prevailing trend toward sustainable development requires recycling and reuse as means to save or preserve resources and limit the generation of wastes (Sitarz 1998).

Among the objectives of environmental policy are to decrease the generation of waste, promote its reuse, and increase the recycling rates of products that have already been used. That is, the generation of waste must reach a compatible level with the ecosystem's ability to assimilate it.

In this respect, Mexico's General Law of Ecological Equilibrium and Environmental Protection (Ley General del Equilibrio Ecológico y la Protección al Ambiente) establishes economic instruments as standard and administrative mechanisms of a fiscal, financial, or market nature through which people take on the environmental benefits and costs generated by their economic activities. Mexican authorities mention the use of the economic instruments of environmental policy for adequate handling of used tires since the problem is their responsibility.

Generation

The generation of waste tires can be estimated by vehicular fleets. Tires can be classified according to two types: used tires with the possibility of retreading and waste tires (useless for their original purpose). In Mexico, the generation of tires of the first type is low. Only commercial passenger and freight vehicles resort to retreads in order to decrease costs. This process extends the product's useful life.

The generation of waste tires for Mexicali was estimated based on waste tire information and vehicular fleet data. In 1998, it is estimated that 364,658 waste tires were generated. Table 1 shows data for previous years. The magnitude of this generation creates particular interest in finding solutions for the reuse of tires with the purpose of avoiding their final disposal on land. Baja California, the rest of the northern border states, and the metropolitan zone of the Valley of Mexico present the highest incidence of waste tires and vehicular fleets per inhabitant.

A common practice in Baja California is to import used tires from the United States to supply part of the state's consumer demand. The importation of used tires along the Mexican border might be due to: (1) the link of the Mexican border zone with the largest source for used tires: the United States; (2) the well-defined market on the Mexican side of the border for used tires that can be sold at lower prices than new tires; and (3) the environmental policies and other regulations related to waste in California and Baja California that are not always coordinated. For example, one option for California to dispose of used tires is to export them—a practice that makes the waste tire disposal issue more difficult for Baja California (Ramírez, Ojeda, and González 2001).

Table 1. Generation of Waste Tires in the Municipality of Mexicali

Year	Vehicular Fleet				Generation* of Tires			
	Buses	Freight Trucks	Auto-mobiles	Total	Buses	Freight Trucks	Auto-mobiles	Total
1987	455	55,298	188,823	244,576	1,235	100,642	243,582	345,459
1988	477	55,795	189,921	246,193	1,432	101,547	244,998	347,977
1989	553	57,566	202,357	260,476	614	104,770	261,041	366,425
1992	237	76,124	151,485	227,846	1,974	138,546	195,416	335,936
1994	762	841	213,729	215,332	3,043	1,531	275,710	280,284
1995	1,175	68,579	160,537	230,291	2,909	124,814	207,093	334,816
1998	1,123	88,222	155,958	245,303	2,909	160,564	201,186	364,659

*Estimates based on vehicular fleet and conversion factors in tires/year: buses 2.59; freight trucks 1.82; automobiles 1.29.

SOURCE: Secretaría de Finanzas del Gobierno del Estado (2002).

The Mexicali Valley has significant problems rooted in the generation of waste tires. A recent study by Ramírez and others (1999), found a large accumulation of waste tires on three sites—El Centinela, INNOR, and Llanset—that totaled approximately 1,929,152 tires. These properties are located in Ejido Emiliano Zapata.

The generation of used tires in the State of California is related to the state's population growth. As the population increases, so do the number of vehicle miles or kilometers traveled and the number of vehicles registered. These indicators represent an increase in the number of waste tires and reusable tires generated. Table 2 data show an estimate of the number of reusable and waste tires generated in California, based primarily on trends and an approximation of population and state industrial growth, since the number of tire shipments are only available at the federal level.

Table 2. Generation, Diversion, and Disposal of Waste Tires in California, 1990–1999 (in millions of passenger tires)

Year	California Population (millions)	Estimated Number of Tires Generated	Reused	Recycled and Other Uses	Renovated		Exported	Imported	Fuel Derived from Tires		Total Diverted Tires	Number of Tires for Confinement	Percentage of Diverted Tires
					Light Load	Heavy Load			Fuel for Energy Production	Incinerators as Fuel Complements			
1990	29.5	27.0	1.0	0.6	0.9	1.4	1.3	0.0	2.4	1.6	9.2	17.8	34.0
1991	30.1	27.5	1.0	0.8	0.8	1.4	1.3	-0.4	4.1	1.7	10.7	16.8	39.0
1992	30.7	28.2	1.1	1.1	0.7	1.4	1.3	-0.6	4.7	2.1	11.8	16.4	42.0
1993	31.1	28.5	1.3	1.5	0.7	1.4	1.3	-0.3	4.7	3.0	13.6	14.9	48.0
1994	31.7	29.0	1.3	1.7	0.7	1.7	1.3	-0.2	5.7	6.0	18.2	10.8	62.0
1995	32.3	29.5	1.5	1.8	0.7	1.7	1.7	-0.6	4.7	6.1	17.6	11.9	60.0
1996	32.6	30.0	1.5	2.3	0.7	1.7	1.7	-1.5	4.3	4.6	16.7	14.8	53.0
1997	33.2	30.4	1.5	5.4	1.0	1.8	1.7	-3.2	3.5	5.5	17.2	13.2	56.6
1998	33.8	30.9	1.5	9.1	1.0	1.8	3.1	-2.2	4.5	3.0	21.8	9.1	70.6
1999	34.0	31.1	1.6	8.6	0.8	1.7	1.5	-2.0	3.8	4.1	20.1	11.1	64.5

SOURCE: IWMB (2000b).

Tire Disposal

Saad, Colín, and Salinas (1996a) explain that tires have historically represented a complex problem with respect to their proper disposal due to their shape, size, physical, and chemical characteristics, as well as the number used and later discarded. Snyder (1998) points out that tires constitute a type of waste that is very slow to degrade in the natural environment. He states that the inadequate disposal of waste tires affects the quality of the environment, propagates illnesses, destroys nature, and contaminates soils. Tires that are disposed of in open spaces, in clandestine dumps, or without controls pose the risk of being burned intentionally. This produces pollution as toxic compounds are emitted, representing a public health problem. Such is the case of waste tires in the State of Baja California, where they are disposed of in open spaces as well as in clandestine dumps.

Beginning in the 1990s, legislative activities began to take place regarding the final disposal of waste tires. The Environmental Protection Law of the State of Baja California stipulates that waste tires must be disposed of at authorized collection facilities from where they are to be sent for treatment, recycling, or final disposal. Collection facilities began to operate under this law.

In Mexicali, disposal of waste tires is carried out in dumps, illegal sites, and collection facilities. Dumps are located in open spaces and official authorization is

Figure 1. El Centinela Tire Dump

SOURCE: Photograph by authors (1999).

granted for the collection of waste tires that are not subsequently treated. The tires are piled up without any handling or disposal control. Once the dump becomes full, it is closed and the tires remain there for years. Such is the case of the site known as "El Centinela," located in the City of Mexicali (see Figure 1). This site was authorized by the now-extinct Secretariat of Urban Development and Ecology (Secretaría de Desarrollo Urbano y Ecología–SEDUE) to serve as a disposal facility for waste tires. The site was in operation from 1985 to 1993.

In 1991, the Cementos Guadalajara factory, located in the City of Ensenada, Baja California, began to operate as a waste tire collection facility. Tires are incinerated in the company's kilns as complementary fuel.

In 1996, the Directorate of Ecology (Dirección de Ecología) authorized the Industrializadora del Norte (INNOR) company for collection and treatment (grinding) of waste tires in the City of Mexicali (see Figure 2). This was the first company to be authorized by the Directorate of Ecology. It was determined that a fee would be charged per tire deposited in order to generate funds to operate collection facilities and recycling systems. The fee was established in 1996 by the Income Law of the State of Baja California. The INNOR company collected 750,000 tires in 1996 and 1997. In early 1998, however, its authorization was revoked due to lack of

Figure 2. Industrializadora del Norte (INNOR) Collection Facility

SOURCE: Photograph by authors (1999).

Figure 3. Llanset Collection Facility

SOURCE: Photograph by authors (1999).

compliance in grinding the tires and meeting the established provisions. To date, this company has not complied with requests to clean up and restore the area.

In 1997, a study was conducted on the technical and economic viability of authorizing another company as a tire collection and recycling center for the state. This company, Llantas y Servicios Técnicos de Baja California (Tires and Technical Services of Baja California–Llanset) (see Figure 3), was established in Mexicali. In 1998, it began to ship the ground product for recycling to the interior of the country, mainly the states of Hidalgo and Jalisco.

Environmental Problems

The inadequate handling and final disposal of waste tires cause serious pollution problems on land, bodies of water, and the air. Tires discarded in dumps or abandoned in canals, vacant lots, and clandestine sites represent a potential danger since they are in the open air and cannot be controlled. Their inadequate handling can cause fires that can burn for weeks or months. The slow degradation and incineration of tires have severe impacts on the ecosystems in which they are deposited as well as negative human health effects.

The accumulation of waste tires directly on land causes a loss of the soil's productive capacity, inhibiting the restoration of the ecosystem's natural conditions.

In addition, when these piles are not controlled or supervised, they become an artificial refuge that promotes the spread of various species of insects, reptiles, and small mammals.

The idea that arid or desert ecosystems are poor and therefore difficult to harm is completely wrong. The arid conditions that rule this natural medium mean that its equilibrium can be easily perturbed by any alteration in the abundance of species, no matter how small this alteration may seem.

In the case of Mexicali, there is a problem specific to the area of El Centinela. Tires that are discarded in this inactive and unsupervised dump represent potential fires. Also, physical (climate, wind, temperature) and chemical (humidity, PH) conditions exist that can cause fires. If there were a fire at this site, it would be difficult to control due to the number of tires and the lack of equipment and resources available to extinguish it.

Air contamination caused by burning tires is a significant problem due to the chemical products found in rubber. One of these products is sulphur, which during the combustion process forms large amounts of sulphur monoxide and sulphur dioxide, both toxic to organisms. Carbon dioxide, carbon monoxide, and volatile organic compounds, among others, are also released (Snyder 1998; Saad, Colín, and Salinas 1996a). In addition to the toxicity of these emissions, it is important to consider the potential effects of smoke and ash on agricultural fields, irrigation canals, livestock, and residential and commercial settlements.

With regard to the local inhabitants' health, Reisman and Lemieux (1997) point out that emissions from the open burning of tires can mean acute dangers in the short term and chronic dangers in the long term for nearby residents and for those who participate in controlling the fire. Depending on the duration and degree of exposure, health effects include irritation of the skin, eyes, and mucous membranes; impacts on the respiratory tract, central nervous system, and blood pressure; and cancer. Reisman and Lemieux also state that emissions from open-air tire burning have been shown to be more toxic or mutagenic than those from an engine or combustor, regardless of the fuel. A mutagenic compound is defined as a substance that causes mutations. For example, tires are 16 times more mutagenic than combustion from residential firewood used in domestic fireplaces.

The combustion of tires produces dense smog that deteriorates visibility and covers the soil. Emissions from the open burning of tires include pollutants such as particulates, carbon monoxide (CO), sulphur dioxide (SOx), nitrogen oxides (NOx), and volatile organic compounds (VOC). Other dangerous pollutants are polynuclear aromatic hydrocarbons (PAH), dioxins, furans, hydrogen chloride, benzene, polychlorinated biphenyls (PCB), and metals such as arsenic, cadmium, nickel, zinc, mercury, chromium, and vanadium. The consequences of such emissions are shown in Table 3.

Other impacts of open tire burning include the generation of significant amounts of liquids and solids that contain harmful chemical substances derived from the smelting of tires. These products can pollute the soil, water surfaces, and aquifers; therefore, adequate precautionary measures are recommended to minimize these impacts (Reisman and Lemieux 1997).

Table 3. Air Pollution Effects on Health and Vegetation

Pollutant	Effects on Health	Effects on Vegetation
Sulphur Dioxide	Irritates eyes and respiratory tract. Reduces lung function and worsens respiratory illnesses such as asthma, chronic bronchitis, and emphysema	Lesions on leaves and reduction of photosynthesis
Nitrogen Dioxide	Irritates the lungs, worsens respiratory and cardiovascular illnesses	Premature fall of leaves and inhibits growth
Carbon Monoxide	Carboxyhemoglobin affects the central nervous system and causes cardiac and pulmonary function changes, headaches, fatigue, sleepiness, respiratory failure, and even death	Premature fall of leaves
Benzene	Leukemia, neurotic symptoms, damages the bone marrow, includes anemia and chromosomal aberrations	
Aromatic Polycyclic Hydrocarbons	The intestines and lungs may absorb these mutagenic and carcinogenic compounds	

SOURCE: INEGI (1994: 319, 320).

Management of Waste Tires

In order to develop a program of integral waste management, it is necessary to evaluate the activities associated with the management of these wastes from their generation to their final disposal, including all related issues. Once this task is carried out, it will then be possible to develop an integral system for management of waste tires. Within this context, the integral management of wastes can be defined as the selection and application of ideal techniques, technologies, and programs to achieve the specific goals and objectives of the management of wastes (Tchobanoglous, Theisen, and Vigil 1994). White (1996) points out that the integral management of wastes must consider waste flows, collection and treatment methods, environmental benefits, economic optimization, and social acceptance within a systematic practice for any region.

A hierarchy can be used to classify actions that are to be implemented through programs within the community. The hierarchy adopted for the handling of tires could be reduction at the source and collection, reuse, and recycling. With this hierarchy as a basis, management programs and systems can be developed in which elements can interrelate and complement one another. The system should evolve jointly with the developed regulations and provide better order and control for its activities.

A management system for waste tires should include alternatives for their handling. Among the main alternatives for reducing waste tires are their reduction at the source with the design of longer lasting tires and the rotation, renovation, and reuse of used tires. The reuse processes that are most common include incineration under controlled conditions, use as an alternate fuel to generate power, pyrolysis, criogenesis, vulcanization, and grinding, among others. Waste tires can also be reused in their original form (as retaining walls and barriers), in strips (for rugs, belts, soles), in small pieces, and as synthetic granulated rubber (as an additive for asphalt pavement).

The collection and reuse of waste tires could be promoted through a fee, tax, or return deposit. Such systems have been used in developed countries, mainly in the United States. In Mexico, a system of return deposit could be implemented to promote the collection and reuse of tires.

Different instruments can be used to suppress pollution and direct production and consumption structures toward the goal of sustainability. At the global level, the economic instruments that are used most for the environmental management of hazardous municipal wastes that are difficult to handle include fees for municipal wastes, fees for products and return deposit systems, and taxes on waste disposal in landfills and by incineration (OECD 1995).

The return deposit system (RDS) is a fee imposed on the price of potentially polluting products. The fee is reimbursed when pollution is avoided or annulled upon the return of product wastes or products themselves. Thus, the objective of this fee is to provide an incentive for reuse or to encourage the return of bottles and products to promote recycling.

The RDS is used mainly in countries that are members of the OECD. This agency works in the environmental arena toward the formulation of policies and tools that contribute to the development, enhancement, prevention, and control of pollutant wastes and emissions. There are multiple advantages to the establishment of an RDS. Among them are the promotion of recycling or reuse programs, reduction of waste flows, and promotion of adequate disposal. All of these allow the consumer to decide between returning wastes and "paying" for not returning them (flexibility); they also reduce audit (inspection) expenses.

Through the use of economic instruments for the environmental management of wastes that require special handing (waste tires), the environmental management and handling of waste becomes a commercial activity in which the RDS provides a mechanism to gage the amount of waste, promoting economies of scale in its collection, transport, reuse, or recycling.

Deposits allow for the financing of the collection phase and transportation of wastes or products. Dispersion of wastes, linked to consumption, is one of the main problems that needs to be solved, not only in terms of economics, but in terms of the environment.

Legislation on Both Sides of the Border

The National Institute of Ecology (Instituto Nacional de Ecología–INE) is the federal ecological authority that controls the importation of used tires into Mexico. This agency is in charge of designing the general ecological policy and the application of different regulatory and environmental management tools. Baja California is the only border state that is open to the importation of used tires. A fee is established annually for the importation of tires by federal and state authorities, as well as union representatives of used tires importers. In 2000, a total of 570,000 authorizations were issued by the government to import used tires.

The payment of the import fee for used tires is processed by a registry of importers. In order to be granted authorization to import, the importers must submit an application to the INE and the General Directorate of Ecology of the State (Dirección General de Ecología del Estado–DGEE). When the application is approved, other measures have to be undertaken with the Secretariat of Commerce and Industrial Promotion (Secretaría de Comercio y Fomento Industrial–SECOFI), the Ministry of Finance and Public Credit (Secretaría de Hacienda y Crédito Público–SHCP), and customs in order to be able to import the authorized quantity. The government of the State of Baja California acts as the managing entity between the used tire importer and the INE.

The General Law of Ecological Equilibrium and Environmental Protection of the State of Baja California, created in 1992, stipulates in Article 138 that waste tires must be disposed of in collection facilities duly authorized by the General Directorate of Ecology and later shipped for treatment, recycling, or final disposal.

With regard to the open burning of tires, Baja California state law provides sanctions for anyone who burns solid substances, materials, or wastes of any kind in the open without authorization from the Municipal Directorate of Ecology. There are also some provisions regarding the material of manufacture, vulcanization, importation, industrialization, utilization, or marketing of tires. Under these provisions, the DGEE or the city council (with advice from the state office) authorizes the creation of centers for tire disposal. Users of these centers are taxed with a fee that is determined by the State Revenue Law. Permits are also issued for marketing or transferring tires equivalent to the number of tires that the interested party can prove were deposited in the authorized centers.

The state law also stipulates that the DGEE will authorize operating permits for businesses that market used tires, but only if they keep a DGEE-approved logbook that includes information on handling, transportation, marketing, reuse, shipment to authorized collection facilities, and final recycling destinations for tires. In addition, subsequent authorizations to import used tires are only granted to those merchants who meet all of the terms stated in their previous authorization. Waste tires should be stored prior to their final disposal in authorized collection facilities.

California legislation is more complete and specific than that of Baja California with regard to the handling and final disposal of tires. California legislation promotes the adequate disposal of waste tires. Assembly Bill 1843 promotes the recycling of waste tires as well as collection facilities (IWMB 2000a).

The bill specified the promotion of the development of markets as an alternative to landfills and collection facilities for whole tires. In order to achieve this objective, Assembly Bill 1843 allowed the Integrated Waste Management Board (IWMB) to grant funds and loans to businesses, companies, and public agencies involved in recycling activities. It also compels the IWMB to develop service regulations for tires to ensure the secure storage of waste tires. The bill also established a permit system for waste tires. A 25-cent fee per waste tire financed these programs. This fee is deposited in the California trust for the management of recycled tires and is transferred to the agency annually by legislature.

State Bill 744 created the registration program for the transport of waste tires as an additional effort to ensure that waste tires are confined to authorized sites. The law also allows for police officers to enforce the requirements for transportation registration. This initiative further reduces illegal transportation and waste tire disposal.

Reuse of Waste Tires

The reuse of waste tires is promoted by charges, taxes, and subsidies. The main processes or items of reuse are: fuel, products, civil engineering, agriculture, exports, and pyrolysis. The latter is the use of the tire in a chemical decomposition process achieved by extreme heat in a controlled condition with little or no oxygen. In the United States, reuse predominates as kiln fuel and in civil engineering. However, reuse is beginning in Mexico.

Saad, Colín, and Salinas (1996b) present the following as primary alternatives to waste disposal:

1.   Source reduction—including tires with a longer life span, rotation to prolong their life, and renovation.

2.   Recycling—through different processes and technologies to convert tires into energy, to obtain byproducts, recuperate material, use them as raw material, and manufacture products.

3. Reuse as products and material—whole tires as reefs and sandbanks, equipment for recreational parks, retaining walls for erosion control, and protective highway barriers; in strips for rugs, belts, joints, shoe soles, and so forth; in shreds to be reused as light material for the construction of roads; as a substitute for gravel in recreational parks, ground up as plastic and synthetic rubber products (such as molded rugs, carpets, and adhesives for plastic); and as synthetic rubber for railroad crossings on roads and as additives for asphalt pavement.

Experiences in Mexico and Other Countries

The problem with waste tires is not exclusive to Mexico. Therefore, it is helpful to observe how other countries have attempted to solve this problem and to what extent they have been successful with their applied measures. Special attention should be placed on those measures that use economic instruments as incentives for their collection and reuse, a practice that is expanding despite minimal international experience.

Mexico's northern border adjoins the United States, the world's largest market of new tires. U.S. production represents 24 percent of the world's tire productivity, while Mexico only represents 1 percent. The United States is also the main generator of used and discarded tires. As a result, the United States has taken more measures in this respect. Hopey (2000) points out that the number of tires that were illegally piled and dumped in the United States decreased from 800 million in 1996 to 500 million in 1998.

Since 1989, California has drastically increased the number of used tires that were diverted from landfills and shipped for reuse and recycling (IWMB 2000). The Integrated Waste Management Board estimates that from 1990 to 1999 the number of recycled tires in California increased by 118 percent, that is, from 9.2 million to 20.1 million. This means that during 1999, a recycling rate of 65 percent was attained. Hopey (2000) notes that U.S. residents generate 276 million tires annually and Californians alone generate 31.1 million waste tires, or about one tire per person (IWMB 2000).

Historically, small fees for disposal in pile-up sites made this method the most popular way to dispose of tires. In the United States, economic instruments are applied most frequently to promote the adequate handling of this waste. In 1991, a total of 27 states had some type of fee for the disposal of used tires. The amounts varied from $0.25 to $1.50 and were used to finance tire reuse programs.

The most common economic instrument for this goal is the application of a fee or tax on new tires (between 1 and 2 percent of retail price), which varies in each state. The ability to solve environmental problems depends on the collected funds from the application of this instrument. In addition to the nationwide environmental fee in the United States, another operative mechanism has also been established: manifest control.

Most states in the United States have imposed regulations that dictate that tires must be processed (cut, shredded, and so on) when shipped to pile-up sites. In Mexico, the reuse of waste tires, under controlled conditions or conditions that do not harm the environment, is incipient. The incineration of tires in cement factory kilns under controlled conditions is at the test level and there are proposals for the processes of pyrolysis and shredding.

Saad, Colín, and Salinas (1996b) point out that two Mexican cement factories have conducted tests in their kilns to use tires as an alternate fuel since the production of cement is intensive in energy consumption. One cement factory has tested the formulation of alternate fuels in kilns in the State of Michoacán and in the City of Ensenada in Baja California.

Recycling and Reuse

In the United States, used tires typically end up in landfills; accumulated in piles, dumps, or garbage heaps; are exported; or are reused. The most common and most rapidly developed reuse method is the production of alternative fuels. This method is popular due to the following advantages: reduction in fuel costs, improvements in fuel production, emission reductions, and so forth. At present, some cement factory kilns are authorized for incineration; other factories are still processing their applications. However, incineration is not without its disadvantages. Among them are the local population's objections to burning, kilns operating at maximum capacity, states have difficulties in obtaining permits for consumption, difficulties in obtaining supplies in less-populated regions, and so on.

Another use that has grown significantly is that as fuel in paper and cellulose factories. The reuse of tires in kilns that generate electricity is important, even when there are high investment costs. Used tires represent only from 10 to 40 percent of the mixture that these kilns need.

By 1994, there were 250.5 million used tires generated in the United States. Their fate was divided as follows: 15 percent for obtaining products, 40 percent as alternative fuel, and 45 percent was not reused. In recycling, export stands out. In reuse as a fuel, cement factory kilns stand out. Another type of reuse is emerging for boilers or electricity generators, but this technology still requires great investments and research for its promotion.

The Scrap Tire Management Council indicates that the reuse of waste tires increased from 11 percent in 1990 to 55 percent in 1994. Its use as fuel predominated, followed by exports and applications in civil engineering. Pyrolysis does not seem to be a technology that will impact the waste tire market. It must be pointed out that fleets renew used tires, mostly in the transportation sector, as a measure to bring down costs. Worldwide, the incineration of tires in cement factory kilns is the most frequent use of used tires.

Conclusion

Massive manufacturing of tires and the difficulty of eliminating them once they are worn out is a major environmental problem along the Mexico-United States border. One single tire needs huge amounts of energy for its manufacturing and, if not properly recycled, contributes to environmental pollution when it ends up at illegal and uncontrolled disposal sites. There are methods for a proper recycling process for these products, but there is a lack of policies to facilitate their collection and the implantation of industries dedicated to recovering or eliminating, in a clean manner, the dangerous components of tires.

The problems that waste tires pose rely on the fact that they are practically indestructible—with their high volume/weight ratio—and, at present, difficult to find suitable markets for the products derived from them. In the United States, the main reusing processes for waste tires are: alternative fuel, products, civil engineering, pyrolisis, and export to other countries, among them Mexico. Of these, tires are reused the most as fuel in cement kilns and in engineering applications. However, in 2000, reusing represented only .71 percent of the total waste tires generated for the year. The remainder ended up in landfills, piled up (scrap tire monofills), and in unknown disposal sites.

In Mexico, the situation is even worse than in the United States because Mexico is only just beginning to reuse waste tires as alternative fuel under controlled conditions. There are some border industries that have invested in granulated rubber.

From an environmental perspective, there must be definitive, clean, and global options proposed for waste tire elimination. Temporary solutions are not good enough since later this waste must be treated again. Alternative uses of waste tires currently do not use large numbers of tires and although some of these are definitive solutions, they do have pollution risks that must be controlled.

References

Diario Oficial de la Federación. 1997. "Ley General del Equilibrio Ecológico y la Protección al Ambiente." México, D.F.: Editorial Porrúa.

Hopey, Don. 2000. "Recalled Tires Find More Uses through Recycling." http//:www.enm.cm/enn-subsciber=archive/2000/09/09162000/krt_tires_315262.asp.

Instituto Nacional de Ecología (INE). 1999. "Instrumentos de política ambiental. Propuestas para establecer el sistema depósito reembolso en residuos clasificados de manejo especial." http://www.ine.gob.mx/dgra/econ_amb/ea_sdr.htm.

Instituto Nacional de Estadísticas, Geografía e Informática (INEGI). 1994. *Estadísticas del medio ambiente*. Aguascalientes: INEGI.

Integrated Waste Management Board (IWMB). 1999a. *California Waste Tire Program Evaluation and Recommendations Final Report*. Sacramento: IWMB.

Integrated Waste Management Board (IWMB). 1999b. *Waste Tire Management Program: 1999 Annual Report*. Sacramento: IWMB.

Integrated Waste Management Board (IWMB). 2000a. "Overview of Tire Management in California." http//:www.ciwmb.ca.gob/Tires/Overview.htm.

Integrated Waste Management Board (IWMB). 2000b. *Waste Tire Management Program 1999 Annual Report*. Sacramento: IWMB.

Organization for Economic Cooperation and Development (OECD). 1995. *Managing the Environment: The Role of Economic Instrument*. Paris: OECD.

Ramírez Barreto, Elizabeth, Sara Ojeda Benítez, and Fernando González Navarro. 2001. "Waste Tire Pile Quantification through Surveying Techniques, Statistical Analysis and Calculus." *Journal of Solid Waste Technology and Management* 27 (1): 15–21.

Ramírez Barreto, Elizabeth, Sara Ojeda Benítez, Fernando González Navarro, Moisés Rivas López, Eva García Durán, and Paulino Luna Juárez. 1999. *Field Characterization of El Cerro Centinela Waste Tire Pile*. Mexicali: Instituto de Ingeniería, Universidad Autónoma de Baja California.

Reisman, Joel I., and Paul M. Lemieux. 1997. "Air Emissions from Scrap Tire Combustion." Environmental Protection Agency (October).

Saad, Laura, Sergio Colín, and Enrique Salinas. 1996a. "Generación de llantas de desecho." Paper presented at the First National Symposium on Hazardous Wastes, 11–13 November, Mexico City, Mexico.

Saad, Laura, Sergio Colín, and Enrique Salinas. 1996b. "Reutilización de llantas de desecho." Paper presented at the First National Symposium on Hazardous Wastes, 11–13 November, Mexico City, Mexico.

Secretaría de Finanzas del Gobierno del Estado de Baja California. 2000. *Dirección de Ingresos*. Documento Interno. Mexicali: Secretaría de Finanzas del Gobierno del Estado de Baja California.

Sitarz, Daniel. 1998. *Sustainable America: America's Environment, Economy and Society in the 21st Century*. Carbondale, IL: Earth Press.

Snyder, Robert H. 1998. *Scrap Tires. Disposal and Reuse*. Warrendale: Society of Automotive Engineers.

Tchobanoglous, G., H. Theisen, and S. Vigil. 1994. *Gestión integral de residuos sólidos, vol. 1*. Madrid: McGraw-Hill/Interamericana de España.

White, Peter. 1996. "So, What is Integrated Waste Management?" *Warmer Bulletin* 49 (May).

23

The Colorado River Delta: An Important Ecosystem for the Mexicali-Imperial Valley Region

José L. Fermán Almada, David W. Fischer, and Alejandro García Gastelum*

Abstract

The makeup of the Colorado River Delta and the Mexicali-Imperial Valley region is based in history, from the physical processes that originally formed the valley and the delta with the movement of the Colorado River to the establishment of the first cultures that settled along the riverbanks and in the delta. Regional activities in contemporary times have generated a dependency between these two zones based on the principal source of regional development: Colorado River water. Such development has provoked a structural change in the delta's ecosystems, turning it into an arid system with greater influences from the marine environment than from the river. The delta's most important ecosystems are the deltaic ecosystem, the wetlands, and the Upper Gulf of California, which are characterized as single environments of global ecological and economic importance. Demand for use of these resources spurred the creation in 1993 by the Mexican government of a natural protected area, the Upper Gulf of California and Colorado River Delta Biosphere Reserve. The creation of this reserve allowed for the establishment of strategies for the sustainable use of natural resources in this zone.

*Fermán Almada and Fischer are Professors and García Gastelum is Technician in the Faculty of Marine Sciences at the Universidad Autónoma de Baja California.

Introduction

The development of the Colorado River throughout the centuries generated the formation of its delta at the river's mouth in the northern part of the Gulf of California (see Figure 1). The constant supply of sediment created a deposit of fine sands and mud, creating the singular environment of the Colorado River Delta and, similarly, the Mexicali-Imperial Valley region.

The relationship between the river and the delta has persisted in different ways throughout history. The first human inhabitants of the region recognized the advantages of the ecosystems of the delta and formed the first human settlements in the area. The artifacts left by these first inhabitants are dated between 12,000 and 10,000 B.C. The remains of arrowheads and other tools help establish the fact that the first inhabitants were the San Dieguito people, ancestors of diverse groups such as the Cucapá, who occupied the delta and the Colorado River's banks.

Figure 1. The Colorado River Delta Zone

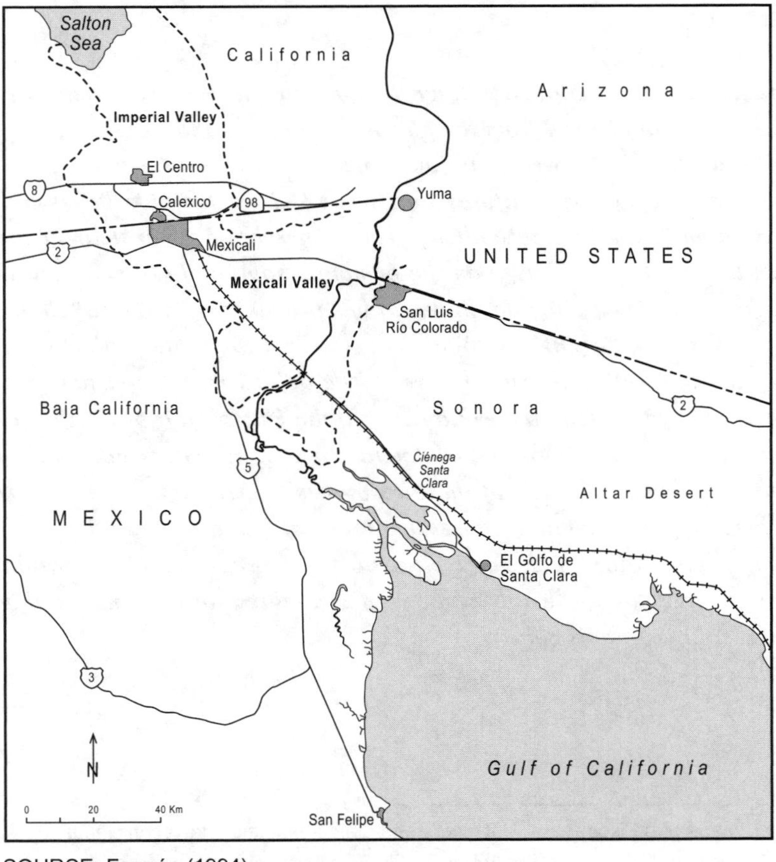

SOURCE: Fermán (1994).

The Cucapá, or "people of the river" as they call themselves, are direct descendents of the Yumans. Their culture was intimately connected to the Colorado River and its delta. The foods they cultivated, collected, hunted, and fished for; the construction materials they used to build their homes; their methods of transportation; and materials for their clothing all depended upon the river. According to their traditions, the river had been part of their lives since creation.

The Cucapá used the riverbanks to plant crops, preparing the rich and humid delta soils after the spring and mid-summer floods. As part of its original ecosystem, the delta presented very dense vegetation, composed of willows, poplars, mesquite trees, and annual plants.

Several fish species were caught in the river, such as desert chubs, mullets, and razorback suckers that were brought to the river with the tide (Minckley 1973). The locals also made trips to the mouth of the river to capture totoaba, shrimp, and other species that reproduce in this area.

Hunting was widely practiced along the riverbanks and their surroundings. Deer, antelope, and bighorn sheep that inhabited the mountains were common prey. Some of these animals were honored and used as symbols of family lineage.

Due to the presence of dams in the higher part of the delta and the ensuing reduction of water flows to the Colorado River, current annual river flows are minimal (in 1935 the flow was almost 17,657 cubic feet/500 cubic meters per second) (Carriquiry and Sánchez 1999). The Cucapá have abandoned agricultural activities; the fish they captured with harpoons, nets, and traps are almost extinct, as are the majority of the animals they hunted with bows and arrows.   With the progressive drying of the delta, the Cucapá are suffering not only the disappearance of their traditional ways of life, but the disappearance of an entire ecosystem within which they lived in harmony for almost two thousand years (SEMARNAP and INE 1995).

The Colorado Delta consisted of vast riparian, freshwater, brackish, and tidal wetlands that covered 1,930,000 acres (780,000 ha) and supported a legendary richness of plant, bird, and marine life. Today, conditions are different. Decades of dam construction and water diversions in the United States and Mexico have reduced the delta to a remnant system of small wetlands and brackish mudflats.

Recently, however, the delta has begun to make a comeback. In the last two decades, floodwater, releases from reservoirs in the United States, agricultural return flows from both countries, and municipal wastewater from Mexico have proved beneficial. Although flood flows are extremely unreliable and irregular and wastewater is high in salinity and pollutants, this water has begun to restore some areas of the delta. Current conditions have allowed wetlands to flourish on about 150,000 acres (60,000 ha) (Luecke et al. 1999).

Contemporary Development

The abundance of fish species of commercial value allowed for the birth and development of new fishing towns in modern times. Aside from constituting the first contemporary human settlements in the desert region, they represent strategic points in the binational region's economic and political life. These communities appropriated the rich marine life and converted the natural wealth into economic riches with the labor of men, women, and children. This brings with it the incorporation and transformation of the cultural ways that an individual or the group held prior to their establishment in fishing villages. The transformation of this inherited culture and the generation of a fishing culture is taking place (McGuire and Greenberg 1993).

The exploitation of the totoaba allowed for the establishment of the first fishing camps, which began in 1920 and lasted until 1975, when the Mexican government restricted totoaba fishing, thus allowing the species to begin to recover. These fishing camps constituted numerous human settlements. Today, they are economically important fishing ports for the states of Baja California and Sonora and their municipalities.

The marked reduction of the totoaba population represented an economic loss for the fishermen. After the establishment of its protection, the rise of the shrimp industry assured the subsistence of fishing communities in the following decades.

The shrimp industry came to replace the economic importance that the totoaba had held for the first half of the twentieth century. Shrimp represented a source of income of fundamental importance for the region and the country. The demise of totoaba fishing continued, followed in the 1980s with an accelerated decline in the volumes of shrimp captured.

Shrimp are a resource currently subjected to intense exploitation. Shrimping has constituted the base for economic development of the fishing populations in the region in the last several decades. There is a significant decline, however, in the amount captured since 1988, which is also reflected in the acute economic impoverishment of the region. Regardless of the prohibition of totoaba fishing, their illegal capture continues to be a problem (Cisneros Mata, Montemayor López, and Román Rodríguez 1995).

Other activities that support the economy of the delta region include shrimp aquaculture on two farms (the first located to the south of the Santa Clara wetland and the second 12 miles [20 kilometers] north of San Felipe) and tourism, which has developed remarkably in the last thirty years.

The Colorado River Delta Ecosystems

The development of agricultural activities in both the Imperial and Mexicali valleys and the delta zone, carried out by the exploitation of Colorado River water through the construction of dams, has generated a change in the delta's environmental conditions. Within the ecosystems that currently make up the delta region, three stand out: the deltaic ecosystem, the Santa Clara wetland, and the Upper Gulf of California.

The Deltaic Ecosystem

Before the construction of the reservoirs on the Colorado River, the delta was considered a positive estuary, meaning that a constant supply of fresh water flowed toward the mouth of the river. Currently, low supplies of fresh water do not compensate for high evaporation rates, conferring anti-estuary characteristics upon it. This means that water flowing in the delta's canals is oriented from the sea to land because of the influences of varying tidal currents that, in this zone, vary from sea level to nearly 33 feet (10 meters) (Thompson 1969). For this reason, these currents are considered to be of the largest and most spectacular in the world, causing large areas of intercurrents (the surface that is flooded or uncovered by the actions of the currents) up to three miles (five kilometers) wide (Mattews 1968).

The delta is characterized as a highly productive zone of diverse habitats, including floodplains, current canals, and islands (principally Montague and Pelican), with the presence of halophyte vegetation (vegetation that resists high salt concentrations). These characteristics make the delta an important reproductive, spawning, and rearing zone for marine species, especially the totoaba *(Totoaba macdonaldi)*, the Delta silverside *(Colpichthys hubbsi)*, whose distribution is restricted to the Colorado River Delta (Crabtree 1989), and many commercial interests such as shrimp *(Penaeus spp.)*, bigeye croaker *(Micropongonias megalops)*, and orangemouth corvina *(Cynoscion xanthulus)*.

The intercurrent canals and zones, floodplains, islands, and halophyte vegetation permit the presence of shore birds that are amply represented in the region by at least eight high diversity resident and migratory species. Some species present in the region are the osprey *(Pandion haeliaetus)*, white and brown pelicans *(Pelecanus erythrorhynchos, P. occidentalis)*, ring-billed gulls *(Larus delawarensis)*, least terns *(Sterna antillarum)*, double-crested cormorants *(Phalacrocorax auritus)*, green-winged teals *(Anas crecca)*, Canada geese *(Branta canadensis)*, American coots *(Fulica americana)*, and clapper rails (Rallus longirostris). The sandpiper *(Calidris spp.)* is noted for its high numbers in the region. The islands that form the delta (Montague and Pelican) are the reproductive sites for birds such as the black-crowned night-heron *(Nycticorax nycticorax)*, great blue heron *(Ardea herodias, Hardea thula)*, laughing gull *(Larus atricilla)*, elegant tern *(Sterna elegans)*, and gull-billed tern *(Sterna nilotica)* (Palacios and Mellink 1992).

The Santa Clara Wetland Ecosystem

The Santa Clara wetland was originally a stretch of lands flooded by the Colorado River that maintained exuberant vegetation. It was dramatically affected and almost obliterated by a lack of fresh water supplies when the Hoover Dam was constructed. Beginning in 1977, however, significant supplies of lightly salted (2–3 ppm) water from the Wellton Mohawk Canal restored the remaining Colorado River wetlands. The wetland has approximately twenty thousand hectares of aquatic surface that extend from the Wellton Mohawk Canal's point of discharge (Glenn, Felger, and Búrquez Montijo 1992; Glenn et al. 1992). The dominant vegetation is cattail (Typha dominguensis), which is surrounded by saline muddy plains and rushes (Juncus sp.), saltgrass (Distichlis spicata), and iodine bush (Allenrolfea occidentalis). Like the El Doctor wetlands (of another origin), the Santa Clara wetland represents important habitats for the desert pupfish (Cyprinodon macularius macularius) and the Yuma clapper rail (Rallus longirostris yumanensis), which live in fresh water habitats. According to Abarca, Ingraldi, and Varela Romero (1993), the Colorado River Delta was the nucleus of the historical distribution of the Yuma clapper rail. With the delta's practical elimination in the last century, the only remaining significant habitat is the Santa Clara wetland, which is important for the potentially reproductive population.

The Upper Gulf of California Ecosystem

The delta's marine portion includes approximately 550,000 hectares belonging to the Upper Gulf of California region. It is characterized by broad intervals of surface temperatures throughout the year (from 54–91°F/12–33°C), large tidal currents of up to 33 feet (10 meters), salinity and turbidity gradients, and coastal lines with soft slopes.

The northern part of the upper gulf is considered one of the most productive marine regions in the world. Its fertility comes from its own hydrodynamics characterized by strong surface currents and currents that bring nutrients to the surface. These characteristics are unique worldwide, making the area rich in endemic marine species (some listed as endangered), highly diverse, and of great socioeconomic importance for the fishermen that reside along its banks. Only 259 fish species have been registered in the upper gulf, compared to 504 known in the southern area. Two ecological factors apparently restrain the upper gulf region: (1) the large annual temperature interval and (2) the broad range of currents that limit the distribution of fish in the Upper Gulf of California. These factors are also responsible for the development of numerous endemic species (fish that only exist in the region) (Walker 1960).

Of the 37 fish species endemic to the Gulf of California, 22 are confined to the upper gulf. All of the fish endemic to the upper gulf can be found in waters of moderate depths (16–328 feet/5–100 meters).

One of the most important fishes in the region is the totoaba *(Totoaba macdonaldi)*, a species endemic to the Gulf of California. The largest totoaba are members of the scianidae family. This species supported intense commercial and sport fishing during the first half of the twentieth century. Its overexploitation, modifications to its habitat, and accidental losses from shrimping boats led to the abrupt decline of its population in the 1970s (Flanagan and Hendrickson 1976).

In 1976, the totoaba was placed in Appendix I of the International Convention Regarding the Traffic of Wild Species (Convención Internacional sobre el Tráfico de Especies Silvestres–CITES) as an endangered species. Similarly, in 1979, the U.S. National Marine Fisheries Service also included the totoaba in the same category (U.S. Fish and Wildlife Service 1979). Currently, it is the only marine fish in the world considered to be in danger of extinction.

There have been at least ten marine mammals registered in the region (Wells, Würsig, and Norris 1981): vaquitas *(Phocoena sinus)*, bottlenose dolphins *(Tursiops sp.)*, common dolphins *(Delphinus delphis)*, pilot whales *(Globicephala melaena)*, sperm whales *(Physeter catodon)*, finback whales *(Baleanoptera physalus)*, blue whales *(Baleanoptera musculus)*, Minke whales *(Baleanoptera acutorostrata)*, gray whales *(Eschrichtius robustus)*, and California sea lions *(Zalophus californianus)*. Among these creatures, the vaquita stands out as a unique cetacean species endemic to Mexico and its distribution seems to be limited to the extreme north of the Gulf of California (Brownell 1986).

The vaquita is the most rare and least understood of the marine mammals (Silber 1990). Little information has been obtained in the 30 years following its initial description. The species is currently considered to be endangered (D'Agrosa, Lennert-Cody, and Vidal 2000).

Social and Environmental Problems

The characteristics of the ecosystems that make up the Colorado River Delta have allowed the region to be considered one of the only coastal regions in the world known for its hydrographic characteristics, high grade of endemic species, the occurrence of both land and marine endangered species, as a habitat for rearing and spawning for many marine species (many of commercial interest), a permanent and seasonal habitat for resident and migratory birds, and an area where the principal socioeconomic activities of the communities are sustained.

The principal economic activity of the population takes place in the primary sector (specifically, fishing). The second most important activity is in the services sector, especially in activities related to tourism. Aquaculture and mining are practically nonexistent.

The development of these activities over the long run has generated environmental problems in the region. These include mainly habitat deterioration, changes in the structure of the plant and animal communities, and decreases in natural populations as a result of human activities or changes associated with the global climate.

The primary threats associated with human activities are derived from the inappropriate handling of resources. Examples of this include the use of Colorado River water, fishing, tourism, salt extraction, hunting activities, agriculture, and the development of urban centers. The impact of these activities is measured by the magnitude of the threats and the grade of susceptibility of the reserve's diverse ecosystems (Fermán 1994).

Delta Management Strategies

Economic problems and the loss of biological resources stemming from the alteration of the upper gulf and Colorado River Delta ecosystems have motivated various efforts to find solutions in Mexico as well as in the United States. The efforts follow the specific needs of selected fishing activities and/or conservation of the region's biological resources. In some cases, these actions were never codified or did not obtain desired results due to their isolated development. In the last few years, the coordination of efforts has been attempted within a global perspective of management and conservation of the Colorado River Delta and the Upper Gulf of California.

In 1974, the area of the Colorado River Delta was declared a reserve for the cultivation and repopulation of all local fish species (*Diario Oficial de la Federación* 1974). Its boundaries were drawn by an imaginary line located at the extreme south of Montague Island from the coast of the Santa Clara Gulf to the Baja California shore.

On August 1, 1975, Mexico's Secretariat of Fisheries (Secretaría de Pesca) established protections for the totoaba that remain in force today. However, efforts to enforce these regulations have not totally eliminated clandestine fishing. On March 2, 1992, the Technical Committee for the Preservation of the Vaquita and the Totoaba in the Upper Gulf of California was created by presidential initiative.

In June 1992, in the port of Mazatlán, Sinaloa, a workshop for the Identification of Priority Marine Areas for Conservation was held. It was organized by the Secretariat of Urban Development and Ecology (Secretaría de Desarrollo Urbano y Ecología) and the World Wildlife Fund to consider the Colorado River Delta and the Upper Gulf of California as the third priority marine area for conservation in Mexico.

On February 19, 1993, at the request of the General Directorate for the Ecological Use of Natural Resources (Dirección General de Aprovechamiento Ecológico de los Recursos Naturales) of the National Institute of Ecology (Instituto Nacional de Ecología) and the Secretariat on Social Development, Wetlands for the Americas (Secretaría de Desarrollo Social, Humedales para las Américas) declared the Colorado River Delta to be an international reserve under the Hemispheric Network of Shore Reserves Program (Programa Red Hemisférica de Reserva de Playeras).

These efforts highlight the ecological importance and need for designing and implementing a conservation program for the Colorado River Delta and the Upper Gulf of California. Such a program would guarantee the protection of biological and ecological values and permit the rational and sustainable use of natural resources.

In March 1993, within the framework of the Technical Committee for the Preservation of the Vaquita and the Totoaba, a document titled "A Proposal for the Declaration of the Upper Gulf of California and Colorado River Delta Biosphere Reserve" was presented to federal entities as well as other governmental and nongovernmental institutions. Working from this document, the Mexican government decreed the Upper Gulf of California and Colorado River Delta a biosphere reserve. This declaration is a possible solution to the conflicts generated by the demand for natural resources and ecosystem protection that supports the diversity of species important to the economy and the environment. The general characteristics that motivated the declaratory process for the reserve include:

1. A 10,000-hectare extension in which distinct delta and upper gulf ecosystems were located, including the lowlands, the estuaries, the canals in the mouth of the Colorado River, and the Santa Clara wetland.

2. The representation of flora and fauna as part of the ecosystems. A low level of deterioration in the reserve's interior should be noted, revealing the high potential for conservation efforts in the zone.

3. High levels of genetic diversity that make the zone important for the conservation of endangered species such as the vaquita *(Phocoena sinus)*, totoaba *(Totoaba macdonaldi)*, desert pupfish *(Cyprinodon macularius macularius)*, and the Yuma clapper rail *(Rallus longirostris yumanensis)*; endemic species such as the Delta silverside *(Colpichthys hubbsi)*; and economically important species such as the blue shrimp *(Penaeus stylirostris)*, brown shrimp *(P. californiensis)*, white shrimp *(P. vannamei)*, and the orangemouth corvina *(Cynoscion xanthulus)*, among others.

This reserve occupies an area of 934,756 hectares constituted by two management zones: The nuclear zone, with 164,779 hectares, and the buffer zone, with 769,976 hectares (see Figure 2), are where the following goals are projected to be carried out:

1. Maintain and strengthen regional economic activities through the sustainable use of natural resources. The conservation of natural resources in the Colorado River Delta and the Upper Gulf of California would allow for the ordered use of the many ecologically and economically important natural resources that, when used inappropriately, negatively impact the region. It would also promote the economic and social welfare of the regional population through the rational use of resources by local inhabitants with

low-impact technological models in accordance with the maintenance of natural populations.

2. Conserve the biological values of the upper gulf and delta ecosystems. Species are found in these zones whose genetic diversity makes the area important for the definition of permanent conservation zones for the endangered species previously mentioned.

Figure 2. Upper Gulf of California and Colorado River Delta Biosphere Reserve Nuclear Zone and Buffer Zone

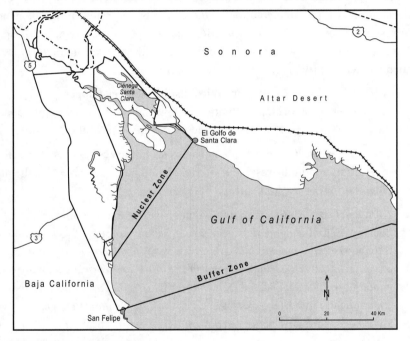

SOURCE: Fermán (1994).

To establish instrumentation of the objectives of the biosphere reserve decree, a management program was developed that incorporated the participation of the local, regional, and international communities. This management program established the specific strategies that define ways to use natural resources as well as their conservation (SEMARNAP and INE 1995). The administrative operation of this program has been carried out by the Reserve Directorate (Dirección de la Reserva), which currently is part of the Commission of Natural Protected Areas (Comisión de áreas Naturales Protegidas), a federal organism.

The management of the Colorado River Delta requires cooperation between Mexico and the United States, among states and resource agencies, and the active involvement of nongovernmental organizations, communities, and citizens. There are different kinds of institutions involved in the management. The only institution with binational authority over surface water resources in the border region is the International Boundary and Water Commission (IBWC), known as Comisión Internacional de Límites y Aguas (CILA) in Mexico. Created in 1889 and restructured in 1944 (Mumme 1996), the IBWC is charged with applying provisions of various boundary and water treaties. Today, the main scope, is to provide environmentally sensitive, timely, and fiscally responsible boundary and water services along the U.S.-Mexican border in an atmosphere of binational cooperation and in a manner responsive to public concerns. In practice, the IBWC has limited its focus to issues of water supply and quality along the border, leaving concerns of environmental protection to the jurisdiction of other Mexican and U.S. agencies (Valdés-Casillas et al. 1998).

National agencies with programs in the Colorado River Delta region include the U.S. Environmental Protection Agency (EPA), Department of the Interior (DOI), and Mexico's Secretariat of Environment and Natural Resources (SEMARNAT). SEMARNAT has jurisdiction over environmental protection, natural resource management, and marine resources management, and it helps develop and implement the nation's Ecology Law (Mumme 1996). Also, within SEMARNAT is the National Water Commission (CNA), which has total jurisdiction over water resources in Mexico.

In the United States, the U.S. Environmental Protection Agency, which regulates water quality, is mandated to participate in international activities. Several U.S. Department of Interior agencies play critical roles. The U.S. Fish and Wildlife Service (FWS) administers the Endangered Species Act and is charged with reviewing federal actions for adverse impacts to endangered species (Mumme 1996).

A Challenge for the Future

The institutional challenges for binational management of the Colorado River Delta region are the growth and transformation of water demand in the border region. These demands present substantive and procedural challenges for domestic and binational institutions. The main issues pertaining to water supply include unresolved transboundary problems of drought management, flood preparedness, groundwater management, and water allocations for environmental purposes. Procedural concerns include public accessibility and procedural transparency of the international agencies, protocols for interagency coordination, and inclusion of domestic stakeholders and nongovernmental bodies in policy development and implementation related to the management of the Colorado River Delta.

The historic relationship between the Mexicali and Imperial valleys with the Colorado River Delta exists mainly because of the need for the river's water for agriculture in the valleys. The development of the valleys through this water has produced social and economic growth which, in turn, has expanded the activities in the Delta region. This region also needs to realize efforts that generate social, cultural, economic, and environmental developments that guarantee improved quality of life for the region's inhabitants. This necessitates the maintenance of binational negotiations that allow for updating policies for the use of natural resources, including water as a principal element. This challenge puts management capacity to the test to achieve simultaneously the integrated definition of development and quality of life for a region that is clearly important in national, binational, and international realms.

References

Abarca, F.J., M.F. Ingraldi, and A. Varela Romero.1993. *Observaciones del cachorrito del desierto* (Cyprinodon macularius), *palmoteador de Yuma* (Rallus longirostris yumanensis) *y comunidades de aves playeras en la ciénaga de Santa Clara, Sonora, México*. Phoenix: Arizona Game and Fish Department.

Brownell, R.L. 1986. "Distribution of the Vaquita *Phocoena Sinus* in Mexican Waters." *Marine Mammals Science* 2: 299–305.

Carriquiry, J.D., and A. Sánchez. 1999. "Sedimentation in the Colorado River Delta and Upper Gulf of California after Nearly a Century of Discharge Loss." *Marine Geology* 158: 125–45.

Cisneros Mata, M.A., G. Montemayor López, and M.J. Román Rodríguez. 1995. "Life History and Conservation of Totoaba Macdonaldi." *Conservation Biology* 9: 806–14.

Crabtree, C.B. 1989. "A New Silverside of the Genus *Colpichthys (Atheriniformes: Atherinidae)* from the Gulf of California Mexico." *Copeia* 3: 558–68.

D'Agrosa, C., C.E. Lennert-Cody, and O. Vidal. 2000. "Vaquita Bycatch in Mexico's Artisanal Gillnet Fisheries: Driving a Small Population to Extinction." *Conservation Biology* 14: 1110–19.

Diario Oficial de la Federación, 30 May 1974.

Fermán, J.L. 1994. "Programa de manejo de la reserva de la biósfera del Alto Golfo de California y delta del Río Colorado." Master's thesis, Facultad de Ciencias Marinas, Universidad Autónoma de Baja California, Ensenada, Mexico.

Flanagan, C., and J.R. Hendrickson. 1976. "Observations on the Commercial Fishery and Reproductive Biology of the *Totoaba Cynoscion Macdonaldi* in the Northern Gulf of California." *Fishery Bulletin* 74 (3): 531–44.

Glenn, E.P., R.S. Felger, and J.A. Búrquez Montijo. 1992. "Oasis in the Colorado Delta, Cienaga de Santa Clara: A Remnant Wetland/Oasis en la Delta del Río Colorado, Ciénaga de Santa Clara: vestigios de un oasis de humedal." *CEDO News/Noticias del CEDO* 4 (1): 14–32.

Glenn, E.P., R.S. Felger, J.A. Búrquez Montijo, and D.S. Turner. 1992. "Ciénaga de Santa Clara: Endangered Wetland in the Colorado River Delta, Sonora, México." *Natural Resources Journal* 32: 817–24.

Luecke, D.F., J. Pitt, C. Congdon, E. Glenn, C. Valdés-Casillas, and M. Griggs. 1999. *A Delta Once More: Restoring Riparian and Wetland Habitat in the Colorado River Delta*. Washington D.C.: Environmental Defense Publications.

McGuire, T.R., and J.B. Greenberg. 1993. *Maritime Community and Biosphere Reserve: Crisis and Response in the Upper Gulf of California*. Tucson: University of Arizona Press.

Mattews, J.B. 1968. "The Tides of Puerto Peñasco, Gulf of California." *Arizona-Nevada Academy of Science* 5: 131–34.

Minckley, W.L. 1973. *Fishes of Arizona*. Phoenix: Arizona Game and Fish Department.

Mumme, Stephen P. 1996. "The Institutional Framework for Transboundary Inland Water Management in North America: Mexico, Canada, the United States, and Their Binational Agencies." Commission for Environmental Cooperation.

Palacios, E., and Eric Mellink. 1992. "Breeding Bird Records from Montague Island, Northern Gulf of California." *Western Birds* 23: 41–44.

Secretaría de Medio Ambiente, Recursos Naturales y Pesca (SEMARNAP) and Instituto Nacional de Ecología (INE). 1995. *Programa de manejo de áreas naturales protegidas I: reserva de la biósfera del Alto Golfo y delta del Río Colorado*. México, D.F.: SEMARNAP.

Silber, G.K. 1990. "Distributional Relations of Cetaceans in the Northern Gulf of California, with Special Reference to the Vaquita, *Phocoena Sinus*." Ph.D. diss., Department of Marine Biology, University of California, Santa Cruz, California.

Thompson, R.W., 1969. "Tidal Currents and General Circulation in the Northern Gulf of California." Pp. 51–55 in *Environmental Impact of Brine Effluents on Gulf of California*. D.A. Thomson, A.R. Mead, J.F. Schreiber, Jr., J.A. Hunter, W.F. Savage, and W.W. Rinne, eds. U.S. Dept. Interior, Office of Saline Water, Research and Development Program, Report No. 387.

U.S. Fish and Wildlife Service, Division of Endangered Species. 1979. "Totoaba; Listing as an Endangered Species." *Federal Register* (May 21) Washington D.C., 44 (99): 29478–29480.

Valdés-Casillas, Carlos, O. Hinajosa-Huerta, M. Muñoz-Viveroz, F. Zamora-Arroyo, Y. Carrillo-Guerrero, S. Delgado-García, M. López-Camacho, E. Glenn, J. Garcia, J. Riley, D. Baumgartner, M. Briggs, C.T. Lee, E. Chavarría-Correa, C. Congdon, and D. Luecke. 1998. "Information Database and Local Outreach Program for the Restoration of the Hardy River Wetlands, Lower Colorado River Delta, Baja California and Sonora, Mexico." A report to the North American Wetlands Council.

Walker, B.W. 1960. "The Distribution and Affinities of the Marine Fish Fauna of the Gulf of California." *Systematic Zoology* 9 (3): 123–33.

Wells, R.S., B.G. Würsig, and K.S. Norris. 1981. *A Survey of Marine Mammals of the Upper Gulf of California, Mexico, with an Assessment of the Status* Phocoena sinus. Washington D.C.: Marine Mammals Commission.

PART FIVE

Social Trends and Culture

24

Education in the Imperial and Mexicali Valleys

Olga Amaral*

Abstract

This article provides an introduction to the educational systems in the Imperial and Mexicali valleys. Presenting a context for the two systems, the essay gives a brief history of education in the region and the development of schools during the settlement period in the early 1900s. The essay also provides some statistics regarding education at the K–12 level as well as some information about higher educational opportunities. Some collaborative efforts currently under way are also described.

Introduction

Higher education plays a key role in shaping any community. The presence of a university is often viewed as an asset, a valuable resource that enhances quality of life in the region. Often, it is the interchange of ideas between universities and other entities within a community that sparks the development of new programs, new trends that affect society, and the nature of debate over intellectual issues. The Mexicali and Imperial valleys are a region of rich traditions steeped in a cultural context that has seen the area evolve from a primarily agricultural economic base to one that is increasingly technological. Higher education institutions within this setting

*Amaral is Assistant Professor in the Division of Teacher Education at San Diego State University's Imperial Valley Campus.

have forged ahead with the development of programs to serve the community, but have struggled to keep up with the ever-changing needs of this dynamic society.

Communities are also shaped by the value of their educational system at the K–12 level. Often, real estate advertisements extol the benefits of selling homes that are within the zones of certain schools, primarily those that have good reputations and are expected to attract parents who research the state of schools in the communities of their choice. These schools, along with higher education institutions, are often a reflection of the needs of the population of a particular area.

A History of Education

History of Imperial Valley Schools

Several years before the Imperial Valley became a viable farming community with the advent of irrigation, the San Diego County Board of Supervisors established two schools near the Colorado River in the Chocolate Mountains (Hendersen 1968: 153). The Laguna and Hedges school districts were established in 1891 and 1896, respectively, primarily to serve children from families involved in the mining industry. Soon thereafter they unified to form the Picacho School District (1906). Unfortunately, this happened just as the mining industry was beginning to decline and thus the number of students served declined as well.

J.R. Havens headed the first family that arrived in the Imperial Valley in October 1901 (Nuffer n.d.: 54). The family settled in a place called Silsbee, lending the school its name. Those completing their studies at the Silsbee School were then sent to San Diego to attend high school. The first teacher (1902) on record at the Silsbee School was Eugene de Burn. By 1904, the school was divided and part of it was moved to Calexico to the corner of Third Street and Imperial Avenue. This site served as both a school and a church.

It was also at about this time that the Imperial School District was established. A pioneer from Nevada named L.E. Carr pitched a tent near Heber, just south of Imperial near the present-day McCabe School. This school was established in 1902 and served a total of 50 students from a large geographical region; many walked as far as eight miles to attend (Hendersen 1968: 153). A third school was established in 1902 in Calexico. This school had a tent with board floors that, at that time, represented an improvement compared to other schools that were simply tents propped by stakes with open-air arrow weed ramadas designed to provide some relief from the sun. The following year, a wood frame school building was erected to serve a total of 113 students. By 1912, Calexico opened its first high school with 21 students and three teachers.

In 1905, a bond for $3,000 was approved for the building of a new Silsbee schoolhouse. It opened in October with a total of 32 students. In 1907, the Eucalyptus

School District was formed to accommodate the growing numbers of students. At the same time, the Magnolia School District was established just half a mile north of the current site of Magnolia School. A teacher's salary at this school in 1908 was $70 per month, or $550 per year. There were 151 days of school during the year. In 1911, the Silsbee School burned down and was rebuilt, only to burn down again in 1935.

The first school in El Centro was established in 1906 (Tout 1931: 285) in the dining room of the Franklin Hotel in the corner of Fifth Street and Broadway. It began with 30 students, but grew so rapidly that by the following year a school building had to be erected to accommodate all the students.

By 1906, the first high school district had been organized. It included Imperial, Sunset Springs, Holtville, Eastside, and Brawley and was named the Imperial Valley Union High School District. By 1908, a second high school district was formed that included the El Centro, Eucalyptus, Silsbee, Deal, Heber, and Adair districts and was called the Central Union High School District.

It was also in 1909 that the Holtville Union High School District was formed. It included the Alamitos, Alamo, Eastside, Holtville, Central, and Verde school districts. It was also in that year that the Mt. Signal School District was organized and a new graduate from San Diego State College/Normal School (now San Diego State University) was asked to teach a total of eight students. It began as a gathering under a ramada, built to provide shade in a climate that could easily reach 120 degrees Fahrenheit in the summer. The first school in this district was finally built in 1924. In 1910, the Calexico Union High School District was formed and Mt. Signal School District was annexed in 1912. This incorporated a total of five elementary schools when the high school district came to include the Jasper portion of the Jasper-Alamitos Union, the Mt. Signal portion of the Mt. Signal Union, and the Calexico School District.

In 1910, Westmorland was a 300,000-acre community just northwest of Brawley that had begun to attract businesses. Its first school site was a screened porch of the home of G.F. Welcome, a pastor and storekeeper. The school served 12 students during its first year. Only one year later, a two-room schoolhouse was built. Three other schools were eventually built in this district: Harding, Roosevelt, and Trifolium. All of these were closed when a new site was found and a new school was built in 1952 to accommodate the students.

Calipatria was another community established early in the Imperial Valley when, in 1914, John Reavis, Luther Brown, and Harry Chandler of the *Los Angeles Times* formed a syndicate to purchase Southern Pacific land for $1,668,970 (Nuffer n.d.: 72). Calipatria's first school opened the same year with 36 students and a new elementary school building was completed in 1921 that cost $15,000.

In 1905, the Imperial Valley had 12 elementary school districts, but as more land opened up for settlement, school growth became more rapid. By 1920, there were 57 school districts. A decline in enrollment beginning at this time resulted in the passage of a controversial bill—AB 46 written by Speaker of the House Jesse Unruh—that forced the consolidation of districts and established many new boundary lines. By 1965, there were 23 school districts remaining.

The largest unified district (by acreage) is San Pasqual. It covers 1,010 square miles from the Mexican border to the Riverside County line to the north and to the sand dunes west to the Colorado River on the California-Arizona border. Only about 1,500 people lived in the district in 1956 and students wishing to attend high school had to travel to Yuma, the nearest city in Arizona. Tuition costs were borne by the entire county. A high school was eventually built in the Imperial Valley and a unified school district formed. Many of the children served were from the Quechan Indian reservation located in the area. As a unified district serving this population, the district now receives federal funding because of its Indian school-age population; however, more than 40 percent of the school population today is Hispanic.

A History of Mexicali Valley Schools

In an essay about life in the early twentieth century in the northern part of the Mexican State of Baja California, Vivanco (1924) describes the region's educational settings. Hundreds of years earlier during the period of the Spanish conquest, the education of this region's inhabitants, mostly Indians, was done by missionaries. The curriculum emphasized Christian doctrine and also covered some elements of mining, agriculture, construction, and domestic occupations. At the beginning of the struggle for independence, many Indians abandoned the missions and fled to safer ground, primarily in the mountains. During the period of about 1821 to 1860 (Vivanco 1924: 315), residents of the area educated their children mainly through private tutors who provided instruction in the homes with some assistance from the clergy. As the numbers grew, the city council of Santo Tomás, the area where most people had settled, agreed to fund the construction of the first school in 1843. Not until 1908 did the Law of Education pass. This law outlined many of the stipulations for basic education, including teaching methods to be used. In 1916, a night school for adults was opened in Mexicali. The previous year, construction began for three rural schools and ended with the completion of the Cuauhtémoc School, which Vivanco called an "imposing building" (1924: 317). The government considered many different issues in setting the course for education in Baja California. One example is the issue of coeducation. Vivanco reports that

> … the district educational instruction has been given to mixed classes, preferential attention, however, being given to the male sex. Later, on the foundation of schools of Ensenada, Tijuana and Mexicali, the sexes were separated, but subsequently the plan of mixed classes was definitely established for Tijuana and Mexicali, the two

sexes remaining separate at Ensenada. Up to now no serious obstacles have been encountered in the co-educational method (1924: 318).

There was also interest in providing continued training for teachers. From 1919 to 1920, the government determined to send three teachers from the Cuauhtémoc School to Los Angeles to take summer courses on "physical culture, domestic economy, manual labor and drawing" (Vivanco 1924: 323). By 1918, the government had issued special examinations and requirements for teacher preparation in an attempt to improve public education.

In 1925, Genaro Coss y León founded the Greg Commercial Academy (Academia Comercial Greg) in Mexicali and in the following year, the Benito Juárez School was also established. In the early 1920s, Vivanco counted a total of 39 separate institutions within the school district of Mexicali, made up of five high schools, nine elementary or primary schools, 22 rural facilities, two night schools, and one prison school. In 1923, there were a total of 2,575 students enrolled and 64 female and 50 male teachers. Vivanco also makes reference to a school built in Mexicali called the Leona Vicario School.

Since then, the region's population has increased tremendously and many new schools have been built. During the academic year of 2000–2001, the government of Baja California's State Educational System reported a total enrollment in Mexicali at the preschool level of 26,242 students, 102,769 in grades one through six, and 40,601 secondary level students. Students in bachelor's programs totaled 11,979, while 7,232 were enrolled in technical schools.

Educational Systems

Education in the United States

Education in the United States is mandatory for all children until the age of sixteen. The general organization of public education in the United States includes preschool settings (with limited public funding to children of low-income families who qualify for the federal Head Start program); elementary schools that include kindergarten (not mandatory in most states) through fifth or sixth grade; junior high schools or middle schools, which are usually sixth through eighth or seventh through ninth grade; and high schools, typically for grades nine through twelve. Upon completion of high school, students receive a diploma and can go on to higher education institutions. Most high schools in the United States are considered to be comprehensive high schools. This means that graduation from these institutions indicates that students have been prepared to go on to institutions of higher education—two- or four-year colleges or universities. Some high schools are considered vocational and focus on preparing students for careers that may or may not require a college education.

Each U.S. state has the legal obligation to educate its children from kindergarten through twelfth grade. As such, it establishes laws that guide the implementation of educational programs. While legislators establish educational laws, state departments of education, led by an elected state superintendent of education, oversee their implementation. Education laws can also be passed at the federal level that always supercede state laws. In California, the state has offices in each county that are responsible for carrying out functions as designated by the State Department of Education. In addition, they can also run programs funded by the state or by the U.S. Department of Education. They also serve as the link between school districts within each county and the State Department of Education. An elected board that gives the responsibility of daily operations to a county superintendent of education runs each county office of education. Figure 1 indicates the organizational structure of the U.S. educational system.

Figure 1. The U.S. and California Educational System

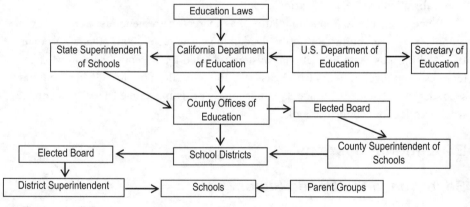

SOURCE: Author's analysis (2000).

Each district within the county has its own hierarchy of leadership. It is run by an elected board that gives power to a superintendent for the day-to-day operations of schools. It is at the district level that curriculum is designed to address state standards that specify what students are expected to know and be able to do in each grade. Methodologies used to implement the curriculum are also chosen at the district level.

Boards at both the district and county levels represent the community and, as such, the interests of parents as well. They are further encouraged, however, to participate in decision-making activities through school-site councils and other governing bodies set up by various programs. Local control of school policies exercised in the United States through individual school districts has traditionally been a very important facet of education and of the U.S. political system. The curriculum taught in schools is often based on standards that describe basic minimal levels of knowledge that a student should have or content frameworks that usually outline basic knowledge with reference to grade levels and according to each content area. Typically, these are developed by state educational agencies or by national organizations for content areas such as the National Council of Teachers of Mathematics (NCTM). The primary subject areas taught throughout the K–12 span include mathematics, English (language arts and reading), social sciences, and science. At each grade level, other subject areas may also be required. These include physical education, computer science, and health education. By the time students reach high school, additional options such as the study of foreign languages, business education, and vocational education may exist. Many school-sponsored extracurricular activities tend to round off students' overall educational experiences and may include participation in sports, clubs, or other after-school programs.

Education in Imperial County

Imperial County had a total student population of 32,898 during the fiscal year of 1998–1999. Of this population, 81.5 percent were Hispanic (California Department of Education 2000). Slightly over 46 percent of the total population was considered to be English learners; that is, students have not developed enough proficiency in English to be able to participate in English-only-speaking classrooms. Many of these students are immigrants or the children of immigrants from Spanish-speaking countries, primarily Mexico.

Imperial County is made up of 16 school districts that range in size from one with 83 students to the largest with over 7,500 students. This is attributed to the fact that the educational system in the United States still strongly clings to the tradition of opting for local control. As such, school boards from very small school districts, when faced with the possibility of merging with other districts and becoming a unified district, often do not accept that option. While this sort of consolidation would result in better economies of scale and would be less expensive to run, some districts prefer to remain independent and find ways of managing their finances. It also allows for control over policies and practices, especially curriculum and personnel choices. The school districts and number of schools in each district are listed in Table 1.

In addition to its public school system, Imperial County also has private schools, some with religious affiliations. The enrollments at some of these schools include many children who reside in Mexico and whose parents cross the border daily to take their children to school. There are also services provided by the Imperial County Office of Education for students in court schools, alternative programs, and continuation schools. Each of the two prisons located in the Imperial Valley also provides educational programs for inmates.

Table 1. Number of Schools by District, Imperial County, 2000

	Name of District	Number of Schools
1	Brawley Elementary School District	3
2	Brawley Union High School District	3
3	Calexico Unified School District	10
4	Calipatria Unified School District	5
5	Central Union High School District	3
6	El Centro Elementary School District	11
7	Heber Elementary School District	1
8	Holtville Unified School District	5
9	Imperial Unified School District	5
10	Magnolia Union School District	1
11	McCabe Union School District	1
12	Meadows Union School District	1
13	Mulberry Elementary School District	1
14	San Pasqual Valley Union School District	4
15	Seeley Union Elementary School District	1
16	Westmorland Union School District	1
	Total	56

SOURCE: California Department of Education (2000).

There are many special programs within schools in the Imperial Valley. Many are provided with special funding opportunities made available by state or federal agencies. Examples include programs that target migrant students, early childhood education programs, after-school programs, technology-enhancing programs, achievement enhancement programs in various curricular areas, and dropout prevention programs.

Migrant education programs provide special tutoring and services to students from families that often travel from one community to another in cycles that mirror seasonal job opportunities, most often agricultural in nature. These services are offered above and beyond those of the schools and include summer programs. The Migrant Program of the Imperial County Office of Education serves as a regional center for the county and also provides day care services and Even-Start opportunities for very young children. It is also a training center for Reading Recovery, a program intended to help children in first grade who experience difficulties in learning to read to improve their reading skills.

Early childhood programs offer opportunities for low-income families to place preschool-aged children in programs designed to prepare them with skills for academic development. After-school programs are mostly state funded and provide opportunities for students to engage in a variety of learning activities that go beyond their academic day. These can include tutoring for students lacking skills in certain curricular areas, such as reading or mathematics, or they can be homework centers. They can also blend academics with activities traditionally considered to be nonacademic, such as sports and hobbies.

Technology programs are increasingly becoming infused into the daily curriculum for students, but, in some cases, this can also be an area that is enhanced for some students through special programs. At times, these are combined opportunities for both students and their parents. These programs are intended to further involve parents in their children's education by bringing them together to work on a common interest, such as learning how to use a computer and software for various purposes. The Imperial County Office of Education also has a Borderlink Program that focuses on helping students to access postsecondary opportunities through activities such as the Scholastic Aptitude Test (SAT, required for admission to many universities) preparation and helping teachers become better prepared to use technology in their own classrooms to enhance instruction for all students.

Dropout prevention programs are varied. One could argue that most programs designed to further educate students or engage them further in learning will increase their motivation and reduce the chances that they will eventually drop out of school. Some programs have this as an explicit goal, while others attempt the same objectives but are more implicit about the intended outcome of the activity and the impact it is expected to have on students' education. This is the case with Student Well-Being Programs, for example. The purpose of this program is to work with students on alcohol, tobacco, and other drug prevention techniques. One additional component of this project includes AmeriCorps volunteers who receive training to provide academic mentoring to students through tutoring and community service projects. Another program is Academic Employment Services, which targets students for employment training and placements in local businesses where they can gain experience.

Programs such as Advancement Via Individual Determination (AVID) work with students who have the potential to go on to postsecondary institutions, but have not followed the right path to do so by the time they graduate from high school. The program leads them through course work that universities will accept and provides them with skills that they will need when working at that academic level. Many of the participants are first-generation college-bound students from families that have no experience in preparing children to attend college. This program is run regionally in collaboration with San Diego and Orange counties.

The California Reading and Literature Project and the California Reading Initiative (grades 7–12) are both academic support services intended to improve students' academic skills, thereby increasing their chances of continuing education with better preparation. They are joint ventures between the Imperial County Office of Education and San Diego State University's Imperial Valley Campus (SDSU-IVC). By collaborating on these efforts, both institutions are able to convey one consistent message to participants regarding issues of literacy development. Similar initiatives are in place for mathematics and the education of English Learners (students for whom English is a second language). An additional initiative for reading intervention is the use of the Corrective Reading methodology sponsored by the joint collaboration of the Imperial County Office of Education and the Sacramento Office of Education.

Alternative education programs are also run at the county level. They include community schools with programs for children temporarily placed in court and juvenile schools. In some cases, these services are for children who find themselves to be wards of the state or children who have not been successful in regular placements and need alternative settings to complete their education.

Some initiatives are generated at the state level and are intended to bring about reforms in education that result in higher achievement. One of these initiatives in California is class-size reduction. Due to this program, most schools in grades K–3 have a maximum enrollment of 20 students in each classroom. Some schools believe that this reform has great potential for higher levels of individualized instruction, resulting in higher achievement levels. Due to this belief, some school districts have extended this reduction to grades beyond K–3. This same initiative is also being implemented in some high schools, particularly in English and mathematics classes, where the stakes are high for students whose graduation in the near future will depend on their passing an exit exam, one heavily assessing students in these basic skills, among others.

Another recent initiative resulted from Proposition 10, a legislative initiative that provides funding for special programs. With this funding, various departments within the Imperial County Office of Education have begun to offer new services to county schools. These include further services provided to preschool children, the beginning of family resource centers in communities, family home care programs to ensure greater safety for children, increasing the toy library, funding for a professional development coordinator to improve the quality of day care and training for preschool teachers, supplying vans to transport teen mothers and their babies to day care so that they can attend school (babies cannot travel in regular school buses), and hiring a behavioral specialist to help parents and teachers better understand how to work with preschoolers.

The county also works with "underperforming" schools to provide them with training and services intended to increase their students' achievement levels. These schools are identified by a formula developed by the State Department of Education that shows their students to be performing at unacceptable levels as determined by the state. These schools are targeted for improvement and the County Office of Education provides assistance in this area.

Special education programs provide special classes for the severely physically challenged. These programs also provide classes within regular schools for those who can be included for part of the day and need only partial special education services. In addition, services are offered for the hearing and the visually impaired. Programs such as Gifted and Talented Education (GATE) programs are run by individual districts without special funding initiatives.

Imperial Valley Regional Occupational Program (IVROP) is a joint partnership between the Imperial County Office of Education and Imperial Valley's high school districts. They provide free and practical hands-on training, career guidance, and job placement assistance. They also provide training to obtain entry-level jobs, update or improve job skills, prepare for advanced training and education, prepare for a college major, earn credits toward high school graduation, and earn a certificate of demonstrated competencies. Some of the projects sponsored by IVROP include:

- CalWORKs Supportive Services: Assesses, tests, and monitors participants

- Environmental, Recycling, and Earth Day Projects: Participants explore, conserve, discover, investigate, create, and evaluate their environment

- Project ACE (Accessing Careers through Education): Children of CalWorks participants and youth in foster care receive services pertaining to case management, integrated academic and vocational classroom instruction, counseling, and work experience

- Project Hope: Participants of CalWorks, the working poor, and former foster care youth receive English as a Second Language instruction and occupational training for the meat-packing industry

- Project PACE (Providing Access to Careers and Education): Participants age 14 to 21 receive academic enhancement, leadership development, summer employment opportunities, and adult mentoring

- Project Power: Intensive English language instruction and vocational training are provided

- Project PRIDE (Promoting Responsibility, Integrity, Determination, and Economic Self-Sufficiency): Provides basic skills training, job coaching, and readiness skills for noncustodial parents, working poor, and former foster care adults age 18 to 24

- Project SOS (Steps for Success): Serves youth age 14 to 21 in certain cities with training and vocational skills

- Project STAR (Students Toward Achievement Results): Meets the needs of a specific target population in the same areas

- Project Trabajo: A welfare-to-work program that focuses on readiness skills, job coaching, and training

- School-to-Career: Provides a Virtual Resource Technology Center, matching students to an education/business mentor

- Project WAMSA (Work Ability Means Skills Applied): Targets students in eighth grade special education classes and gives students a greater understanding of employment opportunities and careers available to them

Student achievement in Imperial County is often below the levels that educators would like to see. This sometimes is attributed to the nature of the population served. For example, children living in poverty tend to score lower on achievement tests throughout the United States. Imperial County is the poorest in California. The unemployment rate in 2000 was 26.3 percent (CEDD 2000), well over five times the state's unemployment rate of 4.9 percent for the same year. Another reason for lower performance is the large population of English learners in the county (46.7%). The state average is only 24.7 percent, accounting for poor performances on achievement tests that are administered only in English. It is important to note, however, that some individual students and individual schools do fit a different demographic profile. Achievement scores for many students are comparable or higher than the national averages (for specific achievement data, see Education Data Partnership 2001).

Education in Mexico

The 1917 Mexican Constitution made K–6 education mandatory for Mexican residents. As the country places a greater emphasis on the preparation of its citizenry, it has increased this requirement and it is now expected that students attend school until the age of 18 (Encarta 2000). The Mexican educational system is not district driven, but rather follows the policies and practices of the Secretariat of Public Education (Secretaría de Educación Pública–SEP). Formed in 1977, this national government body administers all aspects of the K–12 public education system. While many initiatives are now taking place at the state level, the organization of schools, budgeting, policies regarding curriculum, methodologies, and materials remain the responsibility of the federal government. This organizational structure incorporates five administrative areas and two branches that govern operations. These include the Secretariat and Subsecretariat of Education and Social Welfare (Secretaría y Subsecretaría de Educación y Bienestar Social), the Bureau of Administration (Dirección de Administración), the Bureau of Education (Dirección de Educación), the Bureau of Participation (Dirección de Participación), the Socio-Educational Bureau for Planning and Infrastructure (Dirección Social Educativa de Planeación e Infraestructura), the Bureau of Scientific Research (Dirección de Investigación Científica), the Tijuana Delegation, and the Ensenada Delegation.

The Mexican educational system is organized as follows: "educación primaria básica," or basic elementary education, the equivalent of grades K–6; "educación secundaria básica," basic secondary, that is, grades 7–9; "educación media superior," upper secondary, roughly, high school or grades 10–12; and "educación superior," higher education.

There are three forms of basic elementary education offered for different student populations: general, indigenous, and migrant. Basic secondary education also has various modalities to meet the needs of different types of students: general, working students, technical, distance (telesecundaria), and vocational training.

Education at the upper secondary level varies according to the student's professional goals, as follows: "bachillerato general" or "preparatoria," is equivalent to general high school; "bachillerato técnico" or "técnico profesional"—technical high school; and open high school. Open high school is an option available primarily to adult students who would like to complete their upper secondary education. It is generally equivalent to the G.E.D. awarded in the United States.

There are various paths in higher education as well. Normal school *(escuela normal)* trains basic elementary education teachers; higher normal school *(escuela normal superior)* trains basic secondary teachers and offers a doctorate in education for those who would like to teach at normal schools. The intermediate technological education *(educación tecnológica intermedia)* path is usually two years of vocationally-oriented study, equivalent to junior college. University or technological institutions offer four- or five-year bachelor degree programs, specializations (in social and natural sciences, business administration, public health, communications, computer science, law, etc.), master's and doctorate degrees. The system for adult education offers special basic education programs for the incarcerated, cultural missions, literacy, and vocational education.

The Mexican curriculum was last modified in 1993–1994. The emphasis in grades one and two is on Spanish (language arts and reading) with a total of 45 percent of the day devoted to this discipline. In addition, the curriculum incorporates mathematics, community and artistic development, and physical education. From grades three to six, courses of study include Spanish (with only 30 percent of the day devoted to this discipline), mathematics, natural sciences, history, geography, civic education, art, and physical education.

As part of the schools' broader educational efforts, extracurricular activities include career training, adult basic education, and special education and training. Students may also participate in sports and various clubs.

The increase in school enrollments over the past two decades has been dramatic. By 1999, 94 percent of the population in Mexico between the ages of 6 and 14 was enrolled in school. Primary enrollment, including preschool, totaled 17.2 million in 2000. Enrollment at the secondary public school level rose from 1.4 million in 1972 to 5.4 million in 2000. A rapid rise also occurred in higher education. Between 1959 and 2000, university enrollments rose from 62,000 to more than two million (Encarta 2000).

In Mexico, the overall improvement in achievement for all children is also becoming one of the highest priorities for the country. According to the U.S. Department of State, "… [e]ducation is one of the Government of Mexico's highest priorities. The education budget for 2000—$23 billion—represented a 6.8 percent increase over the previous year's figure and 23% more funding in real terms for education in 2000 than in 1994" (2001: 2). Educational funding now represents 27 percent of the budget. Education in Mexico is also being decentralized from federal to state authorities in order to improve accountability. This is part of a general movement in administrative decentralization in Mexico.

Education in Mexicali

During the 1999–2000 academic year, Mexicali had a total student population of 211,291 in 997 schools (Patiño 2001). Of this number, a total of 193,663 students were enrolled in public schools, while 17,628 were in private schools. There are 899 public schools with diverse numbers of students served and 98 private schools. Table 2 provides enrollment figures and numbers of schools by level.

Table 2. Enrollment in Mexicali Schools, 1999–2000

Educational Levels	Enrollment			Schools		
	Public	Private	Total	Public	Private	Total
Preschool	25,578	715	26,293	286	11	297
Elementary	94,953	6,992	101,945	417	28	445
Secondary	37,554	2,440	39,994	130	17	147
Technical College	18,174	3,728	21,902	30	28	58
Teacher College Preparation	2,086	199	2,285	8	2	10
General University	15,318	3,554	18,872	28	12	40
Total	193,663	17,628	211,291	899	98	997

SOURCE: Patiño (2000).

The educational goals for the year 2000 for students in Mexicali focus on making the classroom a place where students can demonstrate what they have learned, where intellectual growth can develop and students can learn how it applies to daily life, and where students learn to get along with others. Interviews with graduates from public schools in Mexicali and individuals who currently have children attending public schools reveal that grade level sequence in K–16 programs is very similar to that of the United States. Unlike the technical names for the various levels of schooling reported in the section on education in Mexico, different terminology is used. For example, students are said to attend grades K–6, referred to as *primaria* (primary). The next three grades (grades 7–9) are referred to as *secundaria* (secondary). They call the last three grades (10–12) *prepa*, which is short for *preparatoria* (preparatory). From this point, students can elect to go to technical schools *(técnicos)* for periods of two years or more, to schools for teacher preparation *(normal)*, or universities that grant undergraduate, graduate, and postgraduate degrees.

The educational system in Mexicali, and in the State of Baja California in general, has remained productive and has a number of initiatives designed to enhance educational services for its student population. The first area of improvement occurs in the realm of basic education and includes four different projects. The first intends to improve the quality and awareness of citizenship and promotes the prevention of corruption and crime. The second promotes social participation. The third focuses on reading, not just for children, but for all community members. The fourth initiative improves the educational infrastructure and brings about new resources for education.

The second major initiative has four projects intended to strengthen equity within basic education. The first component deals with dropout prevention in both urban and suburban communities and is called the Integrated Program for Reducing Educational Gaps (Programa Integral para Abatir el Rezago Educativo–PIARE). The second is the Program for Reducing Gaps in Beginning and Basic Education (Programa para Abatir el Rezago en Educación Inicial y Básica–PAREIB). The third is the Education, Health, and Nutrition Program (Programa de Educación, Salud y Alimentación–PROGRESA), carried out in rural areas. The fourth is a program designed to make free textbooks available to secondary level students.

The third major initiative improves the quality and infrastructure of technical schools and universities. The first project is to improve the infrastructure and services provided to the Vocational College (Colegio de Bachilleres–COBACH), the second to the College of Scientific and Technological Studies (Colegio de Estudios Científicos y Tecnológicos–CECYTE), the third to the National College of Professional Technical Education (Colegio Nacional de Educación Profesional Técnica–CONALEP), fourth to the Technological University *(Universidad Tecnológica)* of Tijuana, and, finally, to increase the promotion of scientific, technological, and humanistic research.

The final area of focus revolves around the enhancement of culture in the state. Resources and attention were given to provide an improved infrastructure, as well as programs for cultural development.

All of these initiatives come at a time when the educational system is witnessing unprecedented enrollment increases. During the 1999–2000 academic year, the State of Baja California saw an enrollment increase from 622,078 to 641,237 (Patiño 2001: 5), representing a 3.08 percent increase in just one year. Resources, however, are being carefully distributed in order for the state to reach its broad goals. This is evidenced by the number of activities and programs supported for the educational enhancement of students. Several additional programs have also contributed to the enhancement of educational services. An example is the identification of children with special or multiple talents related to emotional and cognitive intelligence.

Another is in the area of dropout prevention, where schools with higher percentages of dropouts have instituted measures to assess the extent of the problem and focus attention on preventive measures.

Career education programs are another priority. A total of 31 students in Mexicali have received services that bring students together with professionals to serve as role models. To meet the needs of students in the area of health, for example, students received vision screenings and 14,000 students throughout the state were found to have some form of visual deficiency.

Students are also very involved in sports and competition can be fierce. Last year, for example, the Baja California women's basketball team achieved first place status, while the men's team came in second place. Students also did very well on national tests of physical education.

Students who have special needs can now receive services from the Center for Multiple Care (Centro de Atención Múltiple–CAM). Children with special needs (3,061 students in the state) who cannot be integrated into regular classrooms can receive educational services from CAM (Patiño 2001: 13).

The focus on intercultural education has proven to be a challenge (Patiño 2001: 13). The goal of this initiative is to ensure respect for students from diverse backgrounds, respecting cultural differences and promoting and strengthening traditions and customs. A forum was organized for educators and community members alike to discuss these issues. One of the topics brought forth was bilingual education for the education of migrant children and the education of indigenous groups. There are five indigenous groups in the State of Baja California, including the Cucapá, Cochimí, Kiliwua, Kumeyaay, and Pai-Pai. Mexicali has also seen a small increase (0.1%) in the enrollment of students from these groups in preschool (Patiño 2001: 14). Services to children of migrant workers tend to feature a more flexible curriculum. In addition, an information database is being established so that children can be traced more easily throughout the various states where they attend school, primarily in the states of Sinaloa, Baja California Sur, and Oaxaca, resulting in fewer interruptions in the delivery of their educational services. A similar process is being established for children whose parents migrate between Mexico and the United States. Known as the Mexico-U.S. Binational Migrant Education Program (Programa Binacional de Educación Migrante México-Estados Unidos de América–PROBLEM), it ensures continuity in educational services for target students.

Parents are also beginning to play a larger role in the education of their children. Over five thousand parents throughout the state participated in a number of informational sessions that were offered and dealt with issues such as the role of parents, values, nutrition, hygiene, family violence, family, communication, self-esteem, prevention of sexual abuse, and socialization.

The professional development of teachers has become a consistent goal for the educational system. Teachers are offered numerous training sessions to keep them current on issues affecting the education of their students and to help them learn about various methods for implementing curriculum.

Finally, it is important to note that the initiatives mentioned here are supported by budgeting that keeps these activities focused on goals. Each year, the state accounts for all budget items and their purpose. For example, if the goal is to improve the infrastructure of schools in Mexicali, the report to the government on education (Patiño 2001: 37) will be very specific regarding improvements. In this past year, a total of 15 classrooms and some support facilities were built and a total of 4,339,667 pesos (slightly over $482,185 at the rate of nine pesos per one dollar) were spent on this project.

In a city as large as Mexicali, there are many programs and services available to students at all different levels. This information, while available through the Secretariat of Education, is not necessarily organized in a way that is easily accessible to the public. More research is needed to gain further insight into Mexicali's educational system and its interface with other states and agencies. There is value in conducting further research on the educational system in the greater Mexicali area because it could benefit other programs along the border and the communities at large.

Higher Education

One of the most important facets contributing to the success of society is the educational infrastructure present in the U.S.-Mexican border region to support growth and economic development. In response to an increasing demand for higher-level academic skills within the workforce, schools over the last few decades have begun to introduce and foster programs that promote quality education for all children. This is evidenced by an increase in graduation rates, literacy rates, and the number of candidates advancing to obtain postsecondary education. In the Imperial and Mexicali valleys, opportunities for higher education have been very limited in the past. While opportunities are increasing rapidly, there is still a great need for the expansion of programs to meet local needs.

With the region's demographic and economic growth, the need for higher education programs in the Imperial and Mexicali valleys became increasingly evident in the latter part of the twentieth century. Residents in these communities face the challenge of regional isolation. Prior to the establishment of local universities, residents from the Imperial Valley had to travel 120 miles to reach universities in San Diego or go further to find others. Students from Mexicali had to travel west to Tijuana (also 120 miles east) or to other cities in Mexico. Interviews with community members as part of a study on bilingual education during the fall semester of 1999 revealed that families in this region are traditionally very reluctant to allow children to go away to college. Additionally, many students in local universities admit to attending only because they can remain in the region and stay with their families. A group of high school graduates in the Teacher Education Division at San Diego State University's Imperial Valley Campus reported being nervous to live or work outside the valley in interviews conducted from 1996 to 2000. Many of them find that life beyond the borders of the desert can be quite different from their own cultural experiences as well as without the immediate support of their family. To regain this immediate support, they return to complete their education locally.

The first college in Imperial County was the Heber Collegiate Institute, which opened in December 1908 (Hendersen 1968: 157). It had three faculty members and a dormitory for students. The curriculum included studies in Latin, German, chemistry, Shakespeare, music, and biblical studies. After the death of one of its major contributors, Anthony Heber, the college closed its doors, but the building, while abandoned, still stands.

Imperial Valley Community College

The first higher education institution to flourish in the valleys was the Imperial Valley Community College. It was founded on May 9, 1922, when the Board of Trustees of the Central Union High School District in El Centro passed a resolution to establish this public college. It opened formally in September 1922 and was originally called the Central Junior College. Enrollment grew quickly until the onset of World War II. The decline at that point was sharp, but rebounded and began to increase enrollment once again in the 1950s. The college today serves over 11,000 students, 84 percent of whom identify themselves as Hispanic (Imperial Valley College 1998–1999). Over 63 percent of the student population is female. The largest enrollment of students (17.8%) who complete an associate degree is in the area of business. The breakdown for the others is indicated in Table 3. In addition to associate degrees, the community college also confers certificates in the areas identified in Table 4.

Table 3. Imperial Valley Community College, Associate Degrees Awarded by Area, 1998–1999

Major	Percent Enrolled	Major	Percent Enrolled
Business	17.8	Science/Math/ Engineering	5.9
Liberal Studies	17.3	Early Childhood Education	4.4
Behavioral Science	14.4	English	1.8
Administration of Justice	12.9	Humanities	1.8
Health Science	11.3	Other	5.4
Social Science	7.0		

SOURCE: Imperial Valley College (2001).

Table 4. Imperial Valley Community College,
Certificates Awarded by Area, 1998–1999

Certificate	Percent Enrolled
Health Science	39.8
Business	18.6
Library Technologies	14.2
Behavioral Science	8.8
Other	5.3

SOURCE: Imperial Valley College (2001).

San Diego State University (SDSU), Imperial Valley Campus, Calexico

San Diego State University was first established in eastern San Diego on Montezuma Mesa. It is the oldest and largest higher education institution in the San Diego region. From its foundation as a teacher-training program in 1897, it has grown to offer bachelor's degrees in 87 areas, master's degrees in 76 areas, and doctorates in 13. More than thirty thousand students participate in an academic curriculum distinguished by direct contact with professors.

In 1959, the state legislation approved the establishment of a campus that would serve all of the Imperial Valley. It was likewise an outgrowth for the need to prepare teachers to serve this area. Classes were first held during evening hours at Central High School in El Centro. Shortly thereafter, classes were moved temporarily to Imperial Valley College. When permanent quarters for Imperial Valley College were moved to Imperial, SDSU was notified of the need to find a new facility. At this time, an old high school building in Calexico was offered as the new home for SDSU's Imperial Valley Campus. The three buildings were in desperate need of repair, but the Calexico community, valuing the presence of a university in the city, rallied to raise funds to make improvements to the buildings. An initial investment of $32,366 prepared the premises for classes. The campus was officially dedicated on November 8, 1965 (Hendersen 1968: 160). An earthquake destroyed most of the buildings shortly thereafter and new ones were constructed on the same premises. Today, the campus consists of Mexican-style buildings that have been recently added or refurbished to incorporate current needs, including a library, computer laboratories, faculty offices, classrooms, a student union, and an administration building. The refurbishing continued during the 2001–2002 academic year with renovations being made to the auditorium. The Imperial Valley Campus is a two-year upper-division campus. It is located adjacent to Calexico's civic center and near the Mexican border, providing an opportunity for involvement in a bicultural environment. The campus currently has over eight hundred students who average 28 years of age. A total of 78 percent of the student population is Hispanic and 86 percent receive financial assistance. There are 11 majors offered and four different certificate programs, as shown in Table 5.

Enrollment at SDSU's Imperial Valley Campus continues to grow. To accommodate this growth, the campus needs to expand. Because the current campus is landlocked, the university is planning a new facility in the northern end of the Imperial Valley in the City of Brawley. A groundbreaking ceremony was held at the Brawley site on February 21, 2003. It is expected that more programs will also be available to students as growth continues. An agribusiness program is planned in the immediate future. All programs are accredited as an integral part of SDSU, which is part of the California State University system.

Other institutions in the Imperial Valley also have higher education programs. The University of California system, for example, offers extension programs and classes targeted to specific groups of students. Other institutions, mostly private, also offer services to the local community, mainly through extension courses or long-distance learning.

Higher education opportunities in the Mexicali Valley are much more diverse than in the Imperial Valley. Universities there have been well established far longer and the programs and degrees available to the population through both public and private institutions have a much broader range than those in the Imperial Valley.

Table 5. San Diego State Universitiy's Imperial Valley Campus: Majors, Certificates, and Master's Programs, 2000

Majors	Certificate Programs	Master's Programs
Business Administration	Business Administration	Educational Administration
Criminal Justice Administration	Court Interpreting	Curriculum and Instruction
English	Public Administration	Business Administration (International)
History	Translation Studies	Public Administration
International Business		
Latin American Studies		
Liberal Studies		
Psychology		
Public Administration		
Social Science		
Spanish		

SOURCE: San Diego State University (2001).

Autonomous University of Baja California, Mexicali Campus

The Universidad Autónoma de Baja California (UABC) was founded in the State of Baja California in 1957 and has been growing at a fast pace. In 1961 and 1962, the university included the schools of Economics and Business Administration. Since that time, a number of other schools have been added and have progressed through a series of changes leaving them as they are seen now in Table 6. As shown in the table, UABC divides its programs into three sections: *escuelas* (schools) that only provide undergraduate degrees and *facultades* (colleges) and *institutos* (institutes), which both provide undergraduate as well as graduate studies. While both the *facultades* and *institutos* award degrees, the *institutos* are characterized by conducting more research as opposed to providing courses. More programs are also available on other campuses of the UABC.

During the last two reporting periods of enrollment (1999–2002), UABC has seen an overall increase of 429 students (from 23,294 to 23,723). The breakdown of

Table 6. Autonomous University of Baja California Programs

Schools	Colleges	Institutes
Nursing	Architecture	Agricultural Sciences
Languages	Human Sciences	Veterinary Sciences
Education	Social Sciences and Politics*	Engineering
	Law	Social Research
	Engineering	Geography and History
	Medicine	
	Orthodontistry	
	Accounting and Administration*	

*The Business Administration major is found in the Accounting and Administration College and the Public Administration major is found in the Social Sciences and Politics College.

SOURCE: Imperial Valley College (2001).

Table 7. UABC Enrollments by Region and Program Type

Region	Technical		Undergraduate		Postgraduate		Institutional Total	
	99–02	00–02	99–02	00–02	99–02	00–02	99–02	00–02
Ensenada	0	0	2,705	2,797	99	143	2,804	2,940
Mexicali	192	147	11,133	11,393	305	259	11,630	11,799
Tecate	0	0	193	217	0	0	193	217
Tijuana	0	0	8,527	8,616	140	151	8,667	8,767
Total	192	147	22,558	23,023	544	553	23,294	23,723

SOURCE: UABC (2001).

Table 8. UABC, Mexicali Campus, Undergraduate Programs and Reporting Periods

Program	Reporting Periods	
	1999-2002	2000-2002
School of Social Sciences and Politics		
Public Administration and Political Science	444	378
International Relations	264	288
School of Accounting and Administration		
Public Accountancy	1035	857
Business Administration	809	841
Informational Systems	372	364
International Business	240	333
School of Languages		
English	82	92
Translation (English)	74	84
College of Engineering		
Electrical Engineering	147	147
Computation	615	634
Electronics	594	638
Mechanical Engineering	351	392
Topography	0	0
Computer Systems	498	595
Industrial Engineering	673	853
School of Pedagogy		
Educational Psychology	0	0
School of Nursing		
Nursing	170	179
College of Architecture		
Architecture	497	499
College of Human Sciences		
Communications	546	500
Educational Sciences	316	324
Psychology	496	488
Sociology	35	24
College of Law		
Law	1,265	1,196
College of Medicine		
Medical Doctor and Midwifery	648	654
College of Odontology		
Dentistry	430	451
Institute of Agricultural Sciences		
Engineer of Agronomy	115	113
Engineer of Zoology	17	32
Institute of Research and Veterinary Sciences		
Veterinarian	157	200
Total for Mexicali Campus	11,133	11,393

SOURCE: UABC (2001).

enrollments is featured both regionally and by program type in Table 7. It is important to note that almost half of all students (49.7%) are enrolled at the Mexicali campus, while 36.9 percent are enrolled at the Tijuana campus.

At the undergraduate level, there are a total of 62 programs, of which 11 are offered in Ensenada, 28 in Mexicali, three in Tecate, and 20 in Tijuana. Distribution by undergraduate area is provided in Table 8. In addition, UABC has an enrollment of 259 students in postgraduate programs and 147 in technical programs on the Mexicali campus.

The UABC has a solid background and is recognized nationally as one of the best universities in Mexico. More recent additions in higher education consist of the University Center of Tijuana (Centro Universitario de Tijuana), the Baja California Technological Institute (Instituto Tecnológico de Baja California), and Xochicalco University (Universidad Xochicalco).

The Center for Technical and Higher Education, Mexicali

The Centro de Enseñanza Técnica y Superior (CETYS) was founded in 1961 in the City of Mexicali. This private university has campuses in Mexicali, Tijuana, and Ensenada. CETYS started in a private home with 52 students. At the time of writing this essay, it had a combined enrollment of over 3,500 students. The Mexican Secretariat of Education recognizes CETYS as one of only six centers of excellence among Mexican private universities. In Mexicali, it had an enrollment over 1,700 students, offering a bachelor's degree and a bilingual bachelor's degree. Programs include administration and business with specialties in international accounting, administration, graphic design, international business, and business administration, as well as postgraduate programs. In addition, it offers programs in the social sciences, humanities, and engineering.

CETYS has agreements with various academic institutions, including the University of Calgary (Canada); the Technical University of Nova Scotia (Canada); California State Polytechnic University, Pomona; Arizona State University; San Diego State University; National University, San Diego; University of Arizona; the Autonomous University of Baja California; Sweetwater Union High School District; Diego Portales University (Chile); and Harlem Business School (Holland).

In addition to these universities, there are other entities that provide higher education services to Mexicali residents. Some have technical or professional career programs that do not necessarily lead to degrees. The Technological Institute of Mexicali (Instituto Tecnológico de Mexicali) is one of these institutions. With an enrollment of 5,000, it offers seven specialties in business and engineering. The Training Center for Industrial Work (Centro de Capacitación para el Trabajo Industrial–CECATI) is another. It has three schools with careers in English, mechanics, electronics, textiles, wood, industrial drawing, machinery, and tools and enrolls 3,000 students. The CONALEP has two schools with technical careers and enrolls 1,800 students (Collins and Harmon, 2000). Finally, the College of the Northern Border (El Colegio de la Frontera Norte—COLEF) has a branch research center in Mexicali. There, it has a small, locally based research team that conducts projects pertinent to the Mexicali border region.

The Two Systems Interface

Having participated in a K–12 curriculum task force on Mexico, Elsie Beglar writes that:

> Today, the linkages between the United States and Mexico are greater than ever. People of Mexican descent represent the fastest growing ethnic group in the United States. Issues such as Mexico's foreign debt, the development of a North American Free Trade Zone, 'off-shore' industries, foreign policy, immigration, drugs, cross-border pollution and usage rights to water and maritime resources are bilateral problems that can only be resolved in an atmosphere of mutual understanding and respect for other's history, culture, problems, strengths and perspectives. Indeed, the increasingly multiethnic nature of our own society mandates that our citizens be knowledgeable regarding Mexican culture and society. (2000)

This is not always considered an important part of the U.S. educational system. Even in California, where so many children attending K–12 schools have roots in Mexico, the curriculum rarely addresses the contributions of Mexico or by Mexicans in the region. A much greater curricular focus today is placed on the "basics," usually considered to be reading and mathematics.

There is increasingly more interaction between the two educational systems along the border. It is a natural outcome from the efforts to improve services to communities that share many of the same traits. CETYS, for example, has a tradition of involvement in U.S.-Mexican border environmental issues dealing with air, solid/hazardous waste, pollution prevention, and legislation/policy/regulations, as well as keeping pertinent socioeconomic data. Some current border environmental projects and activities include:

- Classification of wastewater and solids for Colorado River Irrigation District #14

- Assessment of certification, training, and technical assistance needs for water operations personnel in the State of Baja California—joint project with the Mexico-U.S. Foundation for Science (Fundación México-Estados Unidos para la Ciencia–FUMEC)

- Development of a training center for water and sanitation operations personnel in Baja California—joint project with FUMEC

- Development of a system to provide certification, training, and technical assistance to water and sanitation operators in Baja California

Agreements between San Diego State University's Imperial Valley Campus and CETYS include exchange programs for students interested primarily in the area of business, although students are permitted to take courses in other disciplines. This agreement launched student exchanges in the spring of 1999. Since that time, 39 students from CETYS have attended classes at the IVC and 54 IVC students have gone to CETYS. The same type of agreement is in place between SDSU-IVC and UABC. This agreement began in the fall of 1999 and since then 82 students have gone to SDSU while 46 have attended UABC. The IVC also has a joint agreement with the UABC Press. Under this agreement, the Binational Press/Editorial Binacional was founded in 1987 to copublish works that deal with issues related to the university and the joint communities.

In the field of education, exchanges sometimes result in permanent changes in residence for those involved. For example, there are cases of professionals from Mexicali who were lawyers, doctors, chemists, or architects who have crossed the border to the Imperial Valley to change careers and become teachers. Their presence is welcome as there is often a shortage of teachers, especially in the areas of math and science. With some training in pedagogy, professionals can adapt to their new careers. Since many students in K–12 schools are also first-generation immigrants from Mexicali, they benefit from having teachers who are very familiar with their background, their language, and their methods of learning. These professionals still need to meet all requirements set forth by the California Commission on Teacher Credentialing and, often, they meet those requirements by enrolling in programs in the Imperial Valley. Some start with classes designed to improve their English and those already proficient in English participate in teacher preparation courses that lead to teaching credentials. Both the Imperial Valley College and SDSU-IVC play an important role in preparing them to reach their goals.

One important event that links the educational issues pertinent to each side of the border is the Annual Binational Educators Conference at SDSU-IVC. Educators from both valleys come together annually to explore successes, trends, and challenges faced by educators and to learn from one another. It attracts over five hundred participants and offers a wide range of opportunities in a variety of workshop sessions.

Another important service offered by the university system is the training of personnel in the *maquiladora* industry. Sessions are usually tailor-made for the group being served whether it is training in leadership for middle management, public relations, communications, or issues of culture intended to ease the transition of a workforce faced with employer demands different from those they know. Some of these sessions have been offered in Spanish by faculty from SDSU and some have been offered in English, depending on the wishes of the company requesting the service.

An agreement was also forged in 1999 that may have long-term implications for higher education services on the border (McKernan 1999). Two consortia from each side of the U.S.-Mexican border worked on an official agreement to create the Virtual Learning Space, a high-speed computer network linking U.S. and Mexican researchers in diverse fields, including electronics, computer science, management, environmental sciences, biology, telecommunications, and telemedicine. Mexican institutions involved included the Center for Scientific Research and Higher Education (Centro de Investigación Científica y de Educación Superior–CICESE), a government research institution and graduate education center in the areas of oceanography, earth sciences, and applied physics; the Center for Digital Technology Research and Development (Centro de Investigación y Desarrollo de Tecnología Digital–CITEDI); the Autonomous University of Baja California; and Telnor, a regional subsidiary of the Mexican telephone company (Telefonos de México, S.A.–TELMEX).

One of the most promising organizations to be established in the area is the California Center for Border and Regional Economic Studies (CCBRES). Housed at SDSU-IVC, its mission is to inform public and private decision makers of demographic, economic, and social trends in Imperial County and the western border region. Serving as disseminators of information and statistics, the center provides a service that links higher education with the border community. By making these linkages, many facets of each community can be influenced in their decision making because they can base them on statistics dealing with employment rates, housing trends, and businesses established. Educational services, for example, can take this information and respond accordingly by creating programs that will address needs that arise and are documented by the center.

While regional economics, to some extent, drive the interfacing of the two systems, the region's political climate also encourages collaboration and cooperation. There are many regional events that are cosponsored by both communities and the mayors of the sister cities appear together often to address issues pertinent to both. Such events might occur in Mexicali and at times in Calexico.

Challenges

Other scholars have already documented some of the challenges facing educators on each side of the border. Writing about the results of NAFTA on education, Guillermo de los Reyes said that:

... [NAFTA] has made Mexican academics mindful of the fact that U.S. universities in the new economic climate should be regarded as more than teaching institutions— they are a global economic resource that has and will have a profound influence on people who will never visit their campuses. The question of how Mexican researchers and academics are going to come to terms with the situation becomes pressing as NAFTA lowers the protective barriers. The illusion of being an equal partner or of being able to compete in many sectors is dangerous, particularly in the university sector." (1997: 1)

De los Reyes is especially concerned about the rate of pay and level of work when professors from each country compare notes. In the United States, he claims that the average yearly salary for full professors is $86,000, while in Mexico that figure is much lower and the work load tends to be higher in terms of the number of courses taught.

Another challenge educators face is the reality of keeping up with today's technological advances. More and more information is becoming available through distance learning and the impact that this will have on the way students are educated is far from known at this time.

References

Begler, E. 2000. "Key Understandings and Instructional Guidelines for Teaching and Learning About Mexico: Task Force on Mexico in the K–12 Curriculum." http://www-rohan.sdsu.edu/dept/istep/key_understanding.htm.

California Department of Education. 2000. *California Basic Educational Data System, CBEDS, (1997–1999)*. Sacramento: California Department of Education.

California Employment Development Department (CEDD). 1998. *Labor Force Data for Sub-County Areas in California. Local Area Unemployment Statistics*. Sacramento: The Labor Market, Information Division, California Employment Department.

California Employment Development Department (CEDD). 2000. *Annual Average Industry Employment*. Sacramento: The Labor Market: Information Division, California Employment Department.

Collins, K., and R. Harmon. 2000. *The Imperial County and Mexicali Municipio: A Region of Binational Resources*. Calexico: California Center for Border and Regional Economic Studies (CCBRES).

Consulmex of Calexico. 2001. *Information about Schools and Higher Education Institutions in Baja California Norte*. Calexico: In-house Publication.

de los Reyes, Guillermo. 1997. "Higher Education in Mexico." *Annals of the American Academy of Political and Social Science* 550: 96–105.

Education Data Partnership. 2001. "Fiscal, Demographic, and Performance Data on California's K–12 Schools." http://www.ed-data.k12.ca.us.

Encarta Encyclopedia Deluxe. 2000. Microsoft Publishing. http://www.encarta.msn.com/.

EX-XXI Business Center. 2001. http://www.ex21.com.mx.

Hendersen, T. 1968. *Imperial Valley*. San Diego: Neyenesch Printers, Inc.

Imperial Valley College. n.d. *Imperial Valley College, Fact Book. 1998–1999.* Imperial: Imperial Valley College.

Imperial Valley College. 2001. http://www.imperial.cc.ca.us.

Imperial Valley Press. 1999. "Unemployment Figures Released." (10 October): 3.

Instituto Nacional de Estadística, Geografía e Informática (INEGI). 2000. http://www.inegi.gob.mx/.

McKernan, T. 1999. *Marketing and Communications.* San Diego: San Diego State University.

Myers, R. 2000. "Pre-School Education in Mexico: A Social Policy Analysis." http://www/ecdgroup.com/archive/premex.html.

National Research Council. 1996. *National Science Education Standards.* Washington, D.C.: National Academy Press.

Nuffer, D. n.d. *History of Imperial Valley.* Imperial: Imperial Valley Historical Society.

Patiño, N. 2001. *Informe de gobierno, capítulo de educación.* México, D.F.: Secretaría de Educación.

San Diego State University (SDSU). 2001. http://www.ivcampus.sdsu.edu.

Taylor, Lawrence D. 1998. "The Magonista Revolt in Baja California: Capitalist Conspiracy or Rebellion de los Pobres?" *The Journal of San Diego History* 45 (1).

Tout, O.B. 1931. *The First Thirty Years: 1901–1931.* San Diego: Arts and Crafts Press.

Universidad Autónoma de Baja California (UABC). 2001. http://www.uabc.mx/index.php3

U.S. Census Bureau. 1999. *Small Area Income and Poverty Estimates Program.* Washington, D.C.: [Housing] U.S. Census Bureau, Housing and Household Economic Statistics Division, Small Area Estimates Branch.

U.S. Department of State. 2001. "Background Notes: Mexico." http://www.state.gov/www/background_notes/mexico_0101_bgn.html.

Vivanco, A. 1924. *Lower California Up to Date: Mexico and U.S.* Imperial: Pioneers Museum.

25

Housing Trends in the Imperial Valley

G. Jean Laurin*

Abstract

Housing needs in the Imperial Valley can be defined by social issues, affordability, and supply and demand. Major problems associated with housing in the valley are due to an accelerated population growth rate, a sluggish housing construction rate, a lack of housing targeted for middle income families, a large percentage of overcrowded living conditions, and a significant amount of dilapidated housing characterized as unfit for human habitation. In this analysis, some solutions are offered to improve the current situation as well as encourage better housing standards and a healthier environment for those considering to live in Imperial County.

Introduction

Over the last 20 years, social issues and affordability have dominated the housing market, while supply and demand have played only a minor role. During the early 1980s, the primary concern of local government in the Imperial Valley was affordable housing for agricultural and minimum wage workers. This concern coincided with the last great era of government housing subsidies. During this period, if someone wanted to build apartments, Imperial County was the place to do it (Laurin Associates, Inc. 2000). Between 1978 and 1989, there were 1,266 apartment units built in 10 communities (Laurin Associates, Inc. 1997).

*Laurin is Founder and Principal of Laurin Associates, Inc., a housing and demographic data research firm.

With the demise of subsidized housing programs in the late 1980s, developers became creative and began to access the Low-Income Housing Tax Credit Program. This program does not provide direct subsidies to the developer or the resident, but provides a tax credit for units that are affordable to low- and very low-income persons. In 1990, there were 168 low-income senior citizen housing units and 1,098 low-income family housing units for a total of 1,266 low-income units in the Imperial Valley. Between 1990 and the end of 1999, another 477 low-income housing units were added to the housing stock. By January 2000, there were 1,743 low-income apartment units in the county (Laurin Associates, Inc. 2000). This, however, only represented 4 percent of the housing stock and, according to current State Department of Finance figures, 49.1 percent of all households in the county are classified as very low- and low-income by U.S. Department of Housing and Urban Development (HUD) standards.

As defined by government housing experts, housing is affordable when a household spends 30 percent or less of its income on shelter and primary utilities (HUD 2000). This formula holds true for all government programs, but is altered for home ownership programs where shelter costs can exceed 35 percent of household income. In 1980, the median household income in Imperial County was $16,658 (U.S. Bureau of the Census 1980) and the median monthly housing affordability amount was $416. It should be noted that these are median amounts; 50 percent of the households earn less and can only afford less. The median-priced home cost $67,000 (U.S. Bureau of the Census 1990) and interest rates were about 10 percent, making households that earned the median income unable to have homeownership. In 1990 (U.S. Bureau of Census 1990), the median income was estimated at $22,442 and the monthly affordability level was $561. With lower mortgage rates and increased availability of homes, many families were able to purchase homes. The estimated median income in Imperial County is $32,600 (Datum Populus 2000), the median monthly affordability amount is $815, and new homes are priced in the $125,000 to $175,000 price range (Smith-Carter Real Estate 2000). With interest rates in the range of 8.5 percent, a family would require an annual income of $34,500 to afford the least expensive median-priced home, if any were available.

The cost of housing varies widely across the valley. It is least expensive in the more isolated communities, such as Westmorland and Heber; a little more expensive in communities along the major access routes, such as around the Salton Sea, Brawley, and Seeley; and most expensive in the county's urban centers of El Centro, Calexico, and Imperial. The prices of single-family homes in the three urban centers are, to some extent, manipulated by government housing programs, most notably the First-Time Homebuyer Down Payment Assistance Program.[1] These programs set a maximum price that they may help finance. Currently, that amount is $115,200 and virtually no homes are sold for less unless they are extremely small, very poorly located, or in substandard condition.

Table 1. Affordable Housing Unit Construction Trends, 1990–2000

Community/City	Senior Citizen Housing		Family Housing		Total
	1990	2000	1990	2000	
Brawley	20	0	395	64	479
Calexico	46	181	252	79	558
Calipatria	0	0	32	62	94
El Centro	62	0	148	8	218
Heber	0	0	48	0	48
Holtville	0	35	79	0	114
Imperial	40	0	0	0	40
Niland	0	0	38	0	38
Seeley	0	0	38	48	86
Westmorland	0	0	68	0	68
Total	168	216	1,098	261	1,743

SOURCE: Laurin Associates, Inc. (2000).

It is at this juncture that supply and demand will become the driving force in Imperial County's need for housing. The entire valley is on the cusp of a development boom. The *maquiladora* industry just across the border from Calexico remains strong. The port of entry to the east of Calexico will not only ease the border-crossing load at Calexico and San Diego, but it will also increase cross-border traffic. The widening of existing state and local routes and the construction of the newer Route 86 will facilitate truck traffic and transportation from Interstate 8 to the south to Interstate 10 to the north. The buildout of developable lands in San Diego, Riverside, and even Los Angeles counties make the vast vacant lands of the Imperial Valley very attractive. Even the "graying of America" and the need for retirement centers will have a direct impact on the housing need for both permanent and vacationing residents.

Population

A brief look at the population growth and housing construction trends indicates that for the benchmark years of 1980 and 1990, the rate of new housing growth exceeded the population growth rate by a few percentage points. However, for 1985, 1995, and 2000, the population rate far exceeded the residential growth rate (State Department of Finance 1985, 1995, 2000). Between 1990 and 1995, a period of rapid population growth was fueled by the opening of two Department of Corrections facilities and the county's population increased by almost 28 percent (State Department of Finance 1990, 1995), while housing increased by only 11 percent. This period was also a time of volatility in the dollar value of the Mexican peso, which produced a flow of Mexican residents to search for housing in Imperial County. Over the last five years,

Table 2. Imperial County Population Trends, 1980–2005

Year	Number	Change	% Change	Annual % Change
1980	92,135			
1990	109,328	17,192	18.7	1.9
2000	150,066	40,738	37.3	3.7
2005	168,206	18,140	12.1	2.4

SOURCES: U.S. Bureau of the Census (1980, 1990); Datum Populus (2000); AnySite (2000).

population has continued to increase at almost 2 percent per year, while housing has grown by only 1 percent and none of the external impacts have abated.

Housing Construction

Housing shortages always result in higher prices. During the 1980s, housing construction occurred in most of the cities and communities in Imperial County. From 1990 to 2000, almost all population growth in the county took place in Calexico (up 38%), El Centro (up 18%), and Imperial (up 67%) (State Department of Finance 1990, 2000). At the same time, housing units increased by 41 percent in Calexico, 16 percent in El Centro, and 46 percent in Imperial—a shortage of 20 percent in just those three cities. According to the State Department of Finance's Population Research Unit (1990, 2000), over the last 10 years countywide population has increased by 21.5 percent, while housing units increased by 17.2 percent—a difference of 5 percent.

Population and housing growth rates are indications that most people recognize. However, the real determinant of housing need is the household formation rate.

Table 3. Housing Unit Trends, 1985–2000

City	1985	1990	1995	2000	Change 1990–2000	
					Number	Percent
Brawley	5,643	6,434	6,716	6,900	466	7.2
Calexico	4,224	4,799	5,983	6,784	1,985	41.4
Calipatria	783	853	906	931	78	9.1
El Centro	9,003	10,221	11,580	11,889	1,668	16.3
Holtville	1,450	1,494	1,617	1,630	136	9.1
Imperial	1,183	1,415	2,081	2,066	651	46.0
Westmorland	562	608	478	540	-68	-11.2
Unincorporated	10,994	11,533	11,914	13,206	1,673	14.5
County Total	33,842	37,357	41,275	43,946	6,589	17.6

SOURCES: Datum Populus (2000); State Department of Finance (2000).

Households can form even during periods of static population growth as people divorce, young people leave home, and other similar social actions take place. Household size constricts and expands as housing availability changes. For example, when demand exceeds supply, household size increases. This is a strong indication of overcrowding.[2] Likewise, when the housing supply increases, household size declines. Imperial County has the largest household size of any county in California. Some of this can be explained by the large number of Hispanic families that, by tradition, often live in multigenerational households. Within Imperial County, the City of Calexico has the largest household size, with 4.056 persons per household, and Imperial has the smallest, with 3.220 persons per household. The median household size for the entire county has not changed significantly over the last 15 years, increasing from 3.406 persons per household in 1985 to an estimated 3.417 in 2000.

It is estimated that between 1990 and 2000, the number of overcrowded households in Imperial County increased from 6,596 to 8,907, representing 20.5 percent of all households in the county. The actual number is virtually impossible to determine since multiple households and multi-generational families are the norm and are often considered as one reporting unit when residents respond to census and other survey questions.

Overcrowding increases housing demand significantly; every time a new affordable complex opens there are three-to-four times more applicants than the number of units available. However, since the strongest demand for rental housing has been for very low- and low-income affordable units, few new units are built because these are not economically viable without governmental assistance. The most successful local housing finance programs are through the Redevelopment Agency's Affordable Housing Set-Aside Fund.[3] Only the cities of Calexico and El Centro have redevelopment agencies that are successful enough to generate significant funds to assist in housing development. The other cities either do not have an operating redevelopment agency or the agency is underfunded.

Table 4. Persons per Household, Imperial County

Household Size	1990		2000		Change 1990–2000	
	Number	Percent	Number	Percent	Number	Percent
1 Person	5,783	17.6	8,473	19.5	2,690	25.4
2 Persons	8,017	24.4	10,819	24.9	2,802	26.5
3 Persons	5,454	16.6	7,082	16.3	1,628	15.4
4 Persons	5,717	17.4	7,604	17.5	1,887	17.8
5+ Persons	7,886	24.0	9,472	21.8	1,586	15.0
Total	32,857	100.0	43,450	100.0	10,593	100.10
Average Household Size	3.33 persons		3.38 persons		0.05% increase	

SOURCES: U.S. Bureau of the Census (1990); Datum Populus (2000); AnySite (2000).

Chronic overcrowding is a problem that cannot be solved without a three-pronged attack that incorporates: (1) a regional approach to affordable housing needs and issues that will transcend local administrative boundaries; (2) a dedicated commitment on the part of government agencies to finding (and allocating) the funds necessary for the construction and maintenance of affordable housing; and (3) strong building standards and codes coupled with an aggressive code enforcement program that will target slumlords, absentee landlords, and other owners of substandard units. This last action will require an intense public education program, the dedication of sufficient funds to a rehabilitation and renovation program to actually make a difference, and a political climate able to withstand special interest and public pressure.

Housing Conditions

Another significant housing problem in the Imperial Valley is the number of substandard housing units, including both conventional and mobile homes. Approximately one-fourth of all housing units in Imperial County are more than fifty years old (built prior to 1949), totaling just over nine thousand units. An additional 6,500 units are now over forty years old.

Since 1994, Laurin Associates has conducted housing condition surveys in the cities of El Centro, Calexico, and Brawley, as well as in the unincorporated Imperial County areas. The surveys used criteria established by the State of California Housing and Community Development Department (HCD). Each unit was analyzed to determine the condition of its foundation, roof, siding, windows, and doors. Surveyors also noted such items as availability of curb, gutter, sidewalk, and other infrastructure details. Not surprisingly, the unincorporated county area had the highest level of dilapidated units (when cost of repairs would be greater than replacement costs), with just over 12 percent (1,585 units) classified as unfit for human habitation; about 31 percent of these are trailers, mobile homes, or nonresidential[4] structures. The City of Brawley had the second highest level of dilapidated units (9%/604 units), followed by the City of Calexico (8.6%/515 units), and the City of El Centro (4.1%/475 units). As such, an average of 8.4 percent of units in those four cities are

Table 5. Housing Conditions

Community	Dilapidated Units (%)	Substantial Repair Needed (%)	Moderate Repair Needed (%)	Minor Repair Needed (%)	Sound Units (%)
Unincorporated County 1997	12.0	11.0	18.0	14.0	45.0
El Centro 1994	4.1	4.1	9.4	25.9	56.5
Calexico 1996	8.6	12.2	13.9	12.2	53.1
Brawley 1994	9.0	4.6	8.6	20.7	57.1

SOURCE: Laurin Associates, Inc. (1994, 1996, 1997).

dilapidated. If that percentile was then applied to the housing counts of incorporated areas where empirical housing condition data are not available (the cities of Calipatria, Holtville, Imperial, and Westmorland), it is estimated that there would be an additional 427 dilapidated units in the county. This means that countywide, the dilapidated housing count could be as high as 3,606 units. Most of these will never be replaced; as families move to more suitable housing units, another household moves in to take their place.

While little empirical data exist to support the hypothesis that the housing shortage transcends income levels, there is growing anecdotal information from real estate agents and brokers that suggests there is virtually no housing available for the median—or middle-income—wage earner. New single-family and multifamily development is directed toward the working poor and generally priced to be eligible for buyers under government-sponsored first-time homebuyer programs. Additional housing has been constructed for the above-moderate incomes and sales prices range up to $300,000.

Few, if any, new homes have been directed to the middle-income household that is looking for three-bedroom units in the $130,000 to $185,000 price range. The shortage is particularly apparent for rental housing. There are no luxury or executive style apartment complexes targeted for that income group. Rentals are limited to a few isolated condominium or triplex units. The housing shortage is so acute that there are virtually no single-family homes for rent to the general public. Family members rent to family members, friends to friends. The few professionally managed units are occupied by long-term tenants or are not acceptable to many house hunters due to location or condition.

How significant is the housing shortage? Two simple figures provide a definitive answer: (1) as seen in Table 6 the State Department of Finance (2000) estimates that Imperial Valley households will increase by about one thousand per year from now through 2005; and (2) historically, as seen in Table 3, only 659 new housing units are constructed each year (based on the total of 6,589 new housing units constructed in the county from 1990 to 2000). At the construction rate referenced, there is not

Table 6. Household Growth Trends, Imperial County, 1980–2005

Year	Number	Change	% Change	Simple Annual % Change
1980	28,168			
1990	32,857	4,689	16.60	1.70
2000	43,450	10,593	32.20	3.20
2005	48,848	5,398	12.40	2.50

SOURCE: Laurin Associates, Inc. (1994, 1996, 1997).

sufficient new housing being constructed for new households and there is no adjustment for replacement of dilapidated units or mitigation of overcrowding.

Is there a solution? Yes, but only partially. When asked to respond to the strategic vision for the Imperial Valley, the author identified the most important factor as the formation of a strong regional governmental agency with a staff and decision-making authority that can transcend incorporated city boundaries. These single issues will become more critical as federal granting agencies turn more and more to the block granting of resources on a statewide and regional basis. The attempt to reduce the population requirement from 50,000 to 25,000 for "entitlement" cities[5] has already been aborted. It is anticipated that this thrust will continue as HUD streamlines its housing programs and looks for more efficient ways to manage appropriations. A local regional government agency could have broad community and economic development powers, including the ability to apply for and receive grant funds from all public and private sources.

If the 2020 projections for population growth are met, the region could have an additional 100,000 persons living in the Imperial Valley by that year. This new growth will be generated from increased transborder commerce fueled by new border crossings, support industries, increased transportation corridors, and the internationalization of large retailers.

A secondary demand for housing will come from the development of retirement and recreational facilities. As the population continues to age and existing retirement communities either reach buildout or increase in cost, or both, developers are looking for a place in the Sunbelt that will accommodate resort living centers. The Interstate 8 corridor provides such an area, offering good transportation, proximity to metropolitan areas, inexpensive land, and year-round sun.

Endnotes

1. The City of Imperial participates in the state-sponsored HOME program. The cities of Calexico and El Centro use Redevelopment Agency and HOME funds for their first-time homebuyer programs.

2. "Overcrowding" is defined as a unit having more than one person per room in residency.

3. As required by redevelopment agency law, 20 percent of the tax increment received by the agency shall be placed in an Affordable Housing Set-Aside Fund and used to support affordable housing.

4. A "nonresidential" structure includes such buildings as garages, outbuildings, animal corrals, travel trailers, automobiles, abandoned commercial and industrial structures, and so on.

5. An entitlement city obtains HUD and other federal funds directly from Washington, D.C., and does not have to apply and be funded through small city programs operated by the state. Since there is only a finite amount of money, the allocation given to the state is reduced by the entitlements, thus reducing the amount of money available for county programs. As a result, there was strong opposition from the National Association of Counties to the reduction in population as a benchmark for funding.

References

AnySite. 2000. (July). http://www.anysiteonline.com.

Datum Populus. 2000. (July). http://www.DatumPopulus.com.

Laurin Associates, Inc. 1997. *Imperial County Housing Condition Survey and Needs Assessment, 1997*. Sacramento: Laurin Associates, Inc.

Laurin Associates, Inc. 2000. *The Affordable Housing Catalog*. Sacramento: Laurin Associates, Inc.

Smith-Carter Real Estate. 2000. *Imperial County Multiple Listing Service*. El Centro: Smith-Carter Real Estate.

State Department of Finance. 1985. *Population Research Unit Summary Report*. Sacramento: State Department of Finance.

State Department of Finance. 1990. *Population Research Unit Summary Report*. Sacramento: State Department of Finance.

State Department of Finance. 1995. *Population Research Unit Summary Report*. Sacramento: State Department of Finance.

State Department of Finance. 2000. *Population Research Unit Summary Report*. Sacramento: State Department of Finance.

U.S. Bureau of the Census. 1980. *Summary Tape File 3*. [CD-Rom database]. Washington, D.C.

U.S. Bureau of the Census. 1990. *Summary Tape File 3*. [CD-Rom database]. Washington, D.C.

U.S. Department of Housing and Urban Development (HUD). 2000. "Affordable Housing."Community Planning and Development (July). http://www.hud.gov/offices/cpd/affordablehousing/index.cfm.

26

Housing in Mexicali:
An Intraurban Geographic Analysis

Guillermo B. Álvarez de la Torre and
Martha Cristina Dorantes G.*

Abstract

Determining a city's urban structure requires a great deal of social, physical, and economic information, as well as the incorporation of a series of fundamental theories that allow its internal function to be understood. The objective of this essay is to contribute to the knowledge of the internal structure of the City of Mexicali with an analysis of the different housing types according to their quality, ownership status, and geographic location. Thematic maps are used to conclude that there is a higher percentage of rented homes in older sectors of the city than in newer areas, where more people own their homes. They also reveal a pattern in housing quality throughout the different sectors of the city that is unrelated to Mexicali's urban growth pattern.

Introduction

The study of the internal urban structure of cities requires theoretical and methodological antecedents sufficiently sustained and supported in order to obtain a legible and effective picture of how cities function. This, of course, assumes that sufficient information is available to conduct studies on differing levels of specificity, precision, and scale (Bourne 1982). As such, it is important to note that this essay only

*Álvarez de la Torre is Researcher at the Institute for Social Research of the Autonomous University of Baja California, Mexicali, and Dorantes is Master's candidate in Social Sciences at the Autonomous University of Baja California.

attempts to provide additional understanding of the characteristics of the City of Mexicali's urban structure through the spatial distribution of housing by quality. A background on the characteristics of urban growth in Mexicali is provided, as well as on some general housing issues in the region. The thematic map of rental housing shows the center-periphery relationship in the city, revealing the frequency of rented homes by basic geostatistic area (área geoestadística básica–AGEB). Finally, an indicator is proposed that allows for housing quality to be determined and intraurban behaviors to be analyzed. This allows for the determination of low quality housing zones on the periphery and in the center of the city. The map also highlights three AGEBs of high quality housing that (in at least two of the cases) stem from private and public housing initiatives and exemplify the relationship of location to low land prices.

Urban Growth in Mexicali

During the second half of the twentieth century, the northern Mexican border cities were characterized by high demographic growth compared to other regions of Mexico (Tamayo and Fernández 1983; Unikel, Ruiz Chiapetto, and Garza Villarreal 1978). The City of Mexicali showed the highest population growth rates of all border cities in the 1950s (see Table 1).

Beginning in the 1960s, Mexicali experienced a decline in its urban growth rates that ended in the 1980s. Large migrant flows that originated in southern Mexico and were destined for northern Mexico were not as significant as during the first half of the century. The natural population growth rate also diminished, partly as a result of national family-planning programs. Despite the diminishing growth rate, border cities continued to expand in absolute terms.

Table 1. Population Growth by Decade, 1940–1990

City, State	1940–1950	1950–1960	1960–1970	1970–1980	1980–1990
Ciudad Juárez, Chihuahua	8.6	7.3	4.5	2.7	3.7
Matamoros, Tamaulipas	9.8	6.7	4.1	2.9	3.4
Mexicali, Baja California	11.1	9.3	4.2	2.1	2.5
Nuevo Laredo, Tamaulipas	6.7	4.7	4.9	2.8	0.8
Reynosa, Tamaulipas	11.3	7.4	6.2	3.2	3.1
Tijuana, Baja California	11.4	8.7	7.6	2.3	4.8

SOURCES: Dirección General de Estadística (1940, 1950, 1960, 1970); Secretaría de Programación and INEGI (1980); INEGI (1990).

Regardless of the decline in the population growth rate, border cities have continued to grow in size. Figure 1 shows that the density of border cities (the number of inhabitants per hectare) rose from 1940 to 1970. Density ranged from 12 to 60 inhabitants per hectare in 1940 and grew to 50 to 90 in 1970. This indicates that during this period, population grew much more rapidly than the urban area expanded in these cities. Nonetheless, over the next 20 years (1970–1990), a new phenomenon occurred in which the urbanized area demonstrated more dynamic growth. Density rates in border cities were quite similar in 1990 (30–40 inhabitants per hectare). This pattern of behavior toward homogeneous densities in border cities is also noted in medium-sized Mexican cities, revealing one of the most important characteristics in their profiles today.

In this context, the City of Mexicali experienced a significant increase in urban territory due to the demand for urban land to satisfy the needs of the growing population and relieve the demands created by new economic activities that had been established in the city. In 1970, Mexicali averaged 67 inhabitants per hectare. This number fell 35 percent, reaching 43 inhabitants per hectare in 1990. Greater opportunities for access to urban land are also reflected in more housing. In the 1980s, Mexicali's housing growth rate was one of the highest of border cities, following Tijuana and Ciudad Juárez (see Table 2).

The construction of housing in Mexicali in the last 20 years has several origins, including the social, public, and private sectors. During the 1980s, the Baja California

Figure 1. Number of Inhabitants per Hectare in
Mexican Border Cities, 1940–1990

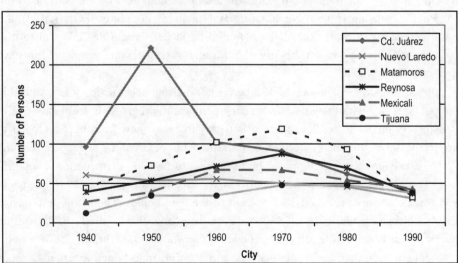

SOURCES: Based on Aguilar Méndez (1992a); Dirección General de Estadística (1940, 1950, 1960, 1970); Secretaría de Programación y Presupuesto and INEGI (1980); INEGI (1990).

Table 2. Housing Growth Rate in Border Cities, 1960–1990

City, State	1960–1970	1970–1980	1980–1990
Ciudad Juárez, Chihuahua	4.3	4.2	4.2
Mexicali, Baja California	4.0	3.5	3.7
Tijuana, Baja California	7.5	4.4	5.2
Matamoros, Tamaulipas	4.1	5.7	2.0
Nuevo Laredo, Tamaulipas	4.3	3.9	1.5
Reynosa, Tamaulipas	5.9	1.7	3.4

SOURCES: Dirección General de Estadística (1960, 1970); Secretaría de Programación y Presupuesto and INEGI (1980); INEGI (1990).

state government implemented a program to offer urban properties for low-income families with the hope of lowering the housing deficit through self-construction. The project was called the Public Housing Development Program (Programa de Fraccionamientos Populares). It developed a series of new neighborhoods in different parts of the city (including El Robledo, Miguel Hidalgo, and Venustiano Carranza) where more than fifteen thousand families were living by the end of the decade.

Government institutions, such as the Institute of National Funds for Worker Housing (Instituto del Fondo Nacional de la Vivienda para los Trabajadores–INFONAVIT), the Institute of Security and Social Services for State Workers Housing Fund (Fondo de la Vivienda del Instituto de Seguridad y Servicios Sociales de los Trabajadores del Estado–FOVISSSTE), the National Bank of Public Works (Banco Nacional de Obras–BANOBRAS), the Bank Operation and Financing Fund for Housing (Fondo de Operación y Financiamiento Bancario a la Vivienda–FOVI), the National Fund for Public Housing (Fondo Nacional de Habitaciones Populares–FONHAPO), and State of Baja California Real Estate (Inmobiliaria del Estado de Baja California), have contributed considerably by providing housing to address working-class demands in Mexicali.

From 1980 to 1990, a total of 46.8 percent of housing construction was financed by the public sector with the goal of producing permanent, progressive, and better quality housing. From 1990 to 1996, there was 61.8 percent of new housing developed by governmental institutions (Dirección de Catastro, Control Urbano y Ecología 1998: 28).

The private sector participated in 23 percent of housing construction from 1980 to 1990 and the social sector participated in 30 percent. From 1990 to 1996, the social and private sectors produced 38.2 percent of the new homes (Dirección de Catastro, Control Urbano y Ecología 1998: 29). These data show that in the last 20 years the public sector has been the principal producer of new housing in the City of Mexicali.

Housing production in Mexicali has, to a point, maintained a rather constant rhythm. From 1960 to 1970, the housing growth rate was 4.0 percent and in the 1980s, 3.7 percent. This rate allowed for greater housing opportunities for those who resided in Mexicali and a decline in housing occupancy density. Table 3 shows an average of five inhabitants per residence in 1980 and 4.1 per residence in 1995. The proportion of owned homes increased from 58 percent in 1980 to 71 percent in 1990.

Infrastructure services to homes have also improved. In 1980, 70 percent of the residences in Mexicali had potable water. That number reached 88 percent by 1995. Drainage or sewerage services also improved from serving 83 percent of households in 1980 to 88 percent in 1995.

According to these factors or indicators, then, it is evident that quality of life has improved in Mexicali. This is manifested in a greater number of families who own their homes, a tendency toward reducing overcrowding, and the extension of water and drainage services.

It is not possible, however, to generalize about the housing conditions throughout the city. With the purpose of better understanding the different levels of housing quality and their intraurban spatial distribution, two thematic maps were created for this essay in which rental housing is analyzed and a quality-of-life indicator is established.

Table 3. Housing Data, Mexicali, 1980–1995

Year	Inhabitants per Household	Percentage of Owned Residences	Percentage of Residences with Piped Water	Percentage of Residences with Sewage Connections
1980	5.0	58	70	83
1990	4.4	71	73	79
1995	4.1	n/a	88	88

SOURCES: Secretaría de Programación y Presupuesto and INEGI (1980); INEGI (1990, 1995).

Rental Housing

AGEB-level information from the eleventh general census of population and housing was used to create the rental housing and housing quality maps of Mexicali (INEGI 1990). AGEBs are boundaries drawn by the National Institute for Statistics, Geography, and Information (Instituto Nacional de Estadística, Geografía e Informática–INEGI) to program and control the collection of census information. The City of Mexicali has 132 AGEBs, five of which are not considered in this essay because they include fewer than eight residences per square kilometer (Baud, Bourgeat, and Bras 1997: 470).

A pattern is evident from the center of the city toward the periphery in Figure 2. Here, the oldest zone in the city is used as the center of the city (it was until 1920). The highest percentage of rented dwellings is concentrated there and, following the city's pattern of historic growth (see Figure 3), the percentage of rented dwellings decreases. That is, the newer the zone, the lower the percentage of rented dwellings. This can be explained by the fact that in the oldest zones, former residents opted to relocate to newly constructed homes, leaving their old homes to be rented. Their mobility is due to transformations in land use and the deterioration of residences in the older zones. The former residents and/or their descendents moved to other neighborhoods or to the periphery in search of better quality of life, residential atmosphere (security, schools, services, and so on), and housing.

Another phenomenon that must also be considered within this topic is that of the new, young homeowner. These new families locate themselves primarily in rented homes in different parts of the city. Once they have enough economic resources to purchase a home or an urbanized lot, people begin to move to residences toward the periphery, where lower cost options exist and more lots and homes are available. Both private and public initiatives have placed new developments primarily in the peripheral zones of the city.

Figure 2. Proportion of Rental Housing in Mexicali, 1993

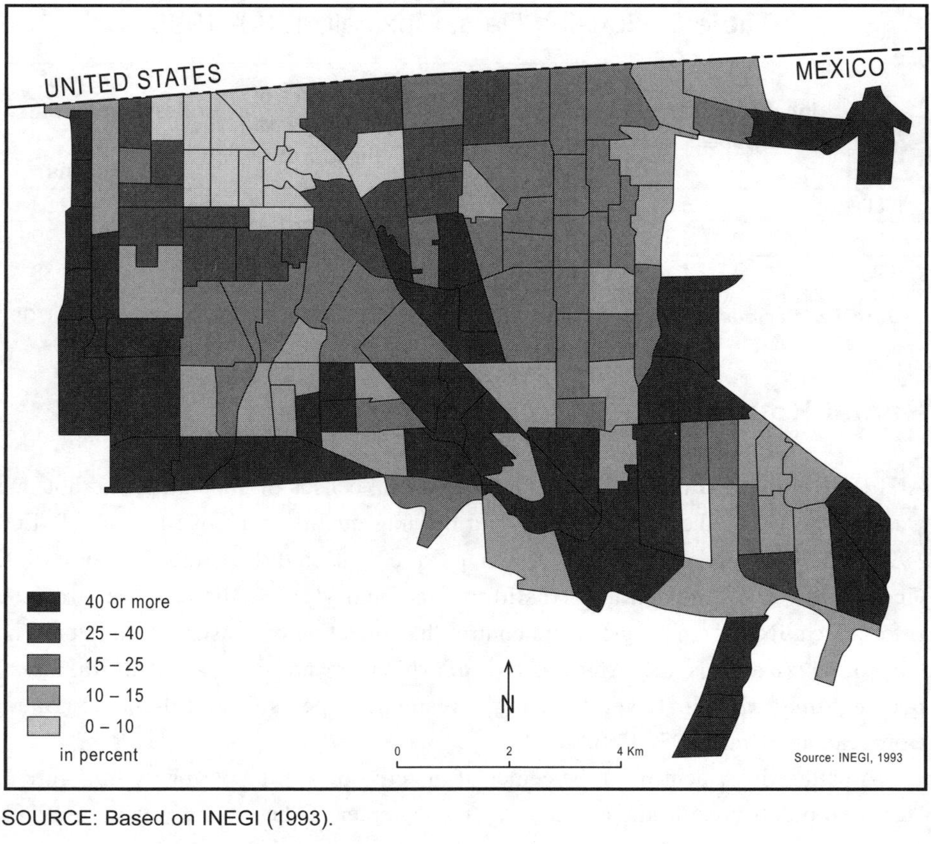

40 or more
25 – 40
15 – 25
10 – 15
0 – 10
in percent

0   2   4 Km

Source: INEGI, 1993

SOURCE: Based on INEGI (1993).

Figure 3. Map of Mexicali's Historic Urban Growth, 1920–1980

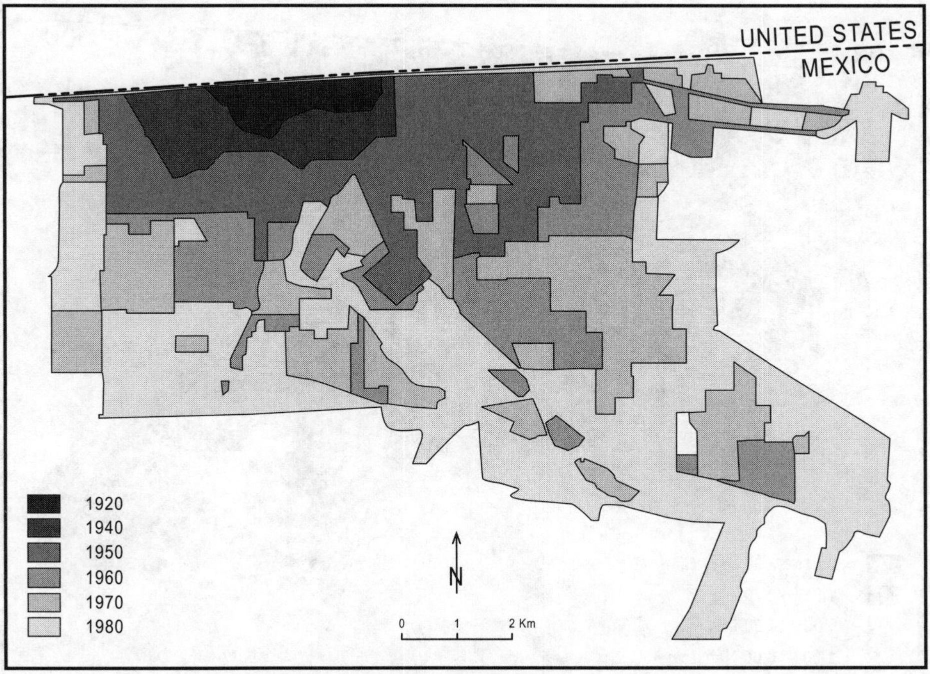

SOURCE: Created by G. Álvarez based on SAHOPE (1995).

Housing Quality

Figure 4 shows the spatial distribution of housing quality at the AGEB level. Housing quality was determined by factorial analysis in which the weight of each variable was determined and, when combined, housing quality could be deduced. The variables selected from the System for the Consultation of Census Information (Sistema para la Consulta de Información Censal–SCINCE) to calculate housing quality included the percentages of residences with piped water, their own kitchen, sewage connections to the general collector system, and block or cement walls. The values of each of the indicators are managed in standard deviations (see COPLAMAR 1982: 27). The result of housing quality is also expressed in terms of standard deviations. Values greater than zero signify that housing quality is better than the city's average and those less than zero indicate the opposite.

Figure 4. Housing Quality in Mexicali, 1993

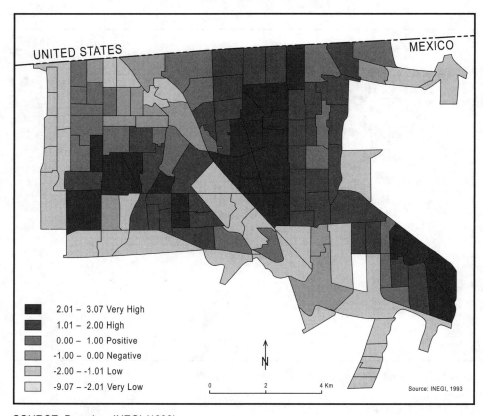

Source: INEGI, 1993

SOURCE: Based on INEGI (1993).

Three important observations can be made from Figure 4:

- No relationships are evident between housing quality distribution patterns and the various periods of historic growth in Mexicali. There is no center-periphery relationship as there is with rental housing.

- Housing quality inferior to the average is found in both the older zone of the city as well as in the periphery (where the newest developments are found).

- Highest housing quality was found in three zones, located in the west, center, and southeast of the urban sector. These zones are surrounded by AGEBs of the second highest level of quality.

From these three observations, the lowest housing quality is found in the center of the city since many homes in this zone have not been modified or renovated and are more than forty years old. The older zone of the city has not been popular for investments in new housing, either to sell or to rent.

A great number of AGEBs with low housing quality are also located in the periphery, given that they are mostly low-income family neighborhoods where housing is primarily constructed by the residents themselves. The location of higher quality housing also responds to the theory that land on the periphery is cheaper. These housing developments are financed by either government institutions or private capital. AGEBs with high housing quality that are located to the extreme southeast of the city are financed primarily by private capital.

Other AGEB groups of high housing quality were located using the theory of exclusivity. When these zones were being developed, they were considered isolated, but nevertheless boasted infrastructure services based on the economic capacity of their inhabitants. One of these groups is located to the extreme west of the city.

Conclusions

The information collected about housing characteristics in Mexicali is important to establish general parameters and to be able to compare it with other urban localities. Nonetheless, it cannot be concluded that these characteristics will behave in a homogeneous manner in any part of the city. Internal forces exist that influence the determination of a variety of housing types, including their location within the city.

The exercise conducted here to determine patterns of housing distribution by ownership and quality allows the city's internal structure to be observed. The number of rented dwellings at the AGEB level is related to the period of growth in Mexicali. The number of rented residences is higher in the older zones of Mexicali. This is a pattern that is also evident in central Mexico's medium-sized cities. This similarity requires a more detailed analysis to determine the factors that make this phenomenon repeat itself in different parts of Mexico.

The distribution of precarious housing principally in the city's periphery is a pattern found in the structure of many Latin American cities (Hartshorn 1992). The degradation process is evident in some neighborhoods located in the older zones of the city. By contrast, the location of acceptable quality housing on the periphery, as a product of public investment, responds to the political localization of cheaper land and promotes the extension of the urban sector.

References

Achen, Christopher H. 1982. *Interpreting and Using Regression.* Newbury Park: Sage Publications.
Aguilar, Adrián Guillermo. 1992. "Dispersión del proceso urbano." Ciudades 12 (October-December).
Aguilar, Adrián Guillermo, Boris Graizbord, and Álvaro Sánchez Crispín. 1996. *Las ciudades intermedias y el desarrollo regional en México.* México, D.F.: CONACULTA and El Colegio de México.

Aguilar Méndez, Fernando Antonio. 1992. *La expansión territorial de las ciudades de México.* México, D.F.: Universidad Autónoma Metropolitana.

Alonso, William. 1964. *Location and Land Use.* Cambridge: Harvard University Press.

Arreola, Daniel D., and James R. Curtis. 1993. *The Mexican Border Cities.* Tucson: The University of Arizona Press.

Baud, Pascal, Serge Bourgeat, and Catherine Bras. 1997. *Dictionnaire de géographie.* Paris: Ed. Hatier.

Bourne, Larry S. 1982. *Internal Structure of the City.* New York: Oxford University Press.

Carter, Harold. 1995. *The Study of Urban Geography.* New York: Halsted Press.

Coordinación General del Plan Nacional de Zonas Deprimidas y Grupos Marginados (COPLAMAR). 1982. "Geografía de la marginación." *Siglo XXI.*

Dirección de Catastro, Control Urbano y Ecología. 1998. *Programa de desarrollo urbano de centro de población de Mexicali, B.C. 2010.* México, D.F.: XV Ayuntamiento de Mexicali.

Dirección General de Estadística. 1940. *Sexto censo de población.* México, D.F.: Dirección General de Estadística.

Dirección General de Estadística. 1950. *Séptimo censo general de población.* México, D.F.: Dirección General de Estadística.

Dirección General de Estadística. 1960. *VIII Censo general de población.* México, D.F.: Dirección General de Estadística.

Dirección General de Estadística. 1970. *IX Censo general de población.* México, D.F.: Dirección General de Estadística.

Hartshorn, Truman A. 1992. *Interpreting the City: An Urban Geography.* New York: John Wiley and Sons.

Instituto Nacional de Estadística, Geografía e Informática (INEGI). 1990. *XI Censo general de población y vivienda.* Aguascalientes: INEGI.

Instituto Nacional de Estadística, Geografía e Informática (INEGI). 1993. *Sistema de consulta de información censal.* México, D.F.: INEGI.

Instituto Nacional de Estadística, Geografía e Informática (INEGI). 1995. *Conteo de población y vivienda.* Aguascalientes: INEGI.

Knox, Paul. 1987. *Urban Social Geography, an Introduction.* Harlow: Longman Scientific and Technical.

Secretaría de Asentamientos Humanos y Obras Públicas del Estado (SAHOPE). 1995. *Plano de crecimiento histórico.* Mexicali: Dirección de Planeación Urbana y Regional.

Secretaría de Programación y Presupuesto and Instituto Nacional de Estadística, Geografía e Informática (INEGI). 1980. *X Censo general de población y vivienda.* México, D.F.: Secretaría de Programación y Presupuesto and INEGI.

Sobrino, Luis Jaime. 1996. "Tendencias de la urbanización mexicana hacia finales del siglo." *Estudios Demográficos y Urbanos* 11 (1).

Tamayo, Jesús, and José Luis Fernández. 1983. *Zonas fronterizas (México/Estados Unidos).* México, D.F.: CIDE.

Unikel, Luis, Crescencio Ruiz Chiapetto, and Gustavo Garza Villarreal. 1978. *El desarrollo urbano de México.* México, D.F.: El Colegio de México.

27

Nongovernmental Organizations in the Mexicali and Imperial Valleys: An Approach to Their Characteristics and Interactions

José A. Moreno Mena and Guadalupe Alonso*

Abstract

This essay presents a brief description of the citizen groups known as nongovernmental organizations (NGO) that dedicate their efforts to benefit a third party in the Mexicali and Imperial valleys. NGOs are civil organizations of an altruistic, philanthropic, and educational character that focus on assistance and service. Several processes of interaction among such organizations from both sides of the border are described. In addition, some examples of their participation to resolve domestic and transborder problems are used to show how their involvement has had a growing influence on public policy over the years.

Introduction

The border cities of Mexicali and Calexico are sister cities that share a common origin since their foundation with the diversion of the Colorado River waters and the ability to irrigate the Mexicali and Imperial valleys. Interactions between their populations have been frequent, including some periods in which Mexicali residents have migrated to the neighboring towns in the Imperial Valley, principally Calexico.[1]

*Moreno Mena is Researcher at the Institute for Social Research at the Universidad Autonóma de Baja California and recipient of a scholarship from the Faculty Advancement Program (Programa de Mejoramiento del Profesorado–PROMEP). Alonso is Educator and Activist for Mariposas Ministry in the City of Calexico.

Such interactions have not only been of a commercial, working, or institutional character; they have also included the realm of cooperation between nongovernmental actors. One example of this is the help given by Imperial Valley residents when contingencies arise on the Mexican side of the border. Philanthropic acts from Imperial Valley organizations toward their neighbors in Mexicali have occurred throughout the history of the two valleys.

Cooperative lobbying activities that influence public policy made by local and national governments, although dating back several decades, began to have relevance in the border region in the mid-1980s.[2] Nongovernmental organizations and community service agencies have existed on the U.S. side for many years and have much experience lobbying at the national level. Nonetheless, they had not interacted with their Mexican counterparts to strengthen their endeavors regarding concrete problems such as migration, health, and so on.

In the last several years, cross-border linkages have begun to develop between citizens organizations in both valleys in an attempt to influence the policies of their respective countries and, at the same time, develop agendas for discussion. This essay provides a brief characterization of the citizen groups known as nongovernmental organizations (NGO) that dedicate their efforts to benefit a third party on both sides of the border. NGOs are civil organizations that focus on providing assistance and services of an altruistic, philanthropic, or educational character. Several interaction processes among NGOs from both sides of the border are described. In addition, some examples of their participation in domestic and transborder problems show how their involvement has had a growing influence on public policy over the years.

Origin, Nature, and Goals of Nongovernmental Organizations in the Mexicali and Imperial Valleys

A characterization of the nongovernmental organizations of these two valleys is a difficult task due to their differing objectives and the multiplicity of their actions. In order to attain this objective, this essay classifies NGOs in Mexicali and then those of the Imperial Valley.

Nongovernmental Organizations in Mexicali

Nongovernmental organizations in Mexicali can be distinguished by several common elements on a general scale. They are made up primarily of middleclass citizens whose goals are not financial, but are to benefit third parties. Although groups exist whose activities do generate funding to maintain their activities—as in the case of some drug rehabilitation centers—most NGOs are not for profit. However, even with drug rehabilitation centers, the primary objective is to help the population affected by drug addiction. In Mexicali, many civil organizations are religious in nature, especially Catholic and Evangelical, but their purpose is primarily social. Participation by women (particularly professionals) is especially strong in their development and activities.

These organizations carry out tasks that federal or local governments are not dealing with or have set aside in favor of other issues. Although NGOs have fewer resources, they are also without the burden of an exaggerated government bureaucracy and are able to help the poorest sectors of their communities.

The primary sources of financing for these groups come from foundations, private donations, and contributions of their own members. They occasionally receive government funding, but their ability to function does not depend on government support. Another aspect common to such groups is a tendency toward the professionalization of their activities, constantly improving their capacity to provide better services.

The majority of these organizations opt to join a civil association to give their activities formal and legal character. Others are registered under a legal device called public benefit institutions, which allows them to enjoy certain governmental prerogatives, but limits their autonomy in internal decision making. In order to obtain government resources or funding from foreign or domestic foundations, a group must meet the requirements mandated by the registry and be listed with the Ministry of Finance and Public Credit (Secretaría de Hacienda y Crédito Público–SHCP).

To achieve credibility and respect, these organizations must draw a boundary between themselves and the government, political parties, and churches; otherwise the citizenry labels them and does not trust them. Although members of the organizations exercise full autonomy with regard to their internal decisions and do not depend upon governments, political parties, or religious groups, certain controls still exist within the local and national judicial frameworks. Additionally, some organizations do not completely separate themselves from party or religious affiliations. NGOs attempt to develop democratic and horizontal decision-making processes, making them attractive to those who oppose the dominant authoritarianism of Mexican politics.

Within the multitude of organizations in Mexicali (see Table 1), two types stand out. First are those groups that work toward the rehabilitation of people addicted to drugs, alcohol, or other substances. Their prevalence denotes the grave situation confronting much of the Mexicali population. Second are those groups that work with the disabled. In this case, the organizations helped more than one thousand people, but the total disabled population in the City of Mexicali is estimated at more than fifty thousand (IIS 2000). The organizations and shelters that offer assistance to children (migrants, homeless, offenders, and others) have been in existence the longest, as is the case of the Desert Juvenile Shelter (Albergue Juvenil del Desierto), which helps migrants who are minors.

Table 1. NGOs in Mexicali

Group Classification	Number	Percentage
Disabled people, children, adults, and health care groups	17	13.6
Women's rights groups	7	5.6
Environmental groups	6	4.8
Human rights groups	2	1.6
HIV/AIDS information and support groups	2	1.6
Community groups	10	8.0
Gay, transgender, and sex worker rights groups	6	4.8
Groups that work with families	5	4.0
Educational development and community training groups	2	1.6
Groups that work with migrants	5	4.0
Rescue groups	2	1.6
Cultural and scientific groups	4	3.2
Groups that work with the elderly	1	0.8
Drug and alcohol rehabilitation groups	36	28.8
Animal rights groups	2	1.6
Sports groups	2	1.6
Groups that work with youth	6	4.8
Philanthropic and charity clubs	7	5.6
Shelter and food for the poor	1	0.8
Others	2	1.6
Total	125	100.0

SOURCE: Moreno Mena (2000).

Undoubtedly, those groups that have the highest level of influence and external dialogue have the greatest influence with the local and federal governments, and are able to present proposals and develop lobbying processes are those that assist women and promote and defend human rights in the migrant worker community. These groups have reached the highest level of maturity in the region. Groups that fall into this category include the women's organization Alaide Foppa; the Coalition for the Defense of Migrants, Mexicali division (Coalición Pro Defensa del Migrante); the Desert Juvenile Shelter; the Center for Assistance for Migrant Workers (Centro de Apoyo al Trabajador Migrante); and the Center for Human Rights and Civic Education (Centro de Derechos Humanos y Educación Cívica). It should be noted that the Mexicali division of the Coalition for the Defense of Migrants has been the only organization in the area to systematize and publish its research in the migratory sphere.

In reality, the majority of groups that work directly with the community do not develop processes for community service. They dedicate themselves to bringing some health and nutrition services to the community. In other words, their work is more about providing assistance than an alternative to the system in place. Only groups such as the Center for Family Care (Centro de Atención Familiar–CENAFAM) and

Education and Community Services (Educación y Servicios Comunitarios–EDUSEC) include in their missions the provision of education and a combination of assistance services and processes to help transform their users and their quality of life.

Gay organizations have remained behind the scenes for years. Even though they have a few meeting and recreation centers in the city, they have not made themselves visible out of fear of repression by a male-dominated (*macho*) culture. Only in the last few years have they begun to surface. Groups that consult, aid, and disseminate information about HIV/AIDS are also present in the region and they are probably among the newest. The majority are made up of medical professionals, but others are run by homosexual groups. The Friendship Program (Programa Amigo) and the AIDS Center of Mexicali (Centro Local Sida Mexicali–CELSIME) are among the most predominant in this category.

Other groups develop campaigns dedicated to the compatibility and dissemination of information and the struggle for a healthy environment. Even though their need is great due to high levels of pollution in the City of Mexicali—from assembly plants, a poorly maintained vehicular fleet, and unpaved roads in marginalized neighborhoods—their development is minimal. This fact reveals the poor environmental culture of the city's population.

Only one group that aids the elderly population is registered in the city, reflecting the low level of importance that society places on the future of older adults. It is also, however, an example of the survival of traditional culture in the city, in which elderly family members live with their relatives. The existence of organizations focused on the promotion, education, and defense of human rights are even scarcer and, like the environmentalists, are the least established. Finally, those groups that promote democratic values, the participation of the citizenry in the public life of the state, and so on, are very few.

A significant number of groups are registered in Mexicali, as can be seen in Table 1. An unknown number of groups also exist that are not registered and develop their activities with resources from their own members, making the creation of a complete directory quite difficult.

The diverse goals of these many groups make them tend to spread out rather than integrate. They usually maintain very open relationships with other groups that work toward the same cause. There is only one case of a local coalition's attempt to aggregate local organizations into a single entity called the Agreement of Nongovernmental Organizations (El Concierto de Organizaciones No Gubernamentales), which existed briefly in the 1990s. This group tried to form a front against the government when it attempted to intervene in the internal life of NGOs and counsel them on government resources that the National Solidarity Program (Programa Nacional de Solidaridad–PRONASOL) was to bring to combat poverty.

Nongovernmental Organizations in the Imperial Valley

In the Imperial Valley, as in much of the United States, the composition of citizen organizations does not differ greatly from that of their Mexican counterparts. On average, their members are of the middle class who have progressed economically, but have altruistic motives.

Although it is difficult to quantify the NGOs in the Imperial Valley, more than one hundred nonprofit citizen groups whose goals are to benefit third parties are formally registered with the appropriate state and federal agencies. Service agencies that receive government funding can be found in this sphere, but their activities are dedicated to benefiting marginalized populations. They are made up of both professionals and volunteers. Even though a portion of their resources comes from the government, this does not imply a loss of autonomy in decision-making practices. Other organizations receive resources through donations by citizens, giving them complete autonomy in their decision-making practices. The binational project, Chimalitquic, and the Civil Philanthropic and Educational Association (Asociación Civil Filantrópica y Educativa) are included in this category.

Along the same lines, some groups organize the development of a community project for which they receive funding from national or international foundations, as is the case of the Library Literacy Project. Of equal importance are service clubs and private institutions that dedicate a portion of their time to the needy population. Some of these organizations include Rotary International, the Lions Club-4, the American Legion Club, and the Boys and Girls Club of Brawley.

Groups of a religious character with social service programs that assist the community include Catholic Charities and the Salvation Army. Some government programs targeted toward the community also incorporate volunteers who do not receive permanent salaries. Several foundations provide financial resources to assistance groups in the Imperial Valley, such as the United Way Agencies, which aid approximately thirty philanthropic organizations in the region. One characteristic particular to NGOs in the Imperial Valley is that they are not involved in politics or political party activities, thus avoiding ideological conflicts.

As in Mexico, U.S. organizations that are based on service or community assistance and require outside resources to develop their social programs have to comply with certain formal prerequisites in order to obtain economic aid. Most importantly, they need to be granted non-profit organization status by the U.S. Department of the Treasury. This requires a formal structure, including a board of directors, by-laws, and incorporation as a not-for-profit organization under the laws of one of the U.S. states. These legal processes usually require the assistance of professionals such as a lawyer and accountant. Once the formal non-profit status has been achieved, usually 501(c)(3), the organization can receive donations and grants and does not have to pay taxes on these sources of funding. Most important, many private foundations and government agencies will provide funding only to non-profit organizations with the proper formal status. Also, donations to these organizations can be used by the donors as tax deductions, an excellent incentive for fund-raising.

Many groups do not obtain formal status, which makes it difficult to obtain funding. Many of these groups are short-lived and often have narrowly focused definitions. They are not easy to identify and follow over time. One such group that does not have formal status is the Mariposas Ministry (Ministerio Mariposas).

The precipitous growth of these groups in the Imperial Valley has been a result of changes in the antidiscriminatory legal frameworks and the incorporation of professional immigrants who have taken advantage of employment and amnesty programs in the late 1980s (see Table 2). Greater participation of the Hispanic population in local organizations is also noted.

Table 2. Legal Immigration to Imperial County, 1986–1996

Year	Number of Immigrants
1986	1,507
1987	1,447
1988	1,488
1990	1,337
1991	1,921
1992	1,735
1993	2,029
1994	1,425
1995	1,159
1996	1,821
Total	15,869

SOURCE: U.S. Immigration and Naturalization Service (2000).

Like their counterparts in Mexicali, Imperial Valley NGOs have not been able to develop articulate processes to form a coalition that encompasses the majority of the groups. One group called the Coalition Against Tobacco and Drugs was able to incorporate a significant number of citizen organizations, but its existence was brief.

Table 3 classifies the NGOs of the Imperial Valley in an attempt to compare them to those of Mexicali, while recognizing the need for a much more detailed research to develop a more complete panorama of those organizations that offer a variety of services.[3] Toward this end, each organization is categorized according to its principal activity.

According to Table 3, NGOs showing the highest levels of growth in the Imperial Valley are those that serve the disabled, followed by rehabilitation groups and organizations that work with families. Groups that provide services to the

Interactions among Citizen Organizations on Both Sides of the Border

Interactions between the two sides of the border have existed since the establishment of Mexican and U.S. settlements. These interactions have not only been in the commercial realm, in the contraction of Mexican labor for agricultural work in the fields of the Imperial Valley, or between local governments. They have also been prominent among the citizens of the region and NGOs. The groups on either side of the border have maintained relationships with one another through informal linkages. This allows them to exchange experiences and, above all, in the case of the Imperial Valley, develop an informal solidarity that transcends boundaries.

Even though Imperial County is considered one of the poorest counties in the United States, its organized citizenry has developed altruistic and philanthropic processes that benefit their neighbors to the south. Perhaps the Hispanic origin of its residents and the familial ties that they maintain with Mexicali, or the fact that they are considered the poorest in such a rich country, influences their desire to help their neighbors. As an example, every year provisions and blankets are distributed to the lowest income neighborhoods in Mexicali by groups of organized workers in the Imperial Valley, without the intervention of government authorities.

Frequently, people with disabilities will be brought across the border so they can be helped by the Valley Orthopedic Clinic. For over twenty years, an informal network has existed among Mexicali neighborhood health centers, the Mexican Red Cross, groups that work with patients (especially children) on the Mexican side, and philanthropic organizations on the U.S. side such as the Lions Club and the Rotary Club. These organizations also work with the Mexican consulate in Calexico and U.S. immigration authorities to allow patients to cross the border even if they do not have a passport.

The Lions Club works primarily with minors and adults with cleft palate and/or vision problems. In this case, the patients are channeled to altruistic doctors in the Imperial Valley or another city in California who do not necessarily belong to a philanthropic organization. The Rotary Club works mostly to help patients with motor disabilities—including those caused by polio—who are channeled to the Valley Orthopedic Clinic.

Coordination with the Valley Orthopedic Clinic is of extreme importance for the disabled in Mexicali. Thanks to its services, Mexican young adults and children can become familiar with a world of opportunities that their country does not offer. Sometimes the clinic diagnoses patients and, according to their level of severity, refers them to the Eye Hospital or Shriners Hospital in Los Angeles or to Children's Hospital in San Diego. In these cases, the institution offers temporary housing for the patient's family and he/she later returns to Mexicali for rehabilitation. Both of these activities are sponsored by social and charitable clubs in the United States.

Table 3. NGOs in Imperial Valley

Group Classification	Number	Percentage
Disabled people, children, adults, and health care	24	16.6
Women's rights groups and antidomestic violence	10	6.9
Civil rights	9	6.2
HIV/AIDS	3	2.1
Community support	5	3.4
Gay, transgender, and sex workers	1	0.7
Groups that work with families	11	7.6
Educational development, literacy, and community learning	7	4.8
Groups that work with migrants	3	2.1
Rescue	1	0.7
Groups that work with the elderly	8	5.5
Drug and alcohol rehabilitation	12	8.3
Animal rights	1	0.7
Groups that work with youth and sport clubs	11	7.6
Service and charity clubs	8	5.5
Groups that provide shelter and food for the poor	3	2.1
Nutrition groups and cooperatives	5	3.4
Groups that distribute information, provide support, and attend to health problems	10	6.9
Consumer and credit help	3	2.1
Groups that work to find missing or runaway children	10	6.9
Total	145	100.1

SOURCES: United Way Agencies (2000); Pacific Bell (2000).

community, however, have had the greatest influence on the population and public policy. Groups that aid families of missing or runaway children also stand out. The number of organizations that fight for civil rights and human rights in general is rather significant for such a small population (approximately 145,000 inhabitants in 2000) (Online Highways 2001). It is interesting to note that, like in Mexicali, there are few gay organizations.

The presence of emergency telephone numbers and community support in all areas is of great importance. In contrast to the scarcity of such services in the City of Mexicali, Imperial Valley boasts countless help lines that are available 24 hours a day and serve the population with information on issues such as suicide prevention, missing children, HIV/AIDS, and so on.

Similarly, relationships between educational groups on either side of the border are very important. Examples include Fiesta Educativa (Educational Festival) from Los Angeles, California. It has been in operation for more than ten years and its objectives are to bring education, information, and training to the parents of disabled children. This organization is supported by parents and professionals who work with special needs and each year a conference is held to discuss relevant issues.

Fiesta Educativa arrived in the Imperial Valley in the late 1990s and since its initiation has tried to involve people on the Mexican side of the border in its activities. It has brought together teachers, parents, and consumers from both sides of the border to share information about judicial frameworks, social issues, health, and education to strengthen and influence positive attitudes for disabled people. This citizens' movement has spurred the assembly of professionals and parents who currently work in Mexico, generating new visions in the educational realm.

NGO Experiences with Transborder Networks and Coalitions in Mexicali and the Imperial Valley: New Forms of Citizen Diplomacy

Cooperation among citizen groups on either side of the border to influence public policy of their respective governments and/or to develop lobbying activities is a relatively new phenomenon. It began to develop in the early 1990s to confront controversial topics such as migration. These processes have been defined as forms of citizen diplomacy (Thorup 1995: 156). This concept was created by the NGOs themselves, revealing that as they develop activities in their county they also involve themselves in issues across the border. It also implies the assumption of roles once considered particular to governmental actors (governmental diplomacy). Thorup also states that "private citizens ... are playing a role of increasing importance in the establishment of the parameters of the exterior political agenda, limiting the capacity of public officials to manage their relationships on a strictly government to government basis, and setting the stage for a much more complex interactive process" (1995: 157).

In the Mexicali-Imperial region, new forms of citizen diplomacy are found principally in the defense of migrant workers' human rights. This is especially evident in responses to anti-immigrant measures developed by the U.S. federal and state governments in 1994 on both sides of the border. Steps taken by border coalitions and networks rose when Operation Gatekeeper, established by the U.S. federal government, was implemented on October 1, 1994, to reroute migrants and step up border security, and when the "Save Our State" (SOS) proposal, better known as Proposition 187 to limit illegal immigration, passed in September 1994.

While the majority of citizen actions by Baja Californians that attempted to influence public policy and relationships between the two countries to benefit migrants took place in the San Diego-Tijuana region, significant events also took place in the Calexico-Mexicali region. Assistance and advice were given on the Mexican side, while mobilizations to defend the rights of migrants took place on the U.S. side to support their Mexican counterparts. These contacts gave birth to several new NGO networks at the local level as well as the transborder level.

To make the problem more visible, organizations in the Mexicali and Imperial valleys participated in simultaneous marches in October 1994. Both events culminated at the international border that divides Mexicali and Calexico. The media described the event in the following manner: "the two countries united at the border fence that divides them ... For more than 45 minutes, borders disappeared and the residents of the two cities united their spirits, their voices, and their protests against Proposition 187" (*El Mexicano* 1994). The next day, representatives from the Plural Binational Mexicali-Calexico Commission—made up of political leaders, popular leaders, and citizens—met at the international port of entry and embarked upon the mission of collecting signatures opposing Proposition 187 to send to government representatives in both countries (their goal was to obtain 100,000 signatures). The types of networks and coalitions that were generated by these issues were not all the same. They included members of civil society from different social classes, races, and religions, signifying an unprecedented level of cooperation.

The Case of Eduardo Zamores

One of the first experiences in which NGOs and organized civil society came together from both valleys was in support of Eduardo Zamores. Zamores was a minor from Mexicali who was shot by U.S. Border Patrol authorities at the Mexicali-Calexico border while trying to cross illegally in 1990 (Avendaño Millán 1996: 23). The response to this act by social groups was unprecedented. The international ports of entry at Tijuana and Mexicali were blocked and protest marches took place on both sides of the border. His death also motivated a regional meeting of human rights organizations in Ciudad Juárez, Chihuahua, in January 1991. The meeting resulted in the temporary creation of a binational human rights coordinator for the border region to work with the NGOs present at the meeting.[4] Even though the resulting network was ephemeral, it signified an important step toward the development of citizen diplomacy.

The Influence of Disabled Groups on the Definition of Attitudes and a Culture of Tolerance

One of the social movements that developed on the U.S. side of the border that influenced a change in Mexican legislation is that which recognizes the rights of the disabled in Mexico. The movement has been in existence for more than twenty years, but it culminated in July 1990 with the Americans with Disabilities Act (ADA). This citizens' movement had its repercussions on the Mexican side as well, generating changes in the judicial framework toward rights of the disabled.

The antecedent to these movements took place in the 1970s in Mexicali with the rise of Club Alma (Soul Club), a social group that brought together youth with physical disabilities. Its goal was to form community counselors who would volunteer to visit other disabled people in the Mexicali Valley and its less-fortunate neighborhoods. At first, the group was primarily social in character, but it soon included religious features.

This movement was funded by a U.S. doctor and his wife who had moved to the City of Calexico to work alongside César Chávez and the United Farm Workers. The doctor also worked in the Calexico Orthopedic Clinic and had connections with participants of the disabled movement in the United States. With the goal of generating changes on both sides of the border, he promoted visits by Americans connected to the movement to Mexicali and so-called "spiritual journeys" in the Imperial Valley, which included members from both countries. Through these visits, disabled youth became familiar with the availability of artificial hand controls, electronic wheelchairs, vans and buses with elevators for wheelchairs, and other helpful devices.

Some of the youth from this group studied in the universities and today are actively involved in Mexicali society. Many were responsible for changes in public policy in the area of urban development, gaining some rights for the disabled. People like Carmen Milán (Físico Limitantes Mexicali, A.C.), Víctor Hugo Flores (current member of President Vicente Fox's cabinet), Hilda de Zavala (Mariposa Ministry, Mexicali), Felipe Montes (Mexican Institute for Social Security *[Instituto Mexicano del Seguro Social–IMSS]*), Miguel Angel Flores (sports star), and Lupita Alonso (Mariposa Ministry, Imperial Valley) are some of those who have initiated the movement in Mexicali and continue to generate changes on both sides of the border regarding rights for the disabled.

Posada Sin Fronteras

In the effort to continue to further transborder linkages, several organizations in the Imperial Valley organized for the first time a highly significant event, primarily for those who fight for the defense of migrant human rights. Posada sin fronteras (*posada*[5] without boundaries) took place on December 17, 2000, as an act of brotherhood between the citizenry on both sides of the border.

This event was rooted in the commemorative activities that formed humanitarian organizations in the cities of Tijuana, San Diego, and Los Angeles over many years. In this case, the California Interfaith Coalition, which brings together Catholics and Presbyterians; the Coalition for Peace and Social Justice, a citizens network from California; the Casa del Migrante Scalabrinni (Scalabrinni Migrant Home); and the Centro Madre Asunta (Madre Asunta Center) for migrant women all contributed.

Although the event had religious overtones due to the significant presence of the Catholic Church, its content was more than religious. Its objective was to further the linkages between the populations in the Mexicali and Imperial valleys, make migrant suffering known, and call attention to public opinion so that governments would take note. It represented a shimmer of hope for those migrants who attempt to cross the border daily in hope of improved quality of life, sometimes meeting death in their attempts.

The event consisted of a march/pilgrimage on both sides of the border. About seventy people on the U.S. side and fifty on the Mexican side participated (*La Voz de la Frontera* 2000: 27–A). Traditional *posada* songs were performed, but their words were adapted to reflect the situation of the migrants. Finally, a symbolic gift exchange took place and the participants from the Mexican side invited the U.S. participants to join them for traditional beverages.

Conclusions

Serious difficulties impede the classification of nongovernmental organizations. A detailed study of their social impact on Mexicali and Imperial Valley communities is lacking. Such a study should analyze their rise, development, and transborder relationships. This essay is only an initial effort to help lead the way.

NGOs need to further their cross-border linkages to develop a common agenda based on scientific research that would allow for an understanding of community needs on both sides of the border. These communities may be divided by a metal fence, but remain united by family ties and friendships that obligate people to cross the border daily to work, study, and live.

For now, the examples given here help to explain the development of a new transborder network and, at the same time, show that while the governments of both countries are losing time discussing their differing points of view, citizen organizations from both sides of the border are constructing agendas for cooperation.

Endnotes

1. The City of Mexicali was flooded in 1902, 1905, and 1906 during the construction of the Colorado River inlet and its population temporarily relocated to its sister city, Calexico. In the 1920s, the majority of Mexicali's public officials lived in Calexico and local governments made several attempts to bring them back, financing the construction of housing in Mexicali in this effort (Aguirre Bernal 1983: 247).

2. This coincides with the rise of NGOs on the national and local levels. See Armendares 1994.

3. There are more than seventy possible service activities in which the organizations could be classified.

4. The list of groups that participated in this new network is long, but worth mentioning because it is one of few cases of binational NGO cooperation. The organizations from Baja California included: Albergue Juvenil del Desierto, Centro de Apoyo al Trabajador Migrante, Asociación de Comités del Pueblo, Unión de Colonos Solicitantes e Inquilinos, A.C., Frente de Organizaciones Sociales de Baja California, and Comité de Solidaridad con Centroamérica. Those from Calexico included: One Stop Education, Por San Diego, and the American Friends Service Committee. From Ciudad Juárez, Chihuahua: Centro de Información y Estudios Migratorios, Casa del Migrante, Comunidades Eclesiales de Base, Comité Independiente de Chihuahua Pro Defensa de los Derechos Humanos. From Albuquerque, New Mexico: Proyecto Organizadora del Suroeste and Proyecto ABC. From El Paso, Texas: Unión de Trabajadores Agrícolas Fronterizos, Coalición Defensora de Derechos Fronterizos, and the National Lawyers Guild (Avendaño Millán 1996).

5. *Posadas* are part of the Mexican tradition surrounding the Christmas holiday. They represent the pilgrimage made by Mary and Joseph to Bethlehem in search of shelter and the birth of Jesus Christ. They typically include songs, prayer, fireworks, and piñatas in the celebration.

References

Aguirre Bernal, Celso. 1983. *Compendio histórico-biográfico de Mexicali*. Mexicali: X Ayuntamiento de Mexicali.

Armendares, Pedro Enrique. 1994. "El año de las ONG's." *La Jornada* (24 September).

Avendaño Millán, Rosa María. 1996. "Las ONG's en Baja California: un acercamiento al trabajo que realizan." *Debate Democrático* 1 (2).

Cambio de Tijuana, 1994, 1 October.

"Carta al Señor presidente de los Estados Unidos Mexicanos de parte de organizaciones y ciudadanos de Mexicali, B.C." 1997. (28 April). Unpublished.

Coalición Pro Defensa del Migrante. 1997. "Peticiones de organismos sociales a la Secretaría de Relaciones Exteriores." (April). Unpublished.

Coalición Pro Defensa del Migrante y Sin Fronteras. 1997. "Oficio dirigido al Congreso de la Unión." (March). Unpublished.

Frente Amplio por la Dignidad. 1994. "Informe del monitoreo realizado por el Frente Amplio por la Dignidad." (November). Unpublished.

Frente Amplio Pro Defensa del Migrante (FPDM). 1997. "Informe y conclusiones del II monitoreo realizado por el Frente Amplio Pro Defensa del Migrante." (April). Unpublished.

Heredia Zubieta, Carlos, and Ricardo Hernández Sánchez. 1996. *La diplomacia ciudadana en la era de la globalización: un punto de vista desde México*. México, D.F.: DECA Equipo Pueblo, A.C.

Instituto de Investigaciónes Sociales (IIS). 2000. *Discapacidad y necesidades sociales*. Mexicali: Instituto de Investigaciónes Sociales, Universidad Autónoma de Baja California.

Joint Declaration of NGOs at the Third Regional Conference. "Informe de la Coalición Pro defensa del Migrante durante 1997." Mexicali. Unpublished.

El Mexicano. 1994. 3 October–30 November.

El Mexicano. 1997. "Apoyo a deportados. Concertan plan emergente de acción." (23 April): 1–A.

Moreno Mena, José A. 1996. "Las organizaciones no gubernamentales: un interlocutor de la sociedad civil." *Debate Democrático* 1 (2).

Moreno Mena, José A. 2000. *Directorio de ONG's en Baja California*. Mexicali: Mimeo.

Online Highways. 2001. "Regions of California." http://www.caohwy.com/y/y06025.htm.

La Opinión de los Angeles, 1994. 1–30 October.

Pacific Bell. 2000. *Smart Yellow Pages, Imperial Valley*. Nevada: Pacific Bell.

Thorup, Cathryn L. 1995. "Diplomacia ciudadana, redes y coaliciones transfronterizas en América del Norte: nuevos diseños organizativos." *Foro Internacional* 35 (2).

U.S. Immigration and Naturalization Service. 2000. "Inmigrantes Admitted to Imperial County California." Fedstats: www.fedstats.gov/.

United Way Agencies. 2000. "Services in Use and with Support." Imperial Valley: United Way Agencies.

La Voz de la Frontera. 2000. "Migrantes piden posada en la frontera." (18 December).

28

The Place and Places of Culture in the Imperial Valley-Mexicali Region

Sheila Dollente and Eduardo Kintero*

Abstract

Both regional and national perspectives figure in the arts and cultural institutions that serve the communities of the Imperial Valley and Mexicali Valley along the eastern portion of the California-Baja California border. Ample facilities exist in both countries for a variety of formal presentations; however, the administration and funding of the arts in Mexico and the United States differs significantly in many instances. Although the sense of binationalism is high, there is surprisingly little patronage by the citizens of either country in the arts events of their neighbor.

Introduction

Just as the desert has an abundance of unique plant and animal life that at first may not be apparent to someone unfamiliar with the local ecology, so does a rich variety of cultural resources abound in the Imperial Valley-Mexicali region, providing opportunities for participation, enjoyment, and education to those who seek them. A broad range of performing arts, visual arts, literary culture, festivals, and museum exhibits fills large and small venues on both sides of the U.S.-Mexican border. In no way is this region a cultural wasteland.

*Dollente is Associate Director of San Diego State University Press and its affiliate, the Binational Press (a joint publishing venture of San Diego State's Imperial Valley Campus and the Autonomous University of Baja California in Mexicali), is Director of the Art Gallery and a humanities enrichment program at the Imperial Valley Campus, and teaches an interdisciplinary course in Liberal Studies for prospective teachers. Kintero is a visual artist who has exhibited throughout Baja California.

Mexicali is the capital of the Mexican State of Baja California and, as such, serves as headquarters for a number of important government-sponsored cultural institutions. The Imperial Valley, in California, boasts a much smaller population distributed among several cities throughout the rural agricultural county. There, private citizens who work together in civic organizations, often as volunteers, provide much of the leadership and funding for cultural events. For both areas, educational institutions play a lead role in presenting major visual and performing artists, writers, and cultural groups from outside the areas, as well as showcasing local talent. Although opportunities for education in the arts are somewhat limited here—when compared to coastal metropolitan regions—there are still dozens of lectures, classes, and workshops available. These border communities consistently produce young artists and writers of the highest caliber who are recognized in state and national competitions.

Space to Flourish: Mexicali

Performance and exhibit spaces in Mexicali include several large theaters, galleries, and museums for patrons in each border community, in addition to dozens of smaller sites. In Mexicali, one of the major venues, the Teatro del Estado or State Theater, is located within two miles of the border with easy access for both Mexican and U.S. residents. Music and dance performances, plays, conferences, and other events are held at this well-appointed location that seats more than one-thousand persons. Attached to the theater are a reading room, bookstore that features quality works by local writers, and the Café Literario. The latter is a small night club where cultural events such as book presentations, music and dance performances, theater productions, and film screenings are regularly scheduled as part of the state capital's cultural calendar. Many of the events at the Café Literario are the work of young, innovative artists and receive wide support from Mexicali's patrons of all ages of the cultural avant-garde.

In addition to the Teatro del Estado, other large performance spaces exist, including the Auditorio del Estado (State Auditorium) and the Teatro del Instituto Mexicano del Seguro Social–IMSS (Mexican Institute of Social Security). During the year 2000, both of these venues hosted international music performances—a folk festival at one and a rock festival at the other. Drama performances, including productions for children, may feature local or state playwrights and acting troupes, all of whom find in the Teatro a worthy stage to exhibit their talents. Actor and director Angel Norzagaray heads the Mexicali a Secas group, which is responsible for managing and programming at the theater. Within a couple of blocks of the main border crossing between downtown Calexico and Mexicali is the House of Culture (Casa de la Cultura). It houses a small theater as well as exhibition spaces for visual arts and multiple classrooms for instruction in dance, music, painting, and other cultural arts. Courses available are always prominently advertised on signage, which fronts the heavily traveled street leading to the Calexico port of entry.

Considerably further from the border, yet still accessible via major Mexicali boulevards, is the Autonomous University of Baja California (Universidad Autonoma de Baja California–UABC). It has on its main campus another large theater used frequently for music, dance, and conferences. One of the program highlights each spring is an international festival of contemporary dance held at this theater and other venues throughout the city. The lobby of the UABC theater is sufficiently spacious to house art exhibits, such as the recent display of portraits of the Mexican literary community by Mexican photographer Rogelio Cuéllar during a national writers' conference. Augmenting this fine facility, an outdoor performance space—Teatro al Aire Libre—adjoins the student center. This beautiful architectural space, largely below ground level, encloses a spacious cafeteria, bookstore, clothing store, and a major art gallery. It provides a popular site for cultural and social interaction on the university campus. The outdoor amphitheater, also below ground level, serves best as a space for student meetings and musical performances. The university has portable stage and lighting equipment that can be utilized here or in any open patio, making the entire grounds a versatile and useful arts space. The main gallery in the student center is complemented by a smaller gallery and a cinema hall that are located within the complex of classrooms for the cultural extension program run by the university. Aside from UABC's main campus, additional university locations and other school sites throughout the city have smaller theaters and galleries. The campus of the Center for Technical and Higher Education (Centro de Enseñanza Técnica y Superior–CETYS)—an institution for both high school and college-level education— has a small theater, exhibition space, and a multifunctional conference center that are widely used for binational gatherings.

By far, the largest and most versatile exhibit space in Mexicali is the Museo Universitario (University Museum), another facility operated by UABC. This museum's exhibits—along with the natural history collection of flora, fauna, and native artifacts of regional tribes that is located next door—are superb educational resources for the border communities and easily accessible via the main traffic corridor into Mexicali from the United States. The museum can accommodate several exhibits at once and almost always incorporates an activity room where children can explore, in depth and hands-on, some facet of the exhibit. During recent years, its programming has included a national traveling exhibit of the famous, fanciful papier-mâché animal figures created by the Linares family of Mexico, a binational exhibit on the wildlife of the Baja California peninsula, an exhibit of the artifacts and sculptural treasures discovered at the Teotihuacán pyramids of central Mexico, a display of Japanese toys, a collection of beaded necklaces by the Cocopah tribe, exhibits of works of art by local and international artists, and a well-produced exposition on the history of money. These also included entertaining and educational components created specifically for children, but that are equally interesting to adults. A small auditorium that is part of the museum complex can be rented by outside groups.

Less obviously a cultural site, yet definitely an impressive resource for families on both sides of the border, El Sol del Niño is an exploration museum specifically for children. This facility boasts dozens of exhibits that invite young people (and their parents) to investigate and participate in the mysteries of science and the natural world. Designed like similar expositions for children in larger metropolitan areas, this attraction exemplifies the opportunities for enrichment that are abundant in this border region.

Within the compound of what was formerly the governor's palace, the Cultural Institute of Baja California (Instituto Cultural de Baja California–ICBC) coordinates a diverse range of cultural activities. It utilizes a myriad of rooms surrounding a central courtyard as offices for the organization of events, graphic design, sound recordings, translation, public relations, and other tasks in support of the arts. The ICBC produces a monthly or seasonal calendar of events and other publicity pieces and provides financial sponsorship for cultural programs, exhibits, and competitions. The administrative facilities available to this organization are as important to the arts and literature of the region as are the galleries and theaters. Recently remodeled, the City Gallery (Galería de la Ciudad) adjoins the courtyard adjacent to the offices and opens onto the street in front of the complex. Visual art exhibits, art performances, and film or video festivals occupy this attractive space throughout the year. The gallery showcases state and local artists as well as those with national and international recognition.

Within a few blocks of the ICBC, several other organizations serve specialized needs of the community. Across the street from the *rectoría*, or general administrative offices of UABC, office and production space is available for Editorial UABC, the university press. Several dozen books are published annually and the office contributes to the publication of several journals focused on cultural and economic development. An outdoor amphitheater occupies a park-like setting on the grounds of the *rectoría*.

Also nearby, the State Institute of Fine Arts (Instituto Estatal de Bellas Artes) houses classroom and practice space for the arts. A significant private facility is the José García Arroyo Gallery. Artist Ruth Hernández Ortega operates this small gallery on the second floor of a building that formerly served as a major public market. The State Library (Biblioteca del Estado) occasionally allots some space to literary conferences and art displays. One of the outstanding features of the library is the large mural in the foyer. The artist is Mexicali resident Carlos Coronado Ortega, whose murals are also permanent works in the foyer of the UABC Theater and the main hallway of the Casa de la Cultura. As with the ICBC, the library and *rectoría* are former state government offices. The conversion of these facilities, outgrown by the state administration, is an indication of the regard for cultural pursuits in Baja California.

A Growing Interest in Cultural Space: The Imperial Valley

State and national support for cultural facilities is not the norm in the United States as it is in Mexico. In the Imperial Valley (or Imperial County), cultural venues are most often built as part of educational facilities. The newest and best-equipped theater in the area is at Southwest High School in El Centro. This campus was designed to incorporate a performing arts academy, with the Southwest Theater serving as an asset to the community as well as to the students. Locally produced versions of Broadway plays supplement a season of a half-dozen touring dramatic and musical performances such as *The King and I*, *Camelot*, singer Crystal Gayle, the Kingston Trio, and Tap Dogs (a tap dance show). Palmer Auditorium, located at Brawley High School, organizes a similar season of performances. Although not an ideal location for an art exhibit, the lobby of this theater is used for displays in an effort to expand the arts available in this northern portion of the county. Many schools in the region have moderate stage facilities incorporated into one end of large multipurpose rooms, and occasionally there is a fully dedicated theater space such as the auditorium at Finley Elementary School in Holtville.

Institutions of higher education provide other important cultural spaces for county residents. Imperial Valley College (a lower-division community college) has a small auditorium in the Health Sciences building and an outdoor amphitheater with a stage and sloped surround, but no built-in seating. The large lounge and eating area in the student center is used for music and drama performances with the addition of a portable stage. The gymnasium, with bleachers, is occasionally pressed into service for cultural events. In a joint effort to advance historical preservation and the visual arts, a vintage train station from Holtville was relocated to the Imperial Valley College campus to serve as a gallery. The landscaping here features native desert plants and a section of the old plank road that used to traverse the desert to the east, connecting local cities to Yuma, Arizona.

In Calexico, just seven city blocks from the U.S.-Mexican border, the Imperial Valley Campus of San Diego State University (SDSU) offers two major cultural venues. Rodney Auditorium, which underwent major improvements during 2001–2002, serves the university and other local schools and organizations as the theater of choice for drama and music performances. This facility seats more than five hundred persons. It has hosted numerous plays, rock concerts, school graduations, conferences, and a filled-to-capacity poetry reading by Chicano poet Gary Soto. The Steppling Art Gallery lies at one end of an open, grass-covered quadrangle, facing the SDSU campus library. Smaller art, drama, or music presentations and conference gatherings take place in the library. The gallery mounts several exhibits during the academic year, bringing artists from Southern California and the border region, as well as occasional artists from areas as distant as Mexico City and New York. Recently, the gallery participated with three other regional institutions as a host venue for a major project by renowned contemporary artist Allan McCollum. The exhibits were part of inSITE 2000, an international installation and performance exposition held every three years along the California-Baja California border. Artist lectures sometimes accompany exhibits of painting, photography, sculpture, ceramics, and other media.

Cultural events, other than visual arts, are staged in the university gallery or the gallery patio. During recent years, activities have included contemporary, folk, and tango dance; folk, rock, country, mariachi, classical, jazz, and blues music; book presentations and poetry readings; international film/video festivals; and small drama productions. The gallery also serves as a gathering place for social activities and receptions. As a special event, each fall university students erect in the gallery, or elsewhere on campus, an exhibit of colorful altars designed to observe the Mexican tradition of *día de los muertos* (Day of the Dead) to honor deceased loved ones, political heroes, or celebrities.

Interest in cross-border culture extends to many other areas of the university as well. SDSU sponsors one of the few university presses in the California State University system and the office of SDSU Press at the Imperial Valley Campus facilitates relationships with authors in Baja California. Recent publications include an eight-book series on Baja California Literature in Translation and titles on postmodern arts such as Russian Futurism and the fluxus arts movement in the United States. The Binational Press was created through a joint publishing agreement with UABC's Mexicali campus. Seven titles on literature, art, language, and dance have been printed in bilingual English-Spanish editions.

In an effort to secure space for cultural programming beyond that in established educational institutions and to preserve the unique architecture of the former post office in El Centro, local citizens worked to have the building registered as a state historical site. The Imperial County Arts Commission is now headquartered there. The facility has exhibit space for visual art and a small stage where classical, jazz, and pop music performances entertain the local audience and where community theater programs are held. Although the basement rooms intended for use as artist workshops are still somewhat undeveloped, there is adequate office and kitchen space on the main floor. This site, known as the Old Post Office Pavilion (OPOP), is well utilized, with additional potential for the future.

A growing facility for cultural preservation is found in the Pioneers Park Museum, which is operated by the Imperial County Historical Society. Individual galleries in the two main buildings feature exhibits sponsored by each of the ethnic groups that have settled in this area since the early twentieth century: Swiss, Mexican, East Indian, Chinese, Portuguese, Filipino, Greek, and many more. In addition, it displays local wildlife; Indian pottery and basketry; the cattle industry; the history of the canal system and the Imperial Irrigation District that manages it; pianos from the early churches and a restored pipe organ; and household furnishings and artifacts that tell the story of the region's early history. Vintage farm implements are arrayed for viewing on the grounds of the museum, which is located directly across the street from Imperial Valley College. Although not a dedicated gallery or performance space, the museum frequently hosts small art exhibits and musical programs. It also provides opportunities for each of the sponsoring ethnic organizations to hold cultural events at the facility. Internationally exhibited artist Allan McCollum designed a permanent piece of public art now installed on the grounds of the Pioneers Park Museum; it is a 15-foot sculpture of a desert sandspike (a naturally occurring sand concretion, generally a few inches in length, found at the base of local Mt. Signal). With its emphasis on both past and present, Pioneers Park Museum is an outstanding resource for the region, built and maintained by local funding and community volunteers.

In another effort to preserve the past, the Ocotillo Desert Museum is still in its planning stage, although the site has been readied and a strong group of volunteers heads the project. Dr. Jay von Werlhof, a renowned anthropologist and former professor at Imperial Valley College, has worked to locate and study the geoglyphs, fish traps, and other traces of earlier Indian cultures in the region that will become the focus of educational displays when this museum is completed.

The largest capacity arena for performances in the Imperial Valley can be found at the county fairgrounds. A roofed grandstand with bench seating opens to a portable outdoor stage where name performers in pop, rock, country, or any of several Mexican styles of music can entertain the large crowds that attend the California Mid-Winter Fair and Fiesta each March. Several smaller stages, both indoors and outdoors, dot the fairgrounds, allowing local and touring artists to perform. Painting, photography, and crafts are also exhibited in a juried exposition during the fair.

Smaller, private venues for the arts in Imperial Valley include several small galleries that sell art and crafts in downtown Brawley and El Centro. A number of clubs and restaurants also provide music groups to entertain their patrons. Occasionally, a business will display the artwork of a local artist.

Cultural Organizations, Programs, and Classes in Mexicali

In Mexico, government, education, and private sectors all offer opportunities to learn more about the arts and to participate in cultural events. Here, the primary and secondary schools have limited hours and resources and are not a major source of cultural education. The university, however, has a flourishing cultural extension program with evening classes in a wide variety of arts. Students can take guitar or percussion lessons, practice crafts, learn flamenco dance, or participate in a wide variety of other programs. As part of its cultural responsibilities, UABC sponsors several high quality music groups: a folk dance ensemble; a folk music troupe (La Choya); a mariachi band (Mariachi Calafia); and a *son*, *salsa*, and Latin jazz band

(Son de Acá). These musicians and dancers are not students recruited from classes, but professionals paid to preserve and disseminate Mexican culture. The engineering department also sponsors a music and singing group—known as a *rondalla*—to present romantic Mexican songs. All of these groups perform frequently in Mexicali and throughout Baja California and are available to make presentations north of the border. These performers have participated in international festivals in Italy, Germany, Brazil, and China in recent years.

In addition to the extensive selection of classes for adults and children at the Casa de la Cultura, other public and private institutions provide a multitude of cultural enrichment experiences for those who wish to learn. The State Institute of Fine Arts offers classes in the visual and performing arts and the ICBC promotes events such as a children's film series and literature workshops. CETYS sponsors a 20-piece jazz band and a *rondalla* with performers drawn mainly from the student population. This campus also regularly hosts cultural workshops with knowledgeable instructors in such areas as film (Alejandro Espinoza), photography (Odette Barajas), and painting (Marcela Alvarado). A state-funded program, ARCO IRIS, provides creative writing workshops for elementary school students and teachers. The José García Arroyo Gallery develops children's talents in the arts through group classes. Organizations for adults include poetry groups and *Imágenes*, a photography club that provides opportunities to learn new techniques and exhibit work. Many private teachers instruct both the children and adults of Mexicali in ballet, painting, music, or other cultural pursuits.

Alternative approaches to the arts are encouraged as young artists and writers support the innovative work in their own genre and in others. The annual A-V TextFest was founded in Mexicali in 1998 to bring together an international slate of artists and their experimental contributions in visual poetry, sound poetry, hypertext, and other forms.

Cultural Organizations and Opportunities in the Imperial Valley

Schools offer cultural programs for the majority of Imperial Valley children and youth. Private music lessons are widely available and some private classes exist for dance and other arts. Most of the high schools sponsor marching bands and many elementary and middle schools maintain music programs, even in the face of ongoing budget cuts for arts education. Many schools have choral groups. Calexico has both high school and junior high mariachi bands. Theater arts, visual arts, and dance instruction receive less attention, but individual schools, most notably Southwest High School, offer some education in these areas. El Centro High School has long been noted for its jazz band. Founded and brought to excellence by Jimmie Cannon, the program continues its reputation under current director Rene Baker. College-level courses in the arts are few, although its instruction is generally first rate.

As in the schools, music opportunities abound within the larger community. Both Cannon and Baker participate in Valley Jazz, a professional-caliber jazz band made up of 15 to 20 local musicians and directed by Cannon. Valley Jazz and several smaller ensembles featuring these musicians (Standing Room Only, Blue Lake Quartet) play at events throughout the year and offer a free Christmas concert in Palmer Auditorium each December as a gift to the community. The Imperial Valley Symphony Orchestra is led by Joel Jacklich with Patricia Saracco also in the role of conductor. The orchestra stages several concerts per year, with informative lectures preceding their performances. The group brings guest performers to the Imperial Valley and sponsors a young musicians competition and scholarships. There are numerous local bands and more informal groups of musicians that play a country, rock, folk, blues, classical, or ethnic repertoire. Brawley hosts a bluegrass festival each fall and an old-time fiddle competition has become a popular event each January at the county fairgrounds in the City of Imperial.

The Imperial County Arts Council is the umbrella organization for the arts. It coordinates music and theater programs and visual art exhibits at the Old Post Office Pavilion. State and federal grants are administered by the Council, which produces a directory of local artists and arts organizations. Adults can avail themselves of specialized groups such as the Imperial Valley Arts Association, which sponsors painting classes and operates a center for its members in El Centro. The North County Coalition for the Arts (NOCCA) sponsors programs in the Brawley area. The Calexico Arts Commission operates along the border to bring opportunities for community-based participation in the arts. One of the Commission's ongoing public art projects is the painting of a lengthy section of the metal fence that marks the border along the western edge of the city. This project, headed by Chicano artist Armando Rascón (a former resident of Calexico), has involved hundreds of hours of labor by students and adults working together to beautify the structure. The Commission also hopes to develop a park along the fence.

The value of arts programs in developing the potential of those in poverty or other underprivileged situations is increasingly recognized through government grants that are channeled through local agencies. Arts in Corrections serves the two state prisons in Imperial County; it provides unique opportunities for artists and educators in visual arts, music, and writing to bring their craft to those who have had little opportunity to explore such cultural experiences in the past. Steps of Success (SOS) is a five-year federal grant program operated by local agencies such as the Regional Occupation Program (ROP), the Boys and Girls Club, and the North County Coalition for the Arts. Students in the age group from 14 to 21 years, and especially school dropouts, are targeted for classes in drawing, photography, violin, guitar, voice, and theater technician skills—all part of a comprehensive package that includes such personal development instruction as anger management and drug and alcohol awareness. Arts are incorporated as useful tools in the promotion of job skills for these youth in the North County area. The arts are an economic boom in other ways. For example, Imperial County supports an active and successful Film Commission to attract producers of television commercials and feature films to the region.

Border Festivals and the Border's Future

On each side of the border, communities celebrate the things that make them special and that bring people together. Throughout the month of October, Mexicali enjoys the Fiesta del Sol, held at Vicente Guerrero Park behind the State Theater. This event is much like a fair, with commercial and club exhibits, local and national performances of music and dance, a carnival, and a dazzling array of food and souvenirs. The California Mid-Winter Fair and Fiesta in Imperial has a similar emphasis on fun and public relations. It has an added focus on youth through the 4-H Clubs and Future Farmers Associations that participate in livestock shows and other judged exhibits with entries in foods, sewing, knitting, crafts, electricity, photography, and other projects. The culture of local agriculture can be explored by walking through the animal barns and talking with the young entrepreneurs who have made sizeable investments of time and money to bring their livestock to the auction ring on the final weekend of the fair.

Other civic festivals include the Holtville Carrot Festival, complete with cooking contests for children and adults, an old-fashioned tractor pull with modern high-horsepower equipment, and a gem and mineral show. Niland hosts the Tomato Festival. Brawley celebrates the beef industry with its Cattle Call Rodeo, cowboy poetry contest, and Western dance at the Planters Hotel. Calexico and El Centro mark the winter holidays with colorful and energetic Christmas parades. An annual Mariachi Festival in the county recognizes the strong presence of Mexican culture north of the border. In Mexicali, an elaborate culture of skill on horseback is preserved in the practice of *charrería*, where a specially designed arena and costumes are part of the tradition that, at first, might appear to be similar to the American rodeo. Both Mexicali and the Imperial Valley honor their patriotic holidays with enthusiasm, gathering large crowds for speeches, music, food, and fireworks.

Religious traditions from many faiths contribute to the infusion of cultural variety in the Imperial Valley-Mexicali region. Both Mexicali and El Centro have Tibetan Culture Centers with ceremonies directed by a Lama of Tibetan Buddhism. Ramadan, the month of fasting by Muslims, and Hanukkah, a remembrance of the triumph of a besieged Jewish settlement from centuries past, are among the specialized celebrations of minority faiths in this region. Both celebrations enrich the cultural understanding of the majority through programs, shared feasts, and educational articles that are annual features in the Imperial Valley Press newspaper. Christians also share evidence of their faith with the community through *posadas* and caroling in December and gathering to serve slices of the *rosca*, or ring of bread and fruit, that is part of the celebration of *el día de los Reyes*, King's Day, on January 6.

Despite the promotion of a binational consciousness by arts and culture administrators and practitioners in both Mexicali and the Imperial Valley, the actual exchange of visitors for the purpose of participating in the arts is not a general habit except among a few individuals or for specific events. The San Diego Symphony's performance in Mexicali draws classical music patrons southward, teenagers flock south to the dance clubs and live music cafés on the weekends, and Mexicali residents head north for the Mariachi Festival or to see popular rock bands in concert at the fairgrounds. When either border community features the artwork of a local artist, friends and family vigorously provide their support by attending the exhibit opening; however, the following month's exhibit might not see any visitors from across the border. News media in both countries make an effort to cover selected events in the nearby cities across the border and, recently, publicity through electronic mail has greatly facilitated binational communication. Whether the scarcity of cross-border arts patronage can be attributed to problems with language, transportation, information, time, or interest, the result is a great deal of official interest in binational arts, but little sustained participation.

Exposure to the culture and vision of the global community expands with international business investments in border *maquiladoras* (assembly plants in Mexico) and increasing opportunities for international travel through student exchange programs in Imperial County high schools and at the university. Communications technology has high priority in the region, as the Internet is useful as a link to neighbors in other countries and continents as the old plank road was in linking Imperial County to Yuma, Arizona, less than a century ago. The wealth of this region has long been found in the mix of ideas and the energy of growth brought to the desert by people looking for the promise of a better life. As a cross-border region, the cultural and educational opportunities found in the Imperial and Mexicali valleys complement one another, making the region flourish in richness and diversity.

29

Transborder Public Art: Murals and Graffiti in the Imperial-Mexicali Valley

Marcia Isabel Campillo López*

Abstract

Murals and graffiti that have emerged in public spaces in the Imperial-Mexicali Valley deal with a variety of subjects that have to do with cross-border regional life. Such works evoke visual narratives on the region's history, portray shared popular icons, and exhibit cryptic languages. These paintings and "writings" jointly reveal a visual world without geopolitical boundaries, clearing the way for the expression of both individuals and groups that inhabit either side of the valley. The murals and graffiti considered in this essay encompass paintings, drawings, and writings found along highways in the cities of Mexicali, Calexico, El Centro, and Brawley. In the cases of Mexicali and Calexico, they also encompass murals within neighborhoods (barrios).

Introduction: Murals and Graffiti, the Basis of Regional Public Art

Public art[1] is included in the creation of open spaces, architecture, and the design of urban roadways. In the framework of visual elements that compete for attention in cities, public art is part of the visual structuring of space. Historically, public art has been characterized as a monumental production that helps create the architectural

*Campillo López is Researcher at the Institute of Social Research at the Universidad Autónoma de Baja California in Mexicali. All photos were taken by author and Carlos Navarro. Images were manipulated by Elsy Gómez and Carlos Navarro.

design of great metropolises. It has played a definitive role in the re-creation of the personalities of cities, the people that inhabit them, and the authorities that govern them. In the process of defining these personalities, the works promoted by artists and social groups converge with the impulses of those who govern the cities. In countries where public art holds an important position in urban design, a majority of monumental art is necessarily defined by a team of urban planners and aided by the collaboration of visual artists. Nonetheless, the formal bond between art and urbanization is loosely regulated outside of large cities and public art is increasingly produced with local resources by local artists and communities. This is the case in the production of public art in the Imperial-Mexicali Valley.[2] Visual works of monumental character are few and unincorporated into urban landscape planning. The aesthetics of public spaces limits them to small areas of the cities. In this context, the works of art considered in this essay, namely murals and graffiti, constitute a joint effort by the citizenry to publicly manifest its own visual representations, even if the dimensions do not reach monumental stature. From another perspective, such unplanned art in public spaces, given its power of expression within the cities, could be the basis for a variety of regional and public visual art realized in two-dimensional mediums. This essay briefly explores the artistic and cultural potential of the paintings and "writings" on the walls of the cities of Mexicali and of the Imperial Valley, describing the motivations of its artists and the reception the works have received from the community based on a shared social history. Photographs of murals and graffiti in the region are included and those elaborated in the last five years are more specifically focused upon. It should be noted that the paintings selected to accompany this essay do not represent the works of an individual artist nor of a group of artists in particular. They are solely representations of the styles of murals and graffiti most common to the region. This is not a guide to the principal works of the valley, but an initial study of the works that have acquired cultural status since their acceptance as part of the daily experience in the cities under study.

The Imperial-Mexicali Valley:
A Shared Social and Cultural Space

The Imperial-Mexicali Valley region shares a social and cultural transborder[3] space defined by the interaction of people on both sides of the border. Since the beginning of the twentieth century, the population of both geopolitical regions was formed principally by migrants. These migrants were attracted to the region by the offer of potential prosperity made by transnational investors. Those migrants who would relocate to northern Mexico or Southern California were spurred by the promise of employment and a better quality of life. Both sides of the border based their development on the agricultural, *maquiladora* (in-bond manufacturing plant), and commercial industries. The working population of each side of the border has thus been made up of primarily agricultural workers, factory workers, and merchants, even when the services sector grew in the second half of the twentieth century.[4] The political division of the two regions was characterized by the different cultural origins of the populations in Mexicali and the Imperial Valley in the first 50 years of development. The considerable growth of the population of Mexican origin in the Imperial Valley, which has increased dramatically in the last three decades, has created a shared cultural base. At the end of the twentieth century, the presence of Mexicans in the Imperial Valley was predominant. The population of Mexican origin in Imperial County was 65.1 percent in 2000. In the most populated cities in the county such as El Centro, Brawley, and Calexico, the population of Hispanic origin was 74.6 percent, 73.8 percent, and 95.3 percent, respectively. In Calexico, across the border from Mexicali, those residents either born in Mexico or of Mexican descent totaled 87.7 percent of the population (U.S. Census Bureau 2000). Fimbres (2000: 108) notes that this "has consequently brought the Hispanization of the city through culture: it is common to hear Spanish spoken in the city, the language that is spoken in the majority of homes, commercial facilities, and office places (the Mexican peso is even accepted in almost all commercial establishments)."

The cultural identity shared by Calexico and Mexicali is observed in the integration of the transborder region and in the fact that the population of both cities is formed by Mexican migrants primarily from the Mexican states of Jalisco, Michoacán, Sinaloa, and Sonora (Fimbres 2000: 102). The Mexican migrant worker is an important part of social and economic dynamics affecting the entire southwestern region. This migratory phenomenon seems to be a dominant factor in the construction of a shared identity in the Imperial-Mexicali Valley, reflecting a daily concern with defining a local personality in the face of the national Mexican culture and a Chicano (Mexican-American) personality in the face of American culture.

Conditions for the Production of Murals and Artistic Graffiti

Undoubtedly, the use of billboards in public places for painting, writing, and sketching is much more common in Mexicali than in Imperial County. The population of Mexicali is six times larger and, therefore, the number of potential muralists and graffiti artists is also greater. Mexicali is also a more accessible place for these types of visual expressions due to its more relaxed restrictions in the use of city walls and more easily acquired permits and financing of such endeavors. Most mural and graffiti activity in Mexicali has been enriched by continual visits by artists and fans of muralism from the Imperial Valley. These visitors involve themselves in the production of neighborhood murals or with graffiti groups that work in the city. In this sense, a space of transborder creation has been formed that supports the development of shared public art.

Land, Work, and Regional History

The murals in the Imperial-Mexicali Valley represent a synthesized way of telling one's own version of the region's history. Be it through mythic description or a reconstruction based on documented evidence, the artists look to synthesize visual elements on the wall that communicate a design particular to those who inhabit the region. With this goal in mind, both artists with formal education and those with no artistic training unite. The narratives produced link regional identity to the workplace, nature (the desert made livable), and social struggles.

The first mural of this genre that still stands was painted in the 1930s in the interior patio of the offices of the Colorado River Land Company, located in the oldest part of the City of Mexicali.[5] This mural narrates the rustic lifestyle in the valley at the inception of its agricultural activity. It shows a harmonious land where those involved in both industry and agriculture made great efforts to make the plains livable. This painting marks the relationship between the development of regional muralism and the production of murals in central Mexico, where muralism was experiencing a boom,[6] expressing the ideologies of the Mexican Revolution of 1910 (Suárez 1974: 381).

Over the next three decades, several attempts to transfer the teachings of Mexican muralism to northern Mexico were made, imitating on occasion, and without much success, the style of Diego Rivera. Regional painters found their own

Figure 1. "American Legion"

Mural narrative of the origins of the California native. The fertility of the land, the legacy of Spanish colonialism, and the indigenous heritage in the region are emphasized. Located in a public parking lot in El Centro, California.

individual forms of expression in their work, including themes based on the defense of the peasantry. The regional dynamics of land seizures and the agrarian struggle in the Mexicali Valley to take back foreign properties for Mexican peasants initiated a thematic tendency for the *mexicalense* (from Mexicali) mural. Farm work as a basis for regional identity and representations of land seizures are subjects repeatedly depicted in murals by local painters and local neighborhood youth, like vignettes of local history that will be transmitted to future generations. The reiteration of the agrarian question suggests a shared idea that farm work could be an emblem of spatial development that both integrates and separates the Mexicali Valley from the Imperial Valley. Mexicans on both sides of the border share the ideas put forth in the early twentieth century by Emiliano Zapata, who claimed that the land belongs to those who work it. This idea is represented first by the Mexican school of muralism and later by Chicano muralism, which reproduces some of the Mexican school qualities. In the late 1960s, Carlos Coronado Ortega painted a mural on a bank

Figure 2. "Corriendo a California"/"Running to California"

Detail of a mural showing the historic route Mexicans took to the United States,
from pre-Hispanic culture to skyscrapers. Located on the exterior of an
industrial building on Imperial Avenue in Calexico, California.

located in the old center of Mexicali. It depicted a field ploughed by financial voracity and robbery of the peasants in the valley who were given credit by investors; it was destroyed when the offices were remodeled. Thirty years later, the pyramidal composition of this mural and the emphasis on the hard work demanded by the fields was repeated in 1997 by Javier Carbó in the Municipal House of Mexicali (Mexicali's city hall) and titled "Collective Individualism." The painter included a small message in the margin, stating, *"Aquél que trabaja escarbando dentro de sí mismo, corre la posibilidad de tener riquezas que compartirle a su humanidad"* (He who works by delving into himself, faces the possibility of having riches to share with [his] humanity). All art is popular art according to Gabriel García Márquez, which is confirmed in this region. The large social space that includes the border cities of Baja California and California will be the source of popular artistic creations charged by anger, nonconformity, and pride, where Mexican and American cultures and other cultural "minorities" will confront one another.

Chicano Muralism, Cultural Confrontation, and Mythic Recollection

The 1960s were a time of struggle for agricultural workers who fought for their rights.[7] This activated the use of walls as an artistic medium to transmit words and images of the protests against the abuse of and discrimination against the already significant population of Mexican origin in the State of California. At this time, California, and particularly the City of Los Angeles, began to show signs of being a receptive place for muralism. Since then, it has emerged as the capital of muralism worldwide (Cockcroft and Barnet-Sánchez 1993: 16). As the Chicano movement grew in strength on the streets of Los Angeles, murals became the backdrop for a collective reflection of cultural identity and the legitimacy of the exercise of citizens' rights in the United States. In them, the struggles of various populations of Latin American origin, African-Americans, and other social sectors considered to be minorities were represented. It should be pointed out that the production of murals of monumental character is less common in Imperial than in other neighboring counties in Southern California, such as San Diego and Los Angeles. Stylistic and thematic continuity is apparent in muralism in Imperial Valley and the rest of the State of California as well as in Mexicali.

The struggles of the population of Mexican origin bring with them the representation of a Mexican-American reality sustained by the reconstruction of Chicano history in the United States. Chicanos use visual narrative elements that place the Mexican migrant descendent population in a context in which the legacies of the first Indians that inhabited the southwestern United States are recognized alongside Mesoamerican civilizations that lived in the times of the conquest and colonization (Gaspar de Alba 1998: 40). In this context, a history that reflects the region at the beginning of the twenty-first century is created. An example of these narratives is found in the mural on Imperial Avenue in Calexico, in which Indians riding horseback impetuously leave the Mesoamerican land (represented by a large pyramid). Several cowboys are also depicted riding toward American skyscrapers. This type of mythic recollection combined with modern imagery used by U.S. artists of Mexican origin carries its influence to the other side of the border to be reinterpreted by Mexicali artists.

Muralists will adopt and further the visual forms of Chicano muralism to depict the reality of the population linked to the migrant lifestyle. The result of this influence on the region's murals is a visual narrative shared by a pre-Hispanic background, but bifurcated in the search for a current definition of "Mexicanness" in each geopolitical context. The challenge to visualize not only their origin, but the way Mexicans have integrated themselves into the American lifestyle is visible in the works of Mexican muralists that paint in the Imperial Valley.

The use of walls to express social problems is reflected in several works in Mexicali. Figure 3 shows a mural painted on a wall on López Mateos Boulevard in the City of Mexicali. It depicts the power of the drug mafias, but was painted over in early 2001.

Figure 3. "El Mero Mero"

Large mural painted on López Mateos Boulevard in the city of Mexicali depicting a scene of drug mafia gambling and transactions.

The Legacy of Mexican Muralism

The direct influence of Mexican muralism—without overlooking Chicano art— arrived to the region during the first half of the twentieth century. However, its definition in the region was not advanced until the second half of the century with the work of Carlos Coronado Ortega. Gabriel Trujillo Muñoz points to two aspects that the muralist incorporated into his artwork: the ideology of nationalism, which includes the context of the Baja Californian identity in a personal and novel way, and the monumentality of the Mexican mural (1993: 5, 12). In this period, the central questions that surrounded the paintings of visual artists and fans of Mexican and Chicano muralism were based on the same theme: the search for a definition of identity. The most notable mural produced in this era by Coronado can be found in the State of Baja California Public Library in Mexicali. Finished in 1976, the mural is an account of the social history of Baja California. The themes of the mural integrate six historical periods: prehistory, the conquest, colonization and missionization, the process of *mestizaje* (the mixture of races), postrevolution, and contemporary identity (Ochoa Zazueta 1977: 56). It remains the most synthetic narrative mural work of regional history.

Muralism won its place in historic art in the twentieth century. In most cases, it became reduced to a sterile form of official Mexican discourse. In Baja California, however, it was revived as a medium for questioning the identity of Mexicans and their history. The mural became a textbook for primary and junior high schools. The cities of Calexico and Mexicali boast murals that creatively illustrate the synthesis of history in either city. On the U.S. side, the integration of national and Mexican heroes

Figure 4. "De la Diversidad Cultural"/"From Cultural Diversity"

Detail of a large mural on the exterior of a school in Calexico,
California. Several figures from U.S. and Mexican history are
represented, guarded by historic monuments, as part of the
multicultural legacy of the Mexican-American population.

Figure 5. "Arte Público en la Línea Internacional"/"Public Art along the International Boundary"

of different cultural origins combined with pre-Hispanic icons is common, including Abraham Lincoln, Benito Juárez, and Martin Luther King, Jr., alongside the Statue of Liberty. The importance of both historical Mexican and U.S. figures that fought for the emancipation of the people alludes to a multiculturalism in which (in theory) all of American society participates. Mexicali muralists, however, almost always follow a nationalistic iconographic tradition, using representations of Emiliano Zapata, Francisco Villa, and Benito Juárez. Few murals break with this tradition; one such case is painted on a public junior high school in Colonia Hidalgo depicting Latin American heroes such as Che Guevara and Augusto Sandino.

At the end of the twentieth century, two decades later, two mural projects demonstrated the ideas of collectivity and border and even used the border fence. "Metamorphosis 2000" is currently being produced directly on the international border fence by plastic artist Armando Rascón of Calexico. Another example is a series of projects initiated by Mexicali artists that also incorporates Californian artists in the effort to convert the divisory fence into an exhibition space for regional plastic artwork. Each project is naturally distinct. "Metamorphosis 2000" encompasses pre-Colombian inspirations along the border with the participation of more than one thousand people and was scheduled for completion in 2002. The project in Mexicali has more to do with the appropriation of the most public space in the region: the border crossing. Whereas art is typically shown in individual galleries to a small audience, moving it to open spaces would expose it to more people. Such a project demands the creation of a way for art to be viewed in the conditions that this public space imposes; namely, the long lines of vehicles waiting to cross the border. The potential for such collective public art projects and their impact on the transborder

Figure 6. "Sagrado Corazón"/"Sacred Heart"

Mural depicting the image of the Sacred Heart. It is located in a park near the Infonavit Cucapá neighborhood in Mexicali. The painting was commissioned and financed by a resident of the neighborhood and painted by a young muralist also from the neighborhood.

community are immense and could be combined with the production of popular murals in a didactic effort to integrate regional muralism.

Popular Icons

The collection of signs and symbols that are used in murals elaborates upon the traditional iconography of the revolutionary and pre-Hispanic Mexican murals and embraces religious and popular imagery in Mexico. Many murals encompass the eclectic interaction of the images of the Virgin of Guadalupe, Francisco Villa, the Flores Magón brothers, the Sacred Heart, Benito Juárez, the pyramids of Teotihuacán, Olmec heads, Sor Juana Inés de la Cruz, Mixtec *grecas* (decorative belts), and the volcanoes of the Valley of Mexico. These popular images acquire a cultural value that exceeds the limits of painting and as more than esthetic products of an artist, they assume a delegated function as collective ideals. In neighborhoods, local residents conserve the murals, repainting them when necessary (generally in anticipation of religious celebrations, such as the Day of the Virgin of Guadalupe on December 12). This is done year after year over the original drawing. The product of the individual is replaced by that of the group that repaints the mural with the devotion that the religious images inspire and the nature with which one would paint his or her own house when necessary. The painting becomes autonomous and legitimizes its significance publicly.

The icon of the Virgin of Guadalupe represents a connection among Chicanos to the Mexican motherland. It is also a symbol of indigenous resistance against colonization,

Figure 7. "Viva la Raza"/"Long Live the People"

Mural depicting diverse iconographic elements of the cholo and Chicano imagination. Painted on the wall of a stationary store in Colonia Industrial, Mexicali, by a young muralist who lives in the neighborhood. It is repainted and adorned with lights on December 12, the Day of the Virgin of Guadalupe.

Figure 8. "Calecia x3"

Conventional forms or signs on the exterior walls of residential buildings in Calexico, California. The signs cover those of other groups who compete territorially.

transformed by the movement into a symbol of Chicano resistance to assimilation and territorial conquest (Gaspar de Alba 1998: 41). On both sides of the valley, the Virgin of Guadalupe is the most frequently represented icon in residential areas and is identified as part of *cholo* art.[8]

The production of murals in the early twenty-first century does not follow the same patterns. Trends follow the graphic creation of a visual identity in the Mexicali Valley, using the mural as an educational tool, a delegated object, the forum for articulating regional problems, or a meeting place with a mobile audience (people that line up to cross the border who are generally unlikely to visit art galleries).

Cryptic Writing

In the 1980s, graffiti was introduced as a form of mural art in California using new techniques and materials. The influence of aerosol paint on this art form gained such strength that it has modified the traditional forms of mural painting. This can be seen in the works of muralist groups in California that combine both techniques (Drescher 1998: 307). Timothy W. Drescher (1998) points to three separate categories of graffiti found in California: (1) "tagging," represented by initials, acronyms, or signs, with the intention of lifting its creator's ego "as often and as widely as possible"; (2) the "wild" style found in large tags, usually of only one color, where an almost undecipherable script is used; and (3) pieces of art or murals, created with aerosol paint. It is in this third category that graffiti becomes public art. It is one of the predominant visual resources in the region. Although one of its most immediate historical relatives is the graffiti on the trains of New York, graffiti found along the

Figure 9. "Tenis.detalle"

Detail of a mural created with spray paint that combines three-dimensional script and caricatures. It is located on the exterior wall of a home in Colonia Industrial, Mexicali. It is an excellent example of composition and color.

border is of a different "flavor" and represents California and Baja California. Many of the graffiti artists in the area belong to gangs on either side of the border and have developed a written language based on shared codes. It is common for youth from El Centro, California, to cross the border into Mexicali to paint graffiti. Graffiti artists in Tijuana leave "DTJ" (*desde Tijuana*/from Tijuana) written on walls as their mark. The markings respond to personal and group promises, not social promises, as in the case of murals (Franco 1995). Graffiti linked to a tradition of *cholo* street murals, even when alternated with the use of popular icons, uses written forms and ludicrous figures or caricatures. The most recent trend in graffiti in Mexicali is the inclusion of characteristics that are found in other contexts, such as "three-dimensional lettering styles and diverse color combinations combined with iconographic figures that represent a reality that is difficult to understand" (see Sánchez Guerrero 2000: 95–100). What gives graffiti local identity is the dynamic that the signs and murals acquire in fights between gangs for territory and expression. Murals created with aerosol paint unite graffiti fans, traditional muralists, and visual artists and writers that normally work with smaller mediums, compelling them to explore public spaces.

Although large cities in California and around the world have legitimized graffiti as an art form—endorsed by the quality of the paintings and their accessibility to large audiences—smaller cities, such as those in the Imperial-Mexicali valleys, are just beginning to value their presence in public spaces. Art found in galleries,

Figure 10. "Back in Business"

Graffiti on the exterior wall of a home in Mexicali demonstrating decorative "tags" in contrasting colors.

museums, libraries, and government buildings does not need the cultural and artistic legitimization of the population. Graffiti, as part of the counterculture, represents the opposition to such art and requires a more careful analysis to distinguish its validity as an artistic language, requiring approval from the general public as well as informed critics. Whether transformed, enriched, erased, or censured, graffiti will continue as an "anonymous" esthetic art form on public walls. What has been written about graffiti in New York is just as valid for the Imperial-Mexicali Valley: "[g]raffiti artwork adds color to a world that often lacks it. And in that the artistic form of graffiti serves the most noble of purposes" (Bronx View 2001). In response to the closed-mindedness of society with regard to urban graffiti, Fernando Vizcarra states that "[i]f we deny the city its purpose as a space for creation, imagination, tolerance, a break with daily life, the restoration of symbols, we put ourselves behind the bars of our own myths and swallow the key" (1996: 27).

Conclusions

What are the criteria for consensus regarding the validity of a work of public art? Who are the legitimate producers of public art? What are the spaces for public art? And, what links the imagination of public art to the development of cities? Artists and producers of public art are influenced by both tradition and provocative innovation. Given these influences, any new art form in the coming decades will repeat themes and ideas from the past. Murals and graffiti are part of the local voice. Their production provides a forum for citizen expression both geopolitically and artistically in public spaces.

These paintings and "writings," whether spontaneous or premeditated, reveal the different sociocultural realities in the Imperial-Mexicali valleys. The works of art allude to the *cholo* art forms of muralism and graffiti in Los Angeles. They also give the observer an understanding of Mesoamerican muralism and the Mexican school of art, which includes muralism as well as Chicano public and gallery art. The different methods of public art discussed in this essay reach all, as they are found in public spaces throughout the region. Both academic and popular painters perceive public spaces as places for art. The need for artistic individuality is the base for regional public art. Yet, the use of common signs, symbols, and messages link the individual to the whole and develops a common culture without geopolitical boundaries.

Endnotes

1. Public art refers to many forms of expression in plastic art, sculpture, and architectural design in open spaces that are within the reach of those who inhabit a specific geographical space. Examples include walls and buildings painted with murals or artistic writings, statues, large-scale sculptures, monumental buildings, artistic performances—art that is expressed as public property. It also includes, however, those art forms that "move" through the networks of a city, such as decorated automobiles and street performers.

2. The Imperial-Mexicali Valley is only one valley—a single social and cultural space that is not limited by the political boundaries of Mexico or the United States. The political space of this Valley refers to the Municipality of Mexicali, one of five in the State of Baja California, and Imperial County. The Municipality of Mexicali had an estimated population of 764,602 inhabitants in 2000, compared to 601,938 in 1990. The City of Mexicali is also the capital of the state. It had 549,873 inhabitants in 2000, compared to 438,377 residents in 1990. Imperial County incorporates several population centers, including Brawley, Calexico, Calipatria, El Centro, Heber, Holtville, Imperial, Niland, Seeley, and Westmorland. The total population of the county in 2000 was 142,361, compared to 109,300 in 1990.

3. The term "transborder" is pertinent to mural and graffiti art in the region because it allows the expressions of public art to overcome the political demarcations of this cultural phenomenon. The etymology of the prefix "trans" means "beyond." The use of this term in cultural research belongs to a much broader discussion that cannot be delved into in this essay.

4. This is, of course, a simplification of the description of the regional working population that allows for relationships to be established with the imaginative identity of the works described here.

5. A clay mural was also produced on the interior walls of the same offices in the late 1910s when Mexicali became a city. It depicted a landscape and technology that had little to do with the social life of the valley at the time. The mural was removed from its original site (Coronado Ortega 2001).

6. An example of the stylistic magnitude of muralism inspired by the Mexican Revolution is this description of the murals of Diego Rivera—a primary figure in the intellectual movement—located in the Secretariat of Public Education (Secretaría de Educación Pública–SEP) building in Mexico City by Teresa del Conde: "… Diego Rivera's murals are not amplified paintings, they are truly monumental works of art that live in tight collusion in the space where they are located and in the visual angle of the spectator. If Diego had not possessed a well-reasoned vision (more than intuition) of the displacement of spaces and elements that either interfere with or aid the visual range that a two-dimensional plane requires, his paintings would have merely told anecdotes and illustrated ideas and customs, but they would not have served as monumental works that integrated with the architecture. … In the SEP murals, the work of the artisan, the factory worker, the peasant, and the teacher is glorified, the festivals celebrated in different regions of Mexico are illustrated, pointing to their traditional

characteristics and their customary context. ... The focus is both pedagogical and critical and deserves to be called revolutionary" (1984: 9–10).

7. Valenzuela Arce says that the word "Chicano" was used pejoratively in the United States: "... it alludes to a poor, working-class, dark-skinned, Mexican. During the 1960s, the sociopolitical and cultural resistance movement against racism and the division of opportunities in this country made the concept known and assumed identity and social, cultural, and political resistance as its reference. Chicano refers to the population born in the United States to Mexican parents" (1997: 56).

8. *Cholo* muralism has been described in the following manner: "All that they are not allowed to say they paint in large street murals, imitating Chicano art of Los Angeles. The figures most frequently represented are Jesus Christ and the Virgin of Guadalupe" (*Diccionario Enciclopédico de Baja California* 1989). *Cholo* art is seeking visibility.

References

Aguilar, Manuel. 2001. Interview by author. Mexicali, Baja California, Mexico (2 December).
Armando Rascón homepage. 2001. http://www.cac.ca.gov/CAC/rascon/news.html (Cited December 2001).
Belkin, Arnold. 1986. *Contra la amnesia: Textos, 1960–1985*. México, D.F.: Universidad Autónoma Metropolitana, Editorial Domés.
Bronx View. 2001. "What is Graffiti?" http://www.bronxview.com/graffiti/whatisgraffiti.html (Cited December 2001).
California Murals. 2001. http://www.muralart.com/california.html (Cited December 2001).
Cimet Shoijet, Esther. 1992. *Movimiento muralista mexicano. Ideología y producción*. México, D.F.: Universidad Autónoma Metropolitana, División de Ciencias y Artes para el Diseño, Libros de la Telaraña.
Cockcroft, Eva Sperling, and Holly Barnet-Sánchez. 1993. *Signs from the Heart: California Chicano Murals*. Albuquerque: University of New Mexico Press.
Cockcroft, Eva, John Pitman Weber, and James Cockcroft. 1988. *Toward a People's Art. The Contemporary Mural Movement*. Albuquerque: University of New Mexico Press.
Cooper, Martha, and Joseph Sciorra. 1992. *R.I.P. New York Spraycan Memorial*. New York: Thames and Hudson.
Coronado Ortega, Carlos. 2001. Interview by author. Mexicali, Baja California, Mexico (2 December).
Del Conde, Teresa. 1984. *Guía de los murales de Diego Rivera en la Secretaría de Educación Pública*. México, D.F.: Secretaría de Educación Pública.
Diccionario Enciclopédico de Baja California, 1989. México, D.F.: Enciclopedias de México, Instituto de Cultura de Baja California.
Drescher, Timothy W. 1998. "Afterword: The Two Decades." Pp. 281–312 in *Toward a People's Art. The Contemporary Mural Movement*, Eva Cockcroft, John Pitman Weber, and James Cockcroft, eds. Albuquerque: University of New Mexico Press.
Dunitz, Robin J., and James Prigoff. 1997. *Painting the Towns. Murals of California*. Los Angeles: RJD Enterprises.
Fimbres, Norma. 2000. "Emigración, inmigración y retorno: el ciclo de los inmigrantes mexicanos en Caléxico, California, EUA." *Revista Estudios Fronterizos* 1 (2).
Fondo de Cultura Económica (FCE). 1967. *La pintura mural de la Revolución Mexicana*. México, D.F: FCE.

Gaspar de Alba, Alicia. 1998. Chicano Art. *Inside/Outside the Master's House. Cultural Politics and the CARA Exhibition*. Austin: The University of Texas Press.

Graffiti. 1995. Produced and directed by Fernando Franco. Universidad Autónoma de Baja California. Videocassette.

Hernández, Ruth. 2001. Interview by author. Mexicali, Baja California, Mexico (2 December).

Ochoa Zazueta, Jesús Angel. 1977. *Coronado Ortega*. Técnica, estilo y mensaje de un mural. Mexicali: Patronato de Asistencia Pública del Estado de Baja California.

Polkinhorn, Harry, Rogelio Reyes, and Gabriel Trujillo M. 1991. *Visual Arts on the USA/Mexican Border/Artes plásticas en la frontera México/Estados Unidos*. Calexico and Mexicali: Binational Press/Editorial Binacional.

Sánchez Guerrero, Alejandro. 2000. "Graffiti y la organización de los crews: diversidad y expansión humana." In *Cultura contracultura. Diez años de contracultura en México. Antología de textos publicados en generación*, Carlos Martínez Rentería, ed. México, D.F.: Plaza & Janés Editores.

Suárez, Orlando S. 1972. *Inventario del muralismo mexicano. Siglo VII a. C.–1968*. México, D.F.: Universidad Nacional Autónoma de México.

Trujillo Muñoz, Gabriel. 1993. *Coronado Ortega*. Mexicali: Universidad Autónoma de Baja California.

Trujillo Muñoz, Gabriel. 2001. Interview by author. Mexicali, Baja California, Mexico (15 December).

U.S. Census Bureau, American Factfinder. 2000. *2000 Census of Population*. http://factfinder.census.gov.

Valenzuela Arce, José. 1997. *Vida de barro duro*. México, D.F.: Universidad de Guadalajara and El Colegio de la Frontera Norte.

Vizcarra, Fernando. 1996. "La ciudad imaginada. Notas sobre cultura urbana." *Revista Semillero de Ideas* 4 (13).

Index

Abejas Arroyo, 36

Academic Employment Services, 359

adaptation, 55–59

affordable housing, 379, 381, 384

African-Americans, 432

Agricultural Commissioner's Annual
  Crop Report, 254

agriculture, 3, 18, 29, 33, 34, 35, 39, 44–47,
  50, 52, 70, 82, 99, 100, 103, 110, 113,
  119–21, 126, 133–35, 137, 143, 146, 151,
  155, 157, 160, 162, 166, 174, 175,
  185–88, 210, 218, 229, 233, 235, 237,
  239–41, 244, 246, 250, 253, 254, 257,
  258, 265, 313, 330, 342, 345, 354, 424,
  430

  abattoir, 253–56

  alfalfa, 41, 102, 231, 232, 234, 247–49,
    253, 254, 257–59

  aquaculture, 338, 341

  asparagus, 102, 121, 248, 249

  beekeeping, 246

  broccoli, 139

  cattle, 120, 230–33, 244, 246, 253–59,

  beef steers, 254

  Brahman breeding, 255

  calf, 233

  Holstein steers, 255

  cauliflower, 139

  cereal producers, 247

  certified seed, 231

  citrus, 133, 139, 144, 146, 246

  corn, 61, 248

  cost of production, 135, 215, 232, 234

  cotton, 38, 48–50, 116, 119, 121, 133,
    146, 172, 211, 218, 246–50, 308

  crop production, 41, 139, 234, 248

  cultivation periods, 248

  dairy, 122, 246, 253–55, 258, 259

    Chino dairy basin, 253, 259

    cows, 253–55, 259

  DDT, 315

  durum wheat, 139

  ferti-irrigation, 246

  fertilizers, 234, 245, 310

  flowers, 247

  fodder, 247

  forage, 234

  fruit trees, 247

  grains, 133, 247, 256

  green onions, 248, 249

  growers, 234, 250, 257

  harvest costs, 232

  hay, 232, 234, 253, 254, 257–59

  lambs, 257

  lemons, 139

  lettuce, 139, 231, 232

  oilseeds, 146, 247

  onions, 121, 248, 249

  pests, 234

  policies, 237

  processing facilities, 235, 253

  rye grass, 247–49

  sheep, 18, 232, 257, 258, 337

  shrimp, 337–338, 343

  silverleaf whitefly, 234

  soil, 26, 102, 119, 237, 238, 337

  sorghum, 247, 248

  sweetpotato whitefly, 234

  vegetables, 19, 22, 24, 121, 133, 139, 146,
    148, 157, 232, 233, 247

  wheat, 121, 122, 139, 148, 211, 213, 218,
    246–50

  yield, 232, 234, 247, 249

air pollution, 263, 267, 272–78, 291, 308

  abatement of air pollution, 277

  carbon monoxide, 263, 267, 269, 270,
    272, 274, 276

  emissions, 267, 274–78, 287, 288, 320,
    326, 328

  lead, 267, 274

  motor vehicle exhaust, 272

  nitrogen dioxide, 267, 269, 270, 276

nitrogen oxide, 274

ozone, 263, 267, 269, 270, 272–74, 276

particulate matter. *See also* PM10 263, 267, 272–76, 269, 270

sulfur dioxide, 267, 269, 270, 274, 276

air quality monitoring, 267, 269

data, 267, 278

network, 269, 270

norms, 267, 278

standards, 267, 273–75, 289

stations, 263, 269, 270, 276

Alamo, 34–36, 115, 229

Arroyo, 34

Canal, 34, 35, 36, 229

River, 115

Alaska, 21

Albergue Juvenil del Desierto, 401

Algodones, 34, 135, 143

All American Canal, 289, 290, 292

Alta California, 20–22, 24, 26, 29

Altar Desert, 38

American Friends Service Committee, 412

American Legion Club, 404

American West, 59

AmeriCorps, 359

Andrade, Don Guillermo, 35, 115, 116

Anglo-Americans, 47, 48, 50, 51

annual growth rate, 117, 118

Antilia, 19, 29

Anza trail. *See* Colorado Desert Trail, 24–27, 59

Arizona, 20, 40, 41, 45, 56, 63, 114, 115, 133, 137, 139, 141, 146, 156, 238, 256, 264, 282, 354, 419, 425

Arizona State University, 373

Army of the West, 26

art, 59, 357, 363, 415–25, 427–30, 432–41

Arts in Corrections 423

Asia, 46, 47, 123, 174, 181

Assembly Bill 1843, 330

Atlantic seaboard, 27

Autonomous University of Baja California. (Universidad Autónoma de Baja California), 269, 310, 312, 371, 373, 375, 417, 418, 420, 421

Editorial UABC, 418

Engineering Institute, 269, 312

Museo Universitario, 417

rectoría, 418

bachelor's degree, 8, 165, 166, 369, 373

Baja California, 3, 5–8, 24, 30, 33, 37–39, 42–45, 49, 55, 56,60, 63, 72, 74, 75, 79–82, 89–91, 93, 110, 114–19, 122, 125–27, 133, 135, 144, 172, 181, 183, 192, 209, 210, 213–19, 237–39, 244, 246, 265, 269, 281–84, 287, 289–92, 293–95, 301, 308–10, 320, 321, 323, 324, 325, 329, 330, 332, 354, 355, 365, 366, 371, 373–76, 408, 415–18, 420, 422, 432–34, 439

Citizens, 408

State Institute of Fine Arts (Instituto Estatal de Bellas Artes), 418, 422

State of Baja California Real Estate (Inmobiliaria del Estado de Baja California), 392

Peninsula, 114, 115, 287, 417

Public Library, 434

Vocational School of Baja California (Colegio de Bachilleres de Baja California–COBACH), 270

Baja California Sur, 75, 115, 117, 366

Baja California Technological Institute, 373

Banco de México, 121

Bank Operation and Financing Fund for Housing (Fondo de Operación y Financiamiento Bancario a la Vivienda–FOVI), 392

basic education, 354, 363, 365

basic geostatic area (área geoestadística basica - AGEB), 390, 393, 395–97

Benito Juárez School, 355

bighorn sheep, 337

Bill of Rights, 58

binational human rights coordinator, 409

block grant, 58

Blue Lake Quartet, 423

Bombay Beach, 68

Border 2012, 73, 266, 267, 310, 311

border czar, 72

Border Industrialization Program, 122, 134,
    210, 211, 213, 308

Border Patrol, 28, 140, 409

border region, 43, 50, 65, 67, 68, 72, 74, 75,
    134, 174, 181, 211, 263, 266, 267, 281,
    283, 287, 289, 308, 310, 345, 367, 374,
    376, 400, 409, 418, 419, 425
    Calexico-Mexicali, 409
    free zone, 49, 122, 126, 209, 210, 211
    Imperial Valley-Mexicali region, 3, 4, 65–
        67, 415, 424
    Mexicali-Imperial Valley, 191, 275, 335,
        336
    San Diego-Tijuana, 73, 75, 408

Border XXI Program, 73, 263, 266, 267,
    269, 310
    Framework Document, 267

boundary spanners, 65, 67, 72

Boys and Girls Club, 404, 423

Bracero Program, 46, 47, 49, 50, 174

Brawley, 46, 68, 74, 156, 162, 232, 253, 255,
    256, 353, 370, 380, 384, 419, 421, 423,
    424, 427, 429
    Cattle Call, 255, 424
    Palmer Auditorium, 419, 423
    Planters Hotel, 424

Brazil, 422

Broadway plays, 419

Brown, Luther, 353

buffer zone, 343

Bureau of Administration (Dirección de
    Administración), 362

Bureau of Education (Dirección de
    Educación), 362

Bureau of Participation (Dirección de
    Participación), 362

Bureau of Scientific Research (Dirección de
    Investigación Científica), 362

Caballero, Felix 24–25

Cabeza de Vaca, Álvar Núñez, 19

Café Literario, 416

Cahuilla, 18, 55

Cantú, Esteban, 35

Calexico, 20, 23, 26, 38, 44, 46, 48, 50, 52,
    68, 73, 74, 126, 156, 162, 186, 229, 270,
    272, 352, 353, 369, 376, 380–84, 399,
    406, 409, 410, 416, 417, 419, 422–24,
    427, 429, 433–35
    Arts Commission, 423
    City of, 48, 50, 73, 74, 186, 383, 384,
        399, 410
    Fifth Street, 353
    Orthopedic Clinic, 406, 410
    Third Street, 352
    Union High School District, 353

Calexico-Yuma railroad, 38

California, 3–8, 18, 20–22, 24–27, 29,
    34–36, 38, 40, 41, 43–46, 56, 59, 60, 62,
    67–69, 74, 75, 99, 100, 107, 108, 110,
    115, 116, 126, 133, 155, 156–58, 166,
    181, 188, 215, 229, 233–34, 237, 238,
    254, 255, 258, 264, 269, 273, 275,
    281–83, 285, 289, 290, 292, 294, 295,
    308, 321, 330, 331, 354, 356, 357, 359,
    360, 362, 374, 383, 406, 408, 410, 415,
    416, 420, 432, 435, 438, 439

California Coastal Commission, 71

Commission on Teacher Credentialing,
    375

Department of Education, 368, 372

Department of Finance, 270, 392, 393,
    394, 397, 399

Population Research Unit, 394
Department of Transportation (DOT), 74
energy crisis, 292
gold, 19, 22, 26, 27, 29
    gold diggers, 26
    Gold Rush, 27, 59, 115
Housing and Community Development
    Department (HCD), 384
Interfaith Coalition, 410
Mid-Winter Fair and Fiesta, 421, 424
Reading and Literature Project, 359
Reading Initiative, 359
State Bill 744, 342
Water Resources Control Board, 75, 259
California Development Company. *See*
    California Land Development Company,
    69, 115, 229
California Development Levee, 34, 35, 36
California Land Development Company. *See*
    California Development Company, 34, 36,
    45, 46
California State Polytechnic University,
    Pomona, 373
California State University, 370, 420
Calipatria, 46, 68, 289, 353, 385
    State Prison, 160
CalWORKs Supportive Services, 361
Canada, 21, 134, 290, 373
Cannon, Jimmie, 422
Cañón de San Martín, 293
Carbó, Javier, 432
Cárdenas, Lázaro, 37, 116
Carr, L.E., 352
Carranza colony, 37, 39
Carretera Unión, 220
Carrizo, 25, 27
Casa del Migrante, 410
Cavendish, Thomas, 21–33
Cementos Guadalajara factory, 324
census, 48, 50, 106, 107, 114, 115, 117, 120,
    122, 125, 127, 128, 145, 148, 150, 168,

229, 383, 393, 395
Center for Assistance for Migrant Workers
    (Centro de Apoyo al Trabajador
    Migrante), 402
Center for Digital Technology Research and
    Development, 376
Center for Family Care, 402
Center for Human Rights and Civic
    Education (Centro de Derechos Humanos
    y Educación Cívica), 402
Center for Multiple Care (Centro de
    Atención Múltiple), 366
Center for Scientific Research and Higher
    Education (Centro de Investigación
    Científica Superior–CICESE), 376
Center for Technical and Higher Education
    (Centro de Enseñanza Técnica y
    Superior–CETYS), 373–75, 417
Centinela State Prison, 160
Central Union High School District, 353,
    368
    Central High School, 369
    Central Junior College, 368
Cerro del Imposible 23
Cerro Prieto, 34, 35, 266, 287–90, 292, 293
    canal, 36
    geothermoelectric power plant, 288, 291
    levee 36
    volcano, 36
Chaffey, George, 17, 115
Chandler, Harry, 353
Chávez, César, 410
Chemgold, 63
Chiapas, 291
Chicago commodities market, 121
Chicano, 419, 429, 431–33, 437, 438, 440
Chief of the Agrarian Department, 37
Chihuahua, 80, 181, 308, 409
Children's Hospital, 406
Chimalitquic, 404
China, 117, 422

Chinese, 33, 35, 46, 117, 420

Chocolate Mountains, 23, 44, 352

cholo, 438–40

Christmas, 126, 201, 423, 424

City Council of Santo Tomás, 354

Ciudad Juárez, 73, 87, 174, 175, 181, 182, 210, 211, 409

Ciudad Morelos, 265

civic organizations, 416

Civil Philanthropic and Educational Association (Asociación Civil Filantrópica y Educativa), 404

civilian labor force, 137, 155, 156, 171, 233

Clean Air Act, 70, 274, 275

Coachella, 273

  Coachella Valley, 285

Coalition Against Tobacco and Drugs, 405

Coalition for the Defense of Migrants, Mexicali division (Coalición Pro Defensa del Migrante), 402

Colima, 291

College of Scientific and Technological Studies, 365

College of the Northern Border (El Colegio de la Frontera Norte), 374

Colmac, 285

Colorado Basin, 37, 40, 41

Colorado Desert, 17–29, 44, 264, 282

Colorado River, 3, 17–22, 24–27, 29, 33–41, 45, 48, 50, 55, 56, 57, 59, 60, 69, 114, 115, 119, 133, 135, 139, 143, 144, 229, 230, 238, 242, 243, 264, 266, 335, 336, 337, 338, 339, 340, 342, 343, 352, 354, 399

  Delta, 29, 37, 45, 113, 134, 146, 152, 282, 287, 293, 299, 335, 336, 338–45

  Colorado River Valley, 18, 20, 24, 25, 26, 27, 38, 40

  Colorado River Delta Biosphere Reserve, 335, 343

Colorado River Flood Control Project, 37

Colorado River Irrigation District, 38, 374

Colorado River Land Company, 33, 35, 36, 37, 38, 39, 46, 115, 116, 430

Colorado River Society of Limited Responsibility of Public Interest, (Sociedad de Responsabilidad Limitada de Interés Público Río Colorado–SRL de IP), 242

Colorado Valley, 265, 282

Colusa, 157

Comisión de Áreas Naturales Protegidas, 344

Comisión Federal de Electricidad, 70, 290, 297

Comisión Internacional de Límites y Aguas (CILA). *See also* International Boundary and Water Commission (IBWC), 37

Commission of Natural Protected Areas, 344

Commodity checkoff program, 258

Compañía Naviera del Golfo de California, 38

Congress of Baja California, 82

conquistadores, 19

constitution, 24, 58, 62, 79, 80

Control of the Process and Use of Pesticides, Fertilizers, and Toxic Substances, 310

Corrective Reading methodology, 360

Coronado Ortega, Carlos, 416, 431, 433

Cortés, Hernán, 19, 287

Coss y León, Genaro, 355

Council Bluffs, 26

Coyote Valley, 60

Coyote Wash, 23

Cuauhtémoc School, 354, 355

Cudahy 34, 36

Cuéllar, Rogelio, 417

Culiacán, 19

cultural Arts, 417

Cultural Institute of Baja California, 418

Data Analysis Office at the National Institute

of Ecology, 270

Davis, Gray, 74

Dawes Act, 61

Day of the Dead. *See* Día de los Muertos, 420

Day of the Virgin of Guadalupe, 437

de Anza, Juan Bautista, 20, 22, 38

de Iturbide, Agustín, 24

de la Madrid, Miguel, 73

de Niza, Fray Marcos, 19

deer, 17, 337

Delta of the Colorado River. *See* Colorado River Delta, 266

Department of Ecology of the State of Baja California (Dirección General de Ecología del Estado de Baja California). *See also* Dirección de Ecología, 274, 276

Department of Finance, 156, 264, 380, 381, 382, 385

Department of International Relations, 73

Desert Center, 285

Desert Juvenile Shelter, 401, 402

Desert Research Institute of Nevada, 263

Desert Shores, 68

Día de los Muertos, 420

Día de los Reyes, 425

Díaz, Melchor, 20, 287

Díaz Ochoa, Jaime Rafael, 83

Diego Portales University, 373

diligencias, 38

Dirección General de Aprovechamiento Ecológico de los Recursos Naturales, 342

Directory of the SLRC Maquiladora Association, 148

Dixieland, 46

Drake, Sir Francis, 21

Drescher, Timothy W., 438

Echeandía, José María, 25

Echeverría, Luis, 121

economically active population, 52, 120,

174, 183, 212

ecosystem, 320, 325, 326, 335–41, 343, 344

Editorial Binacional, 375

educación inicial, 365

educación media superior, 362

educación migrante, 366

Education and Community Services, 403

Education, Health, and Nutrition Program, 365

Educational Festival, 408

Egypt, 22

ejidatarios, 38, 83, 121

Ejido Emiliano Zapata, 321

Ejido Puebla, 217

El Centinela. *See* El Monte Centinela, 21 321, 324, 326

El Centro, 46, 68, 71, 353, 382, 383, 424
    Board of Trustees of the Central Union High School District, 368
    City of, 28, 264, 384
    Southwest High School, 419, 422

El Paso, 73

El Robledo, 392

Elorduy Walther, Eugenio, 83

employee turnover, 199–201, 203, 205, 201

employment, 4, 43, 44, 51–53, 57, 61, 62, 70, 81, 86, 99, 100, 102–04, 107, 113, 115, 116, 117–26, 135, 137, 140, 147–49, 155–58, 160, 162–66, 171, 177–79, 183, 185, 187, 199, 201, 204, 205, 207, 210, 211, 212, 214, 234, 255, 264, 265, 297, 359, 361, 362, 376, 405, 428

empowerment plan, 59

Empress Catherine II, 21

endangered species, 341, 343, 344, 345
    Endangered Species Act, 345

English as a Second Language, 361

English learners, 357, 360, 362

Ensenada, 3, 38, 45, 74, 114, 244, 284, 290, 324, 332, 354, 355, 362, 373

Environmental Protection Law of the State

of Baja California, 323

Environmental, Recycling, and Earth Day
  Projects, 361

Espinoza, Alejandro, 422

Estación Coahuila, 266

Estevanico, 19

estuary, 41, 339

Eucalyptus School District, 352–53

Even-Start, 358

farmworkers, 103, 234

Federal Attorney General for Environmental
  Protection, 274

Felicity, 68

Fernando and Isabela, 19

Figueroa, José, 25

Finley Elementary School, 419

Flores, Miguel Angel, 410

Flores Magón, Ricardo, 116

Flores, Víctor Hugo, 410

Florida, 19

Font, Fray Pedro, 22

Foothills Mountain Range, 45

Foppa, Alaide, 402

Fort Chapala, 25

Fort Leavenworth, 26

Fox, Vicente, 66, 410

France, 21

Franciscan, 19, 20, 22

Franklin Hotel, 353

friars, 20, 21

fuel, 143, 278, 281, 283, 284, 285, 287, 289,
  290, 292, 320, 324, 326, 328, 330, 332, 333

Galveston, 30

Garcés, Fray Francisco, 20

García Márquez, Gabriel, 432

Gayle, Crystal, 419

General Directorate for the Ecological Use
  of Natural Resources, 342

General Law of Ecological Equilibrium and

Environmental Protection, 320, 329

Genetic Improvement, 246

geographical boundaries, 241

Germany, 422

Gila Bend, 61

Gila heavy phase, 238

Gila light phase, 238

Glanton, John, 27

  Glanton gang, 27

Glen Canyon Dam, 37

González Ortega, 114, 266

graffiti, 427–29, 438–40

Grand Canyon, 20, 238

graying of America, 381

Great Depression, 58, 104, 116, 126

Great Plains, 20

Great Society Era, 62

Greater Yuma Port Authority, 143

Green Ecological Party of Mexico, 83

Guaymas, 38

Gulf of California, 3, 36, 38, 39, 41, 114,
  237, 293, 335, 336, 339–43

Gulf of California Shipping Company, 38

habitat, 339, 340, 341

halophyte vegetation, 339

Harding, 353

Hardy River, 36

Harinera del Valle, 219

Harlem Business School, 373

Harpers Well, 23

hazardous waste material, 309, 310

Head Start program, 63, 355

Health Center in Colonia Progreso (Centro
  de Salud en la Colonia Progreso), 270

Heber, Anthony H., 115, 368

Heber, 50, 68, 289, 352, 353, 380

  Collegiate Institute, 368

hedges, 352

hedging instruments, 250

Hemispheric Network of Shore Reserves

Program (Programa Red Hemisférica de
  Reserva de Playeras), 342
Hermosillo Celada, Víctor, 83, 85
Hidalgo, Miguel, 392
High Plains, 256
HIV/AIDS, 403, 407
Holland, 373
Holocene, 60
Holtville, 46, 68, 238, 353, 385, 419
  Carrot Festival, 424
  Union High School District, 353
Hoover Dam, 35, 36, 40, 135
housing, 50, 62, 70, 71, 80, 128, 164, 187,
  201, 216, 282, 376, 379–86, 406
Huelga de los Sentados, 38
human capital, 99, 100, 106, 107, 151
hunting, 18, 337, 342

Illinois, 45
immigrant, 46, 47, 107, 117, 408
immigration, 4, 35, 38, 39, 47, 48, 50, 76,
  117, 374, 406, 408
Imperial Avenue, 352, 431, 433
Imperial Canal, 229
Imperial County. *See also* Imperial Valley,
  3–6, 8, 17, 21, 34–36, 43–51, 53–55,
  57–61, 63, 65–72, 74, 99–110, 113, 114,
  115, 121, 133, 134, 137, 139, 143,
  155–58, 160, 162–66, 168, 171, 185–90,
  191, 192, 199, 229, 230, 232–35, 253–59,
  263–65, 270, 272, 273, 275–77, 281, 282,
  284, 285, 287–94, 297–300, 303, 304,
  307, 309, 312, 316, 335, 336, 351–354,
  357–62, 368, 370, 375, 376, 379–81,
  383–87, 399, 400, 404–06, 408–11, 415,
  416, 419–25, 429
  Agricultural Commissioner. *See also*
    agricultural production, 234, 254
  Air Quality Control District, 285
  Arts Commission, 420
  Arts Council, 423

  Association of Governments, 74
  Board of Supervisors, 46, 68, 73, 352
  Film Commission, 424
  Historical Society, 420
  Office of Education, 356–61
  School Districts, 140
Imperial Dam, 41, 69
Imperial Irrigation District, 69, 230, 420
Imperial Land Company, 46
Imperial Valley College 55, 368, 369, 375,
  419, 421
Imperial Valley Press, 424
Imperial Valley Symphony Orchestra, 423
Imperial Valley Union High School District,
  353
Income Law of the State of Baja California,
  324
India, 117
Industrial Age, 28
Industrial Development Commission, 182
industrial expansion, 210, 294
In-Ko-Pah Mountains, 60
inSITE 2000, 420
Institute for National Funds for Worker
  Housing (Instituto del Fondo Nacional de
  la Vivienda para los Trabajadores
  –INFONAVIT), 392
Institute of Security and Social Services for
  State Workers Housing Fund (Fondo de la
  Vivienda del Instituto de Seguridad y
  Servicios Sociales de los Trabajadores del
  Estado–FOVISSSTE), 392
Instituto Estatal de Bellas Artes, 418, 422
Instituto Tecnológico de Baja California, 373
Integral Systematic Savings, 282, 291, 301
Integrated Environmental Plan for the
  Mexico-U.S. Border Area, 73
Integrated Waste Management Board, 330,
  331
Inter-American Development Bank, 42
Inter-California del Sur railway, 36

INTERGEN, 283, 290
International Boundary and Water
　Commission (IBWC). *See also* Comisión
　Internacional de Límites y Aguas (CILA),
　37, 38, 40–41
　Minute 242, 41
International Wastewater Treatment Plant, 73
Iowa, 26
irrigation district, 38, 42
irrigation modules, 242, 243
irrigation permit, 243
Irrigation and Land Society of
　Baja California, 34
Islas Marías prison, 37
Italy, 422

Jalisco, 325, 425
Japan, 174, 181
Jasper-Alamitos Union, 353
Jenkins, William O., 39
Jesuit, 20
Juárez Valley, 40

Kansas, 26, 256
Kearny, Stephen Watts, 26
Kenworth Mexicana, 211
King Carlos III, 20, 22
King's Day, 425
Kingston Trio, 419
Korean War, 49, 116

La Bomba, 38, 39
La Paz, 38, 115
　Agreement, 73, 266, 310
La Purísima Concepción, 23, 24
La Rosita, 281, 283
labor force, 51, 57, 99, 100, 102, 103,
　106–09, 122, 137, 139, 155, 156, 160,
　166, 168, 171, 174, 233
　force participation rate, 100, 106, 108, 109
Laguna Chapala, 25

Lake Cahuilla, 18
Land and Water Company of Baja California
　(Compañía de Terrenos y Aguas de la Baja
　California), 38, 115
land tenure, 34, 146, 237, 239, 240
Latin America, 4
Laurin Associates, 379–81, 384, 385
Law of Education, 354
Leona Vicario School, 355
Library Literacy Project, 404
Lincoln, Dr. Able B., 27
Lions Club, 404, 406
Local Agency Formation Commission, 68
Los Angeles Times, 353
Lower Colorado River, 18, 56, 133, 134
　Delta, 134, 287, 297
　Economic Report, 410
Luomala, Katherine, 18

Madre Asunta Center (Centro Madre
　Asunta), 410
Magnolia School District, 353
maquiladora, 4, 82, 122–24, 128, 133–35,
　137, 143, 144, 146, 148, 149, 151, 152,
　171, 172, 174–76, 210, 211, 213–15, 221,
　289, 307–13, 316, 317, 381, 428
　industrial parks, 124, 181, 215, 216,
　　218–20, 222, 224
　PIMSA, 187
Mariachi Calafia, 421
Mariachi Festival, 424, 425
Maricopa, 63
Mariposas Ministry (Ministerio Mariposas),
　399, 405
Marshall, James, 26
Matamoros, 174
Mazatlán, 342
McCabe School, 352
McCollum, Allan, 420, 421
Mercantile Bank (Banco Mercantil), 39
Mesa de Otay, 281, 283, 292

Mexicali
  AIDS Center, 403
  City of, 23, 35, 46, 49, 53, 82, 85, 114,
    115, 117, 173, 181, 209, 210, 218, 219,
    220, 245, 270, 288, 307, 311, 313, 324,
    373, 389, 390, 391, 392, 393, 401, 403,
    407, 430, 433
  Colonia Hidalgo, 435
  Colonia Lerdo, 115
  Colonia Morelos, 281
  Colonia Progreso, 270, 281
  Fiesta del Sol, 424
  mexicalense, 431
  Municipal Development Plan of Mexicali,
    85, 91–93
  Municipal House, 432
  Municipality of. *See also* municipio, 3, 33,
    43–45, 48–50, 72, 73, 79, 80, 82,
    84–87, 89, 91–93, 113–15, 117–20,
    144, 172, 209, 210, 212, 214, 215, 263,
    269, 270, 274, 276, 282, 321
  population, 84, 117, 178, 216
  regidores, 81
  Oil Producer of the Valley (Aceitera del
    Valle), 211
  Teatro del Estado, 416
  Guadalupe Victoria, 265
  Vicente Guerrero Park, 424
Mexican Agricultural, Industrial, and
  Colonizing Company of the Colorado
  River (Compañía Mexicana Agrícola,
  Industrial y Colonizadora del Río
  Colorado), 115
Mexican Center for Research on Nutrition
  and Development, 146
Mexican Constitution, 24, 66, 146, 362
Mexican consulate, 406
Mexican Institute for Social Security
  (Instituto Mexicano del Seguro Social),
  125, 176, 416
Mexican Official Norm NOM-807-ECOL-

1995, 315
Mexican Petroleum Company (Petróleos
  Mexicanos–PEMEX), 292
Mexican Red Cross, 406
Mexican Revolution, 49, 116, 430
Mexico City, 19, 24, 35, 37, 70, 419
Mexico-U.S. Binational Migrant Education
  Program (Programa Binacional de
  Educación Migrante México-Estados
  Unidos de América–PROBLEM), 366
Mexico-U.S. Foundation for Science
  (Fundación México-Estados Unidos para
  la Ciencia–FUMEC), 374
Michoacán, 332, 429
migrant, 33, 44–46, 49–50, 53, 358, 363,
  366, 390, 401, 402, 408–11, 428, 429,
  432, 433
  education 358, 366
Milán, Carmen, 410
military, 20, 24–25, 26, 27, 28,
mining, 63, 120, 128, 157, 158, 162, 352,
  354
Ministry of Agriculture, Livestock, Rural
  Development, Fisheries, and Food
  (Secretaría de Agricultura Ganadería,
  Desarrollo Rural, Pesca y Alimentación
  –SAGARPA), 241
Mission Santa Catarina, 24, 25
Montague Island, 339, 342
Montezuma Mesa, 369
Morelos Dam, 41, 242
Mormon Battalion, 26, 27
Mt. Signal School District, 365
Municipal Water Districts of Southern
  California, 70

Nacional Financiera, 39
National Action Party (Partido Acción
  Nacional–PAN), 81
National Bank of Ejido Credit (Banco
  Nacional de Crédito Ejidal), 38

National Bank of Public Works (Banco Nacional de Obras–BANOBRAS) 392

National Bank of Rural Credit (Banco Nacional de Crédito Rural–BANRURAL), 244

National Border Program (Programa Nacional Fronterizo–PRONAF), 174

National College of Professional Technical Education (Colegio Nacional de Educación Profesional Técnica–CONALEP), 270, 365

National Commission for Energy Savings (Comisión Nacional para el Ahorro de Energía–CONAE), 300

National Fund for Public Housing (Fondo Nacional de Habitaciones Populares –FONHAPO), 392

National Institute for Statistics, Geography, and Information (Instituto Nacional de Estadística, Geografía e Informática –INEGI), 393

National Institute of Ecology (Instituto Nacional de Ecología–INE), 267, 270, 273, 329

National Public Subsistence Company (Compañía Nacional de Sussistencias Populares–CONASUPO), 245

National Solidarity Program (Programa Nacional de Solidaridad–PRONASOL), 403

National University, San Diego, 373

National Water Commission (Comisión Nacional del Agua–CNA), 241

Native American, 56, 135, 143
  Anasazi, 19
  Arizpe, 25
  Avi-Kwami, 60, 62
  Aztec, 19
  Bureau of Indian Affairs, 59, 61
  Bureau of Land Management, 63
  Cargo Muchachos, 25

Chief Miguel, 61
Cochimí, 21, 366
Cocomaricopa, 25
Cocopah, 63, 115, 135, 143, 417
Comanche, 30, 55
Cucapá, 35, 115, 117, 336, 337, 366, 436
Desert Kumeyaay, 18, 25, 29
Fort Yuma, 27, 59, 61, 62, 143
Hokan, 55
Hopi, 19, 20
Indian Reorganization Act, 62
Indians, 18–20, 22–25, 27, 59, 61–63, 115, 117, 354, 432, 433
indigenous, 18–22, 25, 27
Keruk ceremony, 60
Kiliwua, 366
Kumeyaay, 18–19, 25, 29, 366
Mastamho, 60
Mohave, 59
Mother Earth, 18
Olmec heads, 437
Pai-Pai, 366
Palaco, 114
Papago, 63
Pima, 19, 25, 63
Quechan, 18–19, 22, 23–24, 25, 27, 55–56, 58, 59, 61–63, 135, 143, 354
reservation, 61–63, 354
reserved lands, 59
Shoshone-Comanche, 55
Southern California Yumans, 59
Takic, 55
Tribal Council, 63
Uto-Aztecan, 55
Yuha, 17, 23, 60
Yuman, 55, 56, 59, 60, 63
Zuni, 19–20

Naval Air Facility, 28
Navarro Cortina, Rafael, 37
Nayarit, 291
Needles, 60, 61

Nevada, 263, 352
New Mexico, 19, 20, 40, 256, 289
New River, 25, 36, 59, 218
  bridge/canal, 36
New Spain, 19, 20
New York, 27, 419, 438, 440
Niland, 46, 68, 270, 424
Nogales, 174, 175
nongovernmental organizations (NGO),
  399–401, 403–06, 408–09, 411
  Agreement of Nongovernmental
  Organizations (El Concierto de
  Organizaciones No Gubernamentales),
  403
Norzagaray, Angel, 416
North American Free Trade Agreement
  (NAFTA), 133, 144, 151, 249
Northern Border Commissioner, 72
Nuevo León, 39

Oaxaca, 366
occupational employment, 155, 163, 165,
  166
Ockerson Levee, 36
Ocotillo, 25, 68, 421
  Desert Museum, 421
Office of Economic Opportunity, 63
Old Anza trail, 25, 27
on-the-job training, 165
Operation Gatekeeper, 408

Pacheco, Romualdo, 25, 28
Pacific Industrial Company, 211
Pacific Ocean, 21
Pacific Soap Company (Compañía Jabonera
  del Pacífico), 37, 219
Palma, Don Salvador, 22, 24
Palo Verde, 68
Paradise Casino, 63
Party of the Democratic Revolution (Partido
  de la Revolucón Democrática–PRD), 83

per capita income, 99–01, 108–10, 188
performing arts, 415, 419, 422
Pescaderos Levee, 36
peso, 121–24, 127, 133, 134, 144, 148–52,
  163, 183, 202, 215, 246–47, 381, 429
Phoenix, 62
Picacho School District, 352
Piedras Negras, 174
Pilot Knob, 35, 229
Pioneers Park Museum, 420, 421
Plaster City, 23, 26
Playas de Rosarito. *See also* Rosarito, 74,
  244, 283, 284, 290, 292
Pollutant Release and Transfer Register, 309
Population
  Imperial County, 9, 11
  Mexicali, 10, 12
  rate, 393
  trends 4-PB, 14
port of entry, 143, 270, 281, 283, 292, 381,
  417
Posada Sin Fronteras, 410
Potable Water Project, 74
prehistoric Imperial-Mexicali Valley, 18
Programa Amigo, 403
Programa de Apoyos Directos al Campo
  –PROCAMPO, 24
prohibition, 48, 116, 338
Project Hope, 361
Project Power, 361
Project Trabajo, 361
Proposition 10, 360
Proposition 187, 408, 409
Public Housing Development Program
  (Programa de Fraccionamientos
  Populares), 392
Public Law 280, 62
Public Law 78, 46
Puebla, 217, 265
Puerto Otis, 39
Puerto Peñasco, 39

pyramids of Teotihuacán, 437

Queen Elizabeth, 21

Rascón, Armando, 435
Reagan, Ronald, 73
Reavis, John, 353
recycling, 320, 323–25, 328–33, 361
redevelopment agency, 383
Redevelopment Agency's Affordable
    Housing Set-Aside Fund, 383
Regional Housing Needs Assessment, 71
Regional Transportation Plan, 70
Religions
    Catholic, 19, 61, 401, 404, 411
    christian, 19, 20, 354
    Jewish, 424
    Ramadan, 424
    Tibetan Buddhism, 424
respiratory illnesses
    asthma, 264, 273
    bronchitis, 264, 273
    emphysema, 264, 273
retail trade, 125, 141, 158, 160, 163, 234,
    265
Rio Grande, 40
Rivera, Diego, 430
Riverside County, 3, 44, 259, 264, 282, 354
Rockwood, Charles. *See also* C.R.
    Rockwood, 115, 229
Rodríguez, Abelardo L., 35, 36
rondalla, 422
Ruffo Appel, Ernesto, 72, 82
Rural Alliance (Alianza para el Campo),
    244–46
rural development, 237, 240, 241, 244, 246
Rural Development Support Center (Centro
    de Apoyo al Desarrollo Rural–CADER),
    240, 241

Sacramento, 26, 75, 360

Office of Education, 356
Sáiz Levee, 36
salt extraction, 342
Salton City, 68
Salton Sea, 34, 68, 114, 230, 264, 266, 283,
    285, 289, 292, 293, 380
    Beach, 68
    Salton Sink, 230
San Andreas Fault, 287
San Diego
    County, 3, 56, 63, 70, 264, 282, 352
        Board of Supervisors, 352
        Water Authority, 70
    Symphony, 425
San Diego State University, 3, 17, 99, 113,
    199, 263, 281, 351, 353, 359, 368, 369,
    373, 375, 415, 419
    Binational Press. *See also* Autonomous
        University of Baja California, 375, 415,
        420
    Imperial Valley Campus, 113, 351, 359,
        368, 369, 370, 375
    California Center for Border and
        Regional Economic Studies, 3
    Rodney Auditorium, 419
    Steppling Art Gallery, 419
    Teacher Education Division, 368
    San Diego State College/Normal School,
        353
San Dieguito, 336
San Felipe, 39, 82, 265, 282, 338
San Francisco, 22, 23
    Golden Gate Bridge, 23
San Gabriel, 21, 23
    Mission, 23
San Jacinto Mountains, 21
San Joaquin Valley, 230, 255
San Juan, 289
San Luis, 27, 34, 36, 42, 114, 120, 133, 134,
    181, 216, 217, 265
San Luis Gonzaga, 39

San Luis Rey, 27

San Luis Río Colorado, 34, 36, 42, 114, 133, 134, 142, 144–46, 149, 151, 181, 216, 217, 237, 238, 240, 248–50

   highway, 217

San Luis Valley, 36

San Pasqual, 26, 354

San Pedro y San Pablo de Bicuñer, 24

San Sebastián, 23

San Sebastian Marsh, 59

Sánchez Taboada, Rodolfo, 37

Santa Ana, 38, 39, 253

   River basin, 259

Santa Clara, 144

   Estuary, 41

   Gulf, 342

   wetland, 338–40, 343

Santa Fe, 40

Santa Rosa de las Raxas, 23

Santa Rosa Mountains, 23

Santa Rosalía, 38

Sandino, Augusto, 435

Saracco, Patricia, 423

Save Our State, 408

Scalabrinni Migrant Home, 410

Scrap Tire Management Council, 332

Sea of Cortez, 20, 114, 265, 266, 283

seated strike, 38

Sebastián Tarabal, 21

Secretariat and Subsecretariat of Education and Social Welfare (Secretaría y Subsecretaría de Educación y Bienestar Social), 362

Secretariat of Agrarian Reform (Secretaría de la Reforma Agraria–SRA), 243

Secretariat of Agricultural Promotion (Secretaría de Fomento Agropecuario –SFA), 39, 244

Secretariat of Agriculture and Development (Secretaría de Agricultura y Fomento), 35

Secretariat of Agriculture and Hydraulic Resources (Secretaría de Agricultura y Recursos Hidráulicos–SARH), 240

Secretariat of Agriculture, Livestock, and Rural Development (Secretaría de Agricultura Ganadería y Desarrollo Rural), 313

Secretariat of Commerce and Industrial Promotion (Secretaría de Comercio y Fomento Industrial–SECOFI), 329

Secretariat of Fisheries (Secretaría de Pesca), 342

Secretariat of Public Education (Secretaría de Educación Pública–SEP), 362

Secretariat of the Environment and Natural Resources (Secretaría de Medio Ambiente y Recursos Naturales–SEMARNAT), 266

Secretariat of the Environment, Natural Resources, and Fisheries (Secretaría de Medio Ambiente Recursos Naturales y Pesca–SEMARNAP), 266–67

Secretariat of the Treasury and Public Credit Secretaría de Hacienda y Crédito Público–SHCP), 243, 290

Secretariat of Urban Development and Ecology (Secretaría de Desarrollo Urbano y Ecología–SEDUE), 324, 342

Secretary of the Interior, 62

Seeley, 46, 68, 380

SEMPRA Energy, 285

shared border environment, 266

Sierra de las Pintas, 237–38

Sierra Madre, 23

Silsbee School, 252, 253

Sinaloa, 22, 366, 429

social security, 125, 143, 176, 410, 416

Socio-Educational Bureau for Planning and Infrastructure (Dirección Social Educativa de Planeación e Infraestructura), 362

Solfatara canal, 36

Sonoita, 38

Sonora-Baja California Railroad, 39, 49

Sonoran Desert, 144, 264, 282

Soto, Gary, 419

Southern California Association of
  Governments (SCAG), 74

Southern California Edison, 70
  Public Power Authority, 70

Southern Pacific Railroad, 34, 39

Spanish colonists, 22, 23

Spanish explorers, 19

specialization, 171, 180, 182, 184, 185, 188,
  191, 210, 212, 215

Statue of Liberty, 435

Sunbelt, 386

Sunset Springs, 353

Support and Services for Agricultural
  Commercialization (Apoyos y Servicios a
  la Comercialización Agropecuaria
  –ASERCA), 245

sustainable development, 266, 320

Sutter, John, 26

Sweetwater Union High School District, 373

System for the Consultation of Census
  Information (Sistema para la Consulta de
  Información Censal–SCINCE), 395

Tecate, 3, 45, 114, 239, 244, 373

Technical University of Nova Scotia, 373

Technological Institute of Mexicali (Instituto
  Tecnológico de Mexicali), 270, 373

Telnor, 376

Tenneco Baja Mexicali Export, 287

Tennessee, 27

Tenochtitlán, 19

Teotihuacán, 417, 437

Texas, 21, 40, 256, 287, 290, 292
  Panhandle, 256

Tijuana, 73–75, 80, 87, 91, 122, 174, 175,
  181, 182, 187, 210, 211, 214–16, 218,
  220, 239, 244, 281, 283, 289, 290, 292,
  310, 315, 354, 365, 367, 373, 391, 408–
  10, 439

Delegation, 362

River, 40

Technological University (Universidad
  Tecnológica), 365

University Center of Tijuana (Centro
  Universitario de Tijuana), 373

Tlaxcala, 291

Torchosa, 36

totoaba, 337, 338, 339, 341, 342, 343

tourism, 48, 125, 133, 135, 140, 141, 143,
  338, 341, 342

trade, 24, 30

transportation, 8, 14
  Imperial County, 13
    Interstate 10, 381
    Interstate 8, 143, 381, 386
    Route 86, 381
  Mexicali, 14

Treaty of Guadalupe Hidalgo, 40, 43

Trujillo Muñoz, Gabriel, 433

Tubac, 21

Tucson, 24

unemployment, 57, 99, 100, 104, 105, 108,
  109, 120, 128, 137, 155–57, 166, 172,
  174, 183, 184, 186, 190, 191, 192, 233,
  234, 308, 362
  insurance, 234

United Farm Workers, 410

United Way agencies, 404

University of Arizona, 373

University of Calgary, 373

University of California, 234, 370
  Cooperative Extension, 229, 232, 253

Unruh, Jesse, 354

Upper Gulf of California, 335, 339, 340,
  342, 343

Upper Pima, 25

U.S. Bureau of Labor Statistics, 104

U.S. Census Bureau, 3–6

U.S. Congress, 45, 61, 62, 267

U.S. Department of Agriculture (USDA), 257

U.S. Department of Commerce, 99, 100

U.S. Department of Education, 356

U.S. Department of State, 364

U.S. Department of the Treasury, 404

U.S. Environmental Protection Agency, 267, 269, 273

    Assistant Administrator for International Activities, 267

U.S. Immigration Service and Border Patrol, 140

U.S. military, 26, 27, 28, 61

U.S. National Marine Fisheries Service, 341

U.S.-Mexican War, 26, 115

Utah, 256

Valle de la Trinidad, 293

value-added, 123, 124

vaquita, 341–43

Vázquez, Gabino, 37

Vázquez viuda de Arellano, Doña Felipa, 37

Vázquez de Coronado, Francisco, 19, 20

Veracruz, 291

Victoria, Manuel, 24

Villa, Francisco, 435, 437

Virgin of Guadalupe, 437, 438

Virtual Resource Technology Center, 361

Vizcarra, Fernando, 440

Vocational Center for Industrial Technology and Services (Centro de Bachillerato Técnico Industrial y de Servicios–CBTIS), 269

Vocational School of Baja California (Colegio de Bachilleres de Baja California–COBACH), 270, 365

Volcano Lagoon, 36

von Werlhof, Dr. Jay, 421

Wal-Mart, 149

wastewater treatment, 73, 74, 216

water, 3, 17, 18, 22, 23, 25–29, 33–38, 40, 41, 45, 48, 50, 57, 62, 67–70, 72–75, 114, 115, 117, 119, 122, 124, 134, 139, 140, 144, 181, 211, 224, 229, 230, 237–39, 241–43, 245, 248, 249, 255, 259, 264, 266, 308, 317, 325, 327, 335, 337–40, 342, 345, 346, 374, 375

Welcome, G.F., 353

Wellton Mohawk Canal, 340

    Drainage Project, 41

Westmorland, 46, 68, 353, 380, 385

    Tomato Festival, 424

wetland, 335, 337–40, 342, 343

Whipple, Amiel W., 28

Williamson, R.S., 28

Winterhaven, 68, 270

World Bank, 42

World War I, 116

World War II, 4, 39, 49, 58, 62, 255, 368

World Wildlife Fund, 342

Wozencraft, Dr. Oliver M. *See also* Wozencraft, Dr. O.M., 115, 229

Xochicalco University (Universidad Xochicalco), 373

Young, Brigham, 26

Yuma, 18, 20–27, 36, 38, 56, 58–59, 61, 62, 133–37, 140–46, 148, 149, 151, 152, 287, 354, 419, 425

    Clapper rail, 340, 343

    County, 116, 133–52, 156,

    Levee, 36

    Proving Grounds, 140, 146

Zamores, Eduardo, 409

Zapata, Emiliano, 431, 435

    Ejido, 321